THE TRUTH
about
HIV

STEVEN RANSOM
& PHILLIP DAY

 Credence Publications

THE TRUTH ABOUT HIV

ISBN: 1-904015-17-4

Please note: The information contained in this book is for
educational purposes only. The Author, Publisher and Reseller
accept no liability for damages arising out of the abuse of the
information contained herein.

Printed and bound in the United Kingdom by

Credence Publications
PO Box 3
TONBRIDGE
Kent TN12 9ZY
England
www.credence.org
1st Ed. VS

TABLE OF CONTENTS

"The next epidemic will be testing abuse."
Dr Ronald Siegel
Dept Psycho-Pharmacology
University of California

"In our 'test for this, test for that' society, this book uncovers the hoodwinking and abuse within the medical and pharmaceutical industry. As the late, great physician, William Ostler, famously stated, 'If the contents of all the medicine cabinets were thrown into the sea, it would be better for mankind, but worse for the fishes.' A great read!"

David Kernew-Barnard,
author *'The Health Plunderers'*

"A magnificent book. Very easy to read and understand, and a real eye-opener for us all. I highly recommend this book as a wake-up call to Africa, to save our continent before it is too late. For, with the knowledge contained in these pages, comes power. God bless the authors and all those who have contributed to this fantastic book."

Winfred Mwebe,
Ugandan health advisor

"Ransom and Day are the Woodward and Bernstein of AIDSgate, exposing the corruption, fraud and lies upon which the multi-billion dollar HIV industry is based."

Alex Russell,
Associate editor, *Continuum Magazine.*

"A perfect read. A masterpiece."

Dr Stefan Lanka,
Vice President of 'Science, Medicine and Human Rights'

"Would you wish to explore the AIDS jungle without risk of becoming lost? Choose Ransom and Day's 'THE TRUTH ABOUT HIV'. It is the perfect guide. Nevertheless, beware! Direct exposure to the facts contained in this book may be hazardous to your mental well-being."

Philippe Krynen, Partage, Tanzanie

ALL TOOLED UP

Thank you for choosing to read *The Truth About HIV*. This book will accomplish the following goals:

- **REVEALING THE DECEIT AT THE HEART OF THE PHARMACEUTICAL INDUSTRY** - This book lifts the lid on the pharmaceutical industry and on corporate business in general, exposing a deceit that extends way beyond the AIDS/HIV story. We bring many fascinating interviews and insights that serve as a valuable reminder not to take accepted cultural and scientific 'truths' at face value. We also report on the real dangers inherent in the latest fad - the medical testing industry.

Phillip Day

- **ENDING THE FEAR THAT CLOUDS MANY LIVES** - We draw attention to the fear-mongering tactics of those agencies promoting the so-called 'global pandemics'. The fear of AIDS/HIV has hung over us these last twenty five years and is still with us today. This book reveals that fear to be wholly unwarranted. With AIDS and HIV, we have been shamelessly duped by colluding officials at all senior levels within government and the conventional medical establishment.

Steve Ransom

- **BRINGING FASCINATING INSIGHT INTO THE REAL NATURE OF AIDS/HIV** - The story of AIDS reads like some crazy Hollywood script. You will discover that AIDS is primarily a series of scientific and political lies, masquerading as medical science, which has come about through man's appetite for money and control. The aim of those in power at the very top is to ensure the lucrative cash-flow from the HIV 'epidemic' remains uninterrupted by continuing to propagate myths and lies.

- **REVEALING THE REAL CAUSES OF THE SO-CALLED AIDS DEATHS ACROSS THE WORLD** - Readers will discover there is a marked difference between African and Western AIDS. As far as Western AIDS is concerned, in almost all instances, blame for the patients' demise can be laid fairly and squarely at the door lifestyle choices and conventional medical treatment. **Dangerous drugs are now being forcefully prescribed to healthy people who have reacted positively to a wide range of extremely unreliable testing procedures** - procedures that are becoming mandated by law - especially the HIV test. For the sake of your future good health, **YOU NEED TO KNOW THIS INFORMATION**.

- **THE AFRICAN (AND NOW ASIAN) 'PANDEMIC'** - We discover the vital role played by harsh but easily reversible environmental factors that contribute so greatly to the illnesses and deaths currently blamed on a 'virus' sweeping these continents.

- **BRINGING MANY CASE HISTORIES** of supposedly terminally afflicted AIDS sufferers **who are now completely healthy!** If you have been given an 'HIV positive' diagnosis by the medical authorities, the diagnosis alone might already be adversely affecting your health. You will discover information in this book on how to start getting better **IMMEDIATELY**. The condition known as HIV/AIDS need NOT be terminal, despite the overwhelming public message to the contrary.

We are not doctors, medical practitioners or healthcare specialists and we do not offer medical advice. The facts presented in this book are intended for information and educational purposes only. Neither does this book instruct the reader to buy products or take any particular course of treatment. However, as a free citizen, you should have the right to informed choice on any treatments, and this is what this book is all about. In the realm of AIDS and HIV at the present time, this is being deliberately denied you.

And the best news of all! Every day, people are recovering from the AIDS/HIV diagnosis! And no, we are not just talking about a few isolated cases. You will read inspiring accounts of how ordinary men and women, sent home to die by the AIDS 'specialists' they trusted,

6

resolved to think for themselves, ask pertinent questions, study the facts and begin treading the path back to health with growing confidence.

This book is dedicated to the men, women and children everywhere who have been labelled HIV positive by establishment medicine. May this book shatter the many myths, precipitate a return to health, in body, mind and spirit, and help set the captives free.

Part 1

WESTERN AIDS

THE MADNESS OF THE
CONVENTIONAL
MEDICAL MIND

THE TERROR OF IT ALL

William was down to 98 pounds and a mess. His face was haunted and sunken, the look that all had come to expect from AIDS. His skin had taken on an unhealthy, ghostly patina. His surroundings mirrored the same sense of neglect and despair – clothes strewn haphazardly about the place, uneaten, fly-infested food and dirty plates piled in the sink.

"OK," said William. "I've read what you sent me. I've decided to do it." I was overcome. "How do you feel about what you have decided to do?" I asked. "I'm gonna die anyway, aren't I...?" he mumbled, shivering and wrapping his arms around himself. My heart went out to him. "Come on, let's do it. Then I'll treat you to some lunch down at the Moustache Café."

William got up and made his way over to the kitchen cupboard. What William did during the next two minutes was to cure him completely of AIDS. Admittedly it would take some months for the body fully to recover. But the direct consequence of William's 'senseless act' (as it was later termed by his doctor) would be that in the space of a single day, in body, in mind and in spirit, William would experience being dragged away from death and back towards the light of health, vigour and sanity.

Today, twelve years after throwing away his AIDS medications, William is an irrefutable example of health and vitality and has been free of AIDS for eleven and a half years. Running his own actors' management agency in Los Angeles with the support of his loving parents, William demonstrates no trace of his former condition. To those who know only the outline of William's story, it seems a miracle has occurred. After all, William once had full-blown AIDS, yet today, impossibly, incredibly, he is now completely healthy. [1]

Apparently there is an AIDS war. The international medical community and the major pharmaceutical companies appear to be pulling out all the stops in an effort to combat a dreadful disease. AIDS, we are told, is only just being contained in the West, thanks

---

[1] Day, Phillip, from personal notes.

largely to the new drugs being developed which have the potential to retard the spread of HIV infection. But, say the experts, the research is very costly and success is dependent upon great amounts of money. Key global health agencies such as The World Health Organization tell us that without funds to buy the necessary drugs, AIDS will devastate the continents of Africa, South East Asia, India, China and now Russia. There seems to be no let-up in the gloomy forecasts or the appeals for money. The latest WHO report tells us that in 2003, an estimated five million adults and children became infected with HIV, and that by the end of the year, an estimated 38 million people worldwide were living with HIV/AIDS. WHO also report that 2003 saw nearly three million deaths from AIDS.[2] WHO has also instituted its 'Three by Five' initiative, whereby the organisation hopes to be treating three million people with AIDS drugs by 2005.

But still, say the experts, there can be no guarantees with these treatments. Nothing about AIDS which was incurable in 1985 is curable today, in spite of the $£billions we have spent. The condoms, the safe/safer sex education programs and plethora of drug treatments seem to be having little impact. Twenty five years into the history of AIDS, the media is still telling us that all the money, the red ribbons, the super-technology, the strident politicians and AIDS rallies in the world seem to be having little effect in the face of this implacable and unrelenting HIV micro-enemy. And for the last quarter of a century, the world has been shivering involuntarily with the titillation and the terror of it all. AIDS - the merciless killer. The story the world has been given.

And the world bought it all.

---

[2] WHO world HIV infection update for 2004 at www.avert.org/worldstats.htm

THE DAWN OF WESTERN AIDS

In late 1980, a young researcher in immunology named Michael Gottlieb, working at the medical centre of the University of California Los Angeles (UCLA), embarked upon a study to examine the immune system. *"I assigned a student to track down for me any unusual cases of immuno-suppression."*[3] With the help of his student, Gottlieb began scouring hospitals and clinics to find evidence of patients demonstrating immune deficiency diseases. By November of that year, Gottlieb had found one such case suffering from a yeast infection in his throat as well as a rare pneumonia that refused to disappear. Gottlieb knew that the *pneumocystis carinii* microbe causing the pneumonia was extremely common across the world. In fact, in a dormant state it is thought to inhabit the lungs of nearly every human on the planet.[4] This pneumonia very rarely strikes anyone other than cancer patients, and then, only those whose immune systems have been severely damaged by the application of chemotherapy or radiotherapy treatments.[5] What attracted Gottlieb's particular interest however was that, in this particular case, the young man had undergone no such chemotherapy treatment and should by rights have been in the peak of health.

Over the following weeks, Gottlieb's search yielded three more cases of immune deficiencies. All displayed the same candidiasis (yeast infection) and *pneumocystis carinii pneumonia* (PCP) Gottlieb had found in his first subject. Also, according to Gottlieb's new testing protocol, each case had 'low' T-cell immune-system lymphocyte counts. By April 1981, Gottlieb was convinced he was on to something.

He contacted Wayne Shandera, a local public health official who had been trained by the Epidemic Intelligence Service or EIS. Gottlieb asked Shandera whether his local health department had any reported immune deficiency cases. Shandera said that he had, and was able to add another patient to Gottlieb's list. Recalls Gottlieb: *"We didn't know*

---

[3] **Ransom, Steven,** from a telephone interview with Dr M Gottlieb, 13ᵗʰ December 1999

[4] **Duesberg, Peter H** *Inventing the AIDS Virus*, Regnery Publishing, Inc. Washington DC, 1996 p.147

[5] Ibid.

what this illness was at the time, but I remember being able to tell the CDC: 'I think we have a new disease.'"[6]

Gottlieb by now had noticed another intriguing factor. All five patients were male and active homosexuals. Gottlieb became convinced he had unearthed something unique. He telephoned the *New England Journal of Medicine*: *"I've got something here that's bigger than Legionnaires'!"* he remarked with excitement.[7] Shandera meanwhile, intrigued too by the homosexual connection, contacted James Curran at the Venereal Disease Division of the Centers for Disease Control (CDC). Curran, in turn, wrote *"Hot Stuff! Hot Stuff!"* on his announcement and had an article on the syndrome hastily published in his agency's *Morbidity and Mortality Weekly Report*. The report came out on 5th June 1981 and implied that the syndrome suffered by the five subjects could represent a major new and hitherto unknown sexually transmitted disease - this despite the fact that the five subjects had experienced no sexual contacts with each other.[8]

Once published, the article attracted other, similar cases which were being reported to the CDC. At this time, the report writers recognised that some of the patients they were studying were suffering from rare, blood-vessel tumours and skin disfiguring lesions known as Kaposi's Sarcoma (KS). Gottlieb's early patients had another striking similarity in common: they were all heavy users of recreational drugs, including nitrite inhalants such as 'poppers', the volatile liquid used by homosexuals to facilitate anal intercourse and heighten orgasm. The CDC did at one point entertain the notion that part of the problem could be a bad batch of 'poppers', but subsequent investigations failed to turn up a 'bad lot', and so the theory was discounted. [9]

Further studies by the CDC confirmed that the men demonstrating such rare and fatal diseases had all been part of the promiscuous homosexual scene for many years, generating many hundreds of sexual contacts. When the CDC began tracing the contacts of those exhibiting

---

[6] Ransom, Steven, telephone interview with Dr M Gottlieb... op. cit.

[7] **Shilts, Randy** *And the Band Played On*, St Martin's Press, New York: 1987, p.63

[8] **Gottlieb, MS, HM Schanker, & A Fan** "Pneumocystis Pneumonia - Los Angeles", *Morbidity and Mortality Weekly Report* 30 (5th June 1981): 250-252

[9] **Etheridge, EW** *Sentinel for Health: A History of the Centers for Disease Control*, University of California Press, Berkeley, CA 1992 p.326

Gottlieb's syndrome, more and more immune deficiency patients appeared. Such 'infection clusters' were producing impressive circumstantial evidence that the syndrome was spread sexually by homosexuals.

Meanwhile in New York, a Dr Friedman-Kein, independent of Gottlieb's research, had also been tracking the same curious phenomenon. Up to this point, the information gathered on this syndrome had largely remained within the confines of the investigative medical authorities. But now its existence was set to reach a far wider audience. Reporting on the work of Dr Friedman-Kein, a *New York Times* article of 3rd July 1981 began:

> *"Doctors in New York and California have diagnosed among homosexual men, 41 cases of an often rapidly fatal form of cancer, with Kaposi's Sarcoma appearing in one or more violet spots anywhere on the body. The cause of the outbreak is unknown. Doctors who have made the diagnoses are mostly in the New York City and San Francisco Bay area, and are alerting other physicians in an effort to identify more cases. Dr Friedman-Kein described the appearance of the outbreak as rather devastating."*

While the CDC investigators concentrated their efforts on tracing the sexual contacts provoked by each newly discovered patient, Kaposi's Sarcoma and Opportunistic Infections task force members[10] were examining the plausibility of a new apocalyptic fear. Building on the circumstantial premise that Gottlieb's new syndrome was sexually transmitted, the CDC was now speculating: *Was this syndrome, to date found only in homosexual drug-users, now spreading into the heterosexual population?* Using the infection pattern of hepatitis B as the model, investigators began their search.

Interestingly however, they did not conduct their research across the usual cross-section of the populace. To determine the spread of Gottlieb's syndrome into the heterosexual population, they began by examining non-homosexual heroin addicts and haemophiliacs.[11] Before too long, the researchers were able to confirm the same worrying

---

[10] KSOI - another division of the CDC
[11] Duesberg, Peter H, *Inventing...* op. cit. p.135

statistics: the group they were examining had a low T-cell (immune lymphocyte) count and, sure enough, they also shared a number of immuno-deficient health disorders.

But even though the illnesses they recorded in this new group were, in some cases, not even similar to the diseases suffered by Gottlieb's homosexuals, the CDC once again classified these two groups as falling into Gottlieb's new 'emerging immune deficiency epidemic'. Homosexuals, haemophiliacs and now heroin addicts. Rationally or otherwise, it appeared the new epidemic was spreading.

From the sidelines, however, a number of independent researchers were not happy with the manner in which the CDC had been amassing their data. As we will later discover, one or two even went so far as to accuse the CDC of fabricating a new epidemic just to keep appropriate sections of their work force in well-paid employment. Such accusations are not as far-fetched as they first appear. A brief examination of what became known as 'the swine flu outbreak' brings to light the actions of one particularly powerful, yet little known section of the US medical research community, the Epidemic Intelligence Service (EIS), a department within the Centers for Disease Control.

The interestingly named Epidemic Intelligence Service was formed in July 1951 by Alexander Langmuir, an associate professor at Johns Hopkins University School of Hygiene and Public Health. Langmuir had persuaded US health officials and Congress to grant the CDC special contingency powers to deal with future, potential, public health emergencies. The Epidemic Intelligence Service thus came into being and was granted significant spending powers and unlimited access across the medical institutions to give advanced warning of any perceived health threat, however remote. Such was the autonomy enjoyed by the EIS that one of Britain's senior epidemiologists, Dr Gordon Stewart, described them as *"the medical CIA."* [12]

The considerable budget allocated to the EIS helped fund the positioning of agents into local health departments and corporations throughout the United States and even abroad. Acting as the eyes and ears of the CDC, the mission of these agents was primarily to act as

---

[12] Ibid.

guardians of America's health and report on even the most insignificant outbreaks of illness. Such was the mandate of the EIS that, from the outset, finding new diseases and tracking existing viruses and bacteria became fundamental to its worth and purpose.

In January 1976, five soldiers succumbed to a particular strain of flu. The EIS was the first to sound the alarm, and named the emerging outbreak 'swine flu', based on the prevailing speculation that pigs had served as the reservoir for the supposed virus. Such were the frightening predictions put out by the EIS concerning the destructive potential of the 'new' disease that President Ford and Congress panicked, allocating large funds for another flu vaccine – a sum of money which would spread itself liberally down through the epidemic research chain. The program stalled however when insurers discovered that the vaccine itself could produce extraordinary side-effects, ranging from severe fevers and malaise to paralysis and death.[13]

To the intense chagrin of the White House, except for the five soldiers, no flu epidemic ever materialised, and nothing remotely akin to an epidemic ever ventured onto the horizon. Unless Congress could be convinced the danger was real, the lucrative vaccine program would be terminated, severely depleting the coffers of the CDC. A battle plan was needed and fast. In their book, *Anatomy of an Epidemic*, Gordon Thomas and Max Morgan-Witts describe the CDC's preparations:

> "The large Auditorium A, located in CDC headquarters in Atlanta, became the command centre - called the 'war room.' Set up especially for this occasion, it contained banks of telephones, teleprinters, and computers, the hardware for an unprecedented monitoring system which, to work, also required a typing pool, photocopy machines, and doctors sitting at rows of desks in the center of the room."[14]

The CDC and the EIS worked around the clock, week after week, following up every rumour of flu outbreaks. And then, on the horizon, a sighting! A cluster of pneumonia cases appeared in Philadelphia. This pneumonia had manifested itself in a group of elderly American Legion

---

[13] **Ellison, Bryan** *Rethinking AIDS* Homepage: www.rethinkingaids.com, December 1999
[14] Ibid.

members several days after returning home from their July convention. Was this remote link all that was needed to rescue the funding? The EIS sprang into action. On Monday 2nd August, within three hours of receiving word of this outbreak, EIS officers flew up to Philadelphia. They were joined by dozens of experts from the CDC.

On arrival, the CDC began wilfully feeding rumours that this was the start of the swine flu epidemic they had predicted. To cover the rampaging 'swine flu' story, the CDC assigned none other than former EIS employee Lawrence Altman, now chief medical correspondent to the *New York Times*. Needless to say, Altman rose to the challenge magnificently. The *New York Times* ran its piece on the 'emerging swine flu epidemic'. The American public quivered at the notion of a virulent pathogen sweeping the country. Congress was spooked enough to change its mind and approve the CDC's request for a mass swine flu vaccine program. What came next was nothing short of a catastrophe.

Over 50 million Americans were inoculated during the next months, ultimately producing at least 1,000 cases of severe nerve damage and paralysis, dozens of deaths, and nearly $100 million in liability claims. As if that were not enough, within days of the legislative approval for the vaccine program, the EIS was compelled to acknowledge that the minor pneumonia outbreak was not actually related to swine flu at all.

The EIS rode out the whole sorry affair by blaming the outbreak on some newly isolated bacterium. In reality, those stricken American Legion ex-servicemen were later found to be an elderly group, several with kidney transplants, who had all become extraordinarily drunk at their convention – combined risk factors quite capable of compromising the ability of the immune system to resist certain minor infections. Under these circumstances, minor outbreaks of flu or other opportunistic syndromes are relatively common, though rarely fall into the public spotlight. What made this situation disturbingly different was that, in their pursuit of a disease and a dollar or two, the CDC's only success had been in bringing virtual panic and not a little death to America, compelling many millions to accept an untested and unsafe vaccine treatment they otherwise would not have taken – all over a harmless bacterium that can be found in the plumbing system of almost any building.[15]

With little outward sympathy for either the CDC or the EIS, Congress was considering a drastic reduction in their budget. It was now 1981, and the CDC were in dire need of some national threat to health to revive their tarnished image and avert an imminent cash crisis. In that same year, AIDS appeared. And as Bryan Ellison, co-author of *Inventing the AIDS Virus*, wryly comments, *"not a moment too soon."*[16]

But back to the story at hand. The Centers for Disease Control were now contacting hospitals across the US in an effort to trace patients with unusually low immune system T-cell counts. Jackson Memorial Hospital in Miami reported that, while they had no cases exactly fitting the CDC requirements, they had recently taken in a number of undernourished Haitian boat people. The physical hardships endured during their extremely arduous sea journey had left all passengers with tuberculosis, salmonellosis, and a variety of gut parasites, leading to diarrhoea and malnutrition.[17] On the strength of that description alone, the CDC were satisfied the Haitians were suffering from Gottlieb's 'new syndrome'. Conclusion: The 'epidemic' had now spread to Haiti. The unsubstantiated but very professional-looking speculation was now snowballing. Could the 'outbreak' have originated in Haiti itself? Harry Haverkos from the EIS was sent to Haiti to study that possibility first-hand.

Joan Shenton, author of *Positively False,* has also studied the Haitian problem, but from a very different perspective. Her chapter entitled "Whatever Happened to AIDS in Haiti?" gives a penetrating insight into the political and social havoc wreaked so indiscriminately by the 'big boys' from across the water:

"The effect of all of this on Haiti was dramatic. The tourist industry collapsed and with it the economy. In the US, Haitians all over the country lost their jobs. Incensed by this, Haiti's Minister for Health, Ari Bordes, demanded the CDC

---

[15] Duesberg, Peter H, *Inventing...* op. cit. pp.56, 144
[16] Ellison, Bryan, *Rethinking AIDS*, op. cit.
[17] **Shenton, Joan** *Positively False*, Tauris Publishers, 1998

strike Haiti off their list of risk categories. The CDC reluctantly agreed, and with a little juggling of statistics, they reallocated the Haitians to different specific disease groups."[18]

But the damage had already been done. Even though the range of diseases found in the largely undernourished Haitian population were different to those being reported on mainland America, the definitions for Gottlieb's 'immune deficiency syndrome' were simply expanded further to include the Haitian diseases. In what amounted to no more than a cynically contrived, data-stretching exercise, the little island of Haiti was ruined almost overnight with an unwarranted 'frightening disease' tag, was then exited just as quickly and left to pick up the pieces of its shattered economy.

Back to mainland America and the growing 'crisis'. The CDC were now taking known and classified conditions such as TB, malnutrition and salmonellosis and reclassifying them as 'strange unknowns' under the umbrella of Gottlieb's syndrome. As a result of adding more diseases to the syndrome profile, it appeared to the public that an epidemic was emerging and growing at an alarming rate. The CDC then embarked on a program to publicise the new syndrome, and in July 1982 named it the Acquired Immune Deficiency Syndrome, or AIDS. Announcing it as 'BIG' they then solicited the help of powerful politicians Henry Waxman (Los Angeles) and Philip Burton (San Francisco).[19] As AIDS was apparently 'decimating' their constituents, both men wasted little time raising a furore inciting Congress to consider emergency spending programs to combat the new AIDS threat. The first in a series of emotionally charged media articles appeared as a result of the political lobbying of these men, whose efforts later succeeded in diverting millions of additional dollars into the coffers of the Centers for Disease Control.

Waxman and Burton's high profile orchestrations were difficult to ignore. Soon every major newspaper, news agency and talk-show was getting in on the act. By late 1982, hundreds of articles were appearing in the news media about the new syndrome known as AIDS. *Time* and *Newsweek* ran front-page stories of the mystery killer syndrome and hypothesised about its danger to world populations. Gruesome 'before

---

[18] Ibid.
[19] Duesberg, Peter H, *Inventing...* op. cit. p.151

and after' pictures of the victims appeared. On 12th April 1983, *Newsweek* ran its cover on the subject and labelled AIDS "The Public Health Threat of the Century". Every article began asking the same central questions: *What was causing it? Who was most at risk? What was being done by government to combat this new apocalyptic threat to public health?*

Bizarre and fanciful predictions of entire populations being wiped out appeared in the less responsible tabloids across the globe. The question hotly debated in medical circles became: *Was AIDS caused by a virus or bacteria?* And just as the bounty on Jaws led to shark hunters of all shapes and sizes putting frenziedly out to sea in the search for the dreaded great white, so too did AIDS attract the immediate attention of the virus hunters. And then, one press conference in April 1984 changed the whole future of AIDS and AIDS research. A hunter had apparently speared a new virus – the virus identified as Human Immunodeficiency Virus, or HIV.

But not all were convinced by the orthodox party line that had rapidly formed concerning AIDS, or that a new virus had even been found. But the AIDS monster had been unleashed and the subsequent juggernaut became unstoppable. Shortly after the announcement that HIV was the cause of AIDS came news of a new 'HIV identification' procedure, now commonly known as 'the HIV test'. The test was marketed to a fearful public as highly specific and accurate. A suspected carrier could now be tested. The social penalty the test exacted on the 'positive ones' would very quickly become apparent.

If the AIDS monster was big, its media machine was gargantuan. Reliant only upon the unsubstantiated information fed to them by this tiny cluster of AIDS 'professionals', front pages across the world were telling us that HIV could live on toilet seats for up to three weeks. It lurked on the doorknobs of homosexual bedrooms. By late 1986, the world was awash with documentaries featuring tales of HIV-infected, killer prostitutes with grudges against males, or sex-crazed rape villains blackmailing defenceless housewives with HIV infection. Firemen became fearful of giving car-crash or drowning victims the kiss of life. Dentists squirmed for the first time when they looked into an open mouth. Says one 'positive' individual who remembers all too well:

"I was treated like a leper and a fiend. My family abandoned me. They refused to eat with me until checking it was safe with the doctor. When I had dental treatment, the dentist wore a helmet and a visor. I became so afraid I might infect others, I would wash my hands over and over again with bleach until they were raw."[20]

The declared pathological make-up of AIDS was a horror. Here was a virus that could creep into your system and remain dormant for up to ten years before striking. All over the world, doctors began announcing a new and shocking diagnosis: *"You have HIV, the virus that causes AIDS. There is no cure."* One day - nothing. The next, lesions all over the body, barrier nurses face-masking around you, friends and relatives making excuses and disappearing. And then the spasms, the haemorrhaging and the croaking of your last breath before becoming another one of the horrifying, mounting AIDS statistics.

The press scare stories became so virulent that virtual panic broke out in the gay communities of the Castro, San Francisco and West Hollywood, Los Angeles. Rallies of the fearful hit the streets of the major cities throughout the world. Various media began widening the catastrophe and AIDS was soon reported spreading into middle-class heterosexuality, generating real fear in those originally deemed outside the high-risk groups. Newspapers fed the public bewildering stories of poor souls who, upon receiving the dreaded HIV-positive result, climbed the stairs to the hospital roof and launched themselves into oblivion.[21] Husbands, wives and lovers began to whisper, *"Not tonight, Joseph/Josephine,"* looking at each other, wondering if perhaps their previous history had now rendered them irreversibly 'armed and biologically dangerous'.

Through the power of the media, AIDS united the public with princesses, politicians and the paparazzi. Television brought the

---

[20] Shenton, Joan, op. cit.

[21] *"I'd Shoot My Son if He Had AIDS."* So ran the UK's *Sun* newspaper headline on 14th December 1985. The headline was accompanied by a photograph of Dad holding a shotgun to his son's head. Commenting on this, Kenneth Thompson, author of *Moral Panics*, stated *"The coverage managed to combine some of the most potent images of threats to normal life, family breakdown, infanticide, teenage sexuality, homosexuality and contagious disease."* (**Thompson, Kenneth** *Moral Panics*, Routledge Press, 1997. An analysis of how perceptions are shaped and reflected through the media over time).

average man and woman to the 'virtual' bedside of Rock Hudson, Liberace, Freddie Mercury, Arthur Ashe, their gaunt faces and final harrowing days broadcast around the world. From the portrayal of Tom Hanks' AIDS sufferer in the movie *Philadelphia* to Britain's most popular soaps, *East Enders, Casualty* and *Holby City*, the myths and fables about AIDS were dramatised and driven home into an unquestioning, collective psyche. The incontrovertible message? AIDS was stalking the planet. Everyone was a target. Everyone was at risk. The future was bleak. [22] [23]

Unless, of course, you studied the facts.

In beginning to unravel the incredible deception that has been woven around the myth of AIDS, we have so far examined the role played by the CDC, EIS and the media in helping to establish AIDS as a 'crisis'.[24] There were, however, a number of other key players fulfilling critical roles in the formative years of AIDS. Let us focus our attention on one of these individual in particular, that most celebrated of virus hunters, Dr Robert Gallo, the man who introduced the world to the idea of HIV and soon after, his special test by which to identify 'the virus'. *The perfect revolving door?*

Let us wind the clock back a few years to George Orwell's apocalyptic 1984. America is in the grip of a new and terrifying enemy, predicted to wipe out entire nations in the coming few decades....

---

[22] In November 1986, the UK government announced a £20 million ($28.5 million) advertising campaign, which included leaflets delivered to every door, nationwide posters, radio, TV and cinema coverage of the horrors of AIDS.

[23] *"Why Must The Innocent Suffer?" Daily Express* 25th September 1985. *"AIDS: The NEW Holocaust." Sunday Telegraph*, November 1985. *"All Are Potential Victims." Sunday Times*, November 1985. See also *Guardian Newspapers*, 14th September 1995: *"Angel of Death"* - the story of a mysterious young woman who had apparently infected nine men within a six-month period. Despite the £10,000 offered by various newspapers for her name and whereabouts, no 'angel' was ever traced. The hundreds of UK and overseas journalists who had converged on the tiny Irish town of Dungavon all left within a few days.

[24] "CDC Flouts its Own Human Rights Rules", *Plain Dealer Online*, 8th November 1998. *"...fashioning scientific partnerships on nearly every inhabited continent, and undertaking medical research without obtaining basic agreements to avoid abuses. Medication was dispensed without assurance that patients be fully informed, monitored for safety or free to refuse experimental drugs in all 96 research projects conducted by the CDC in the last 10 years,"* say investigators Epstein and Sloat.

23

NATIONAL ENQUIRER OR
RATIONAL ENQUIRER?

*"Endless loop - n. See loop, endless. Loop,
endless - n. See endless loop."* **Isaac Asimov**

23rd April 1984, and the National Academy of Sciences auditorium in Washington DC was packed with journalists and television crews abuzz with anticipation. US Health Secretary Margaret Heckler emerged and greeted the assembly, declaring: *"Today we add another miracle to the long honour roll of American medicine and science. Today's discovery represents the triumph of science over a dreaded disease."*

The miracle Heckler announced was that a team of virologists led by Dr Robert Gallo had isolated a virus that was apparently causing AIDS. This was a tremendous announcement and the enormity of Heckler's words, coming at a time when the climate of AIDS-induced fear was at its pinnacle, could not be overestimated. Speaking of Gallo's work as an all-American miracle discovery, Heckler reminded the public of the gratitude it owed to medicine for triumphing over this dreaded disease.

And then it was Dr Gallo's turn: *"Dr Gallo, Sir! Dr Gallo, this way! Sir, this way!"* chorused the hordes, the whirring and flashing banks of cameras more befitting a royal arrival. The jostling photographers vied for that special Gallo victory pose to accompany the following day's world editorials which would triumphantly announce: *"The beginning of the end of the scourge of AIDS!"*

With no demanding questions being asked of Dr Gallo, the likeable, but rather nervous-looking doctor produced what he described as photographic evidence of the cornered virus and briefly outlined the supporting science behind his discovery. And all the time, the flashing and the whirring. Gallo's discovery was the news of the decade, the answer the world had been yearning for, the relatively unknown doctor now quite fittingly fêted as the saviour of the human race.

But there was a big problem, as AIDS critic David Rasnick stated:

"With that announcement, Gallo had publicly leapfrogged across the scientific process - across peer-review and analysis, across the very checks and balances of science."[25]

Gallo had committed the cardinal sin as far as transparency of scientific reasoning was concerned. At the time of his press announcement, he had allowed no independent body initially to verify his claims. How very different the future of AIDS and HIV might have been, had Margaret Heckler opened the press conference thus:

"Science and research must be studied in the context of all the interested parties involved. The questions centre on determining the relative weight of the various allies in the 'fact-creating' process - e.g. funding bodies, businesses, departments of state, professions and other scientists. In analysing scientific debates, <u>one should always ask what social, institutional, political and philosophical interests lie behind often apparently 'neutral' and 'technical' knowledge claims.</u>"[26]

An important piece of advice, ten years too late and in any case forgotten in the fanfaronade of the public canonisation of Dr Gallo. After all, for the good of mankind, science and scientists had been pulling out all the stops to bag possibly the biggest killer this planet had experienced since the bubonic plague of the 15th century.[27] And of course, in this all-out mercy mission to save so many human lives, it goes without saying that nothing improper would have been taking place... *doesn't it?*

To our very great cost, and hence the reason for this book, we shall see that such trust and benevolence extended towards the science supporting AIDS and HIV are misplaced and naïve in the extreme. A special panel of the National Academy of Sciences would, a few years after the Gallo announcement, be meeting to discuss:

---

[25] **Rasnick, David,** "Blinded By Science", *Spin Magazine*, June 1997

[26] University of Manchester Institute of Science & Technology (UMIST) research methodology course handout, 1994

[27] For insight into the environmental factors behind the Great Plague, please see **Ransom, Steven** *Wake Up To Health In The 21st Century*, Credence Publications, 2004

"...a persistent pattern of behaviour on Dr Gallo's part of repeated misrepresentation, suppression and distortion of data, and the misrepresentation of findings in such a manner that would enhance Dr Gallo's claim to priority."[28]

The above panel was by no means be the only one urgently convened over the years following the 1984 press conference to discuss the methodology of Dr Gallo, the founding father of the alleged HIV. What exactly was this man getting up to in the closeted, almost impenetrable world of beakers, bunsen burners and centrifugal separation? Before we visit the Gallo laboratories in Bethesda, Maryland, it might serve us firstly to examine the scientific and medical culture into which the AIDS phenomenon/crisis reared its head in the first place. Establishing what attitudes prevailed at the time concerning the theories on illness and contagious disease will highlight why the search for the cause of AIDS was so dominated by the virus hunters.

The National Institutes of Health (NIH) in America began in 1887 as the Hygienic Laboratory. An insignificant organisation at the time, it was actually affiliated to the Public Health Service, which itself was affiliated to the US Navy. The NIH has since retained its military connections, the Surgeon General to this day wearing a white uniform. In the 1930s Congress created the National Cancer Institute (NCI), which became the first subdivision of the NIH to focus on any particular illness, and the parent organisation thus became known as the National Institutes of Health. James Shannon became the director of the NIH in 1955, taking up his position at a time when the US was experiencing the effects of polio.

James Shannon persuaded Congress to release considerable amounts of money to fund an all-out medical war against polio. But with the natural waning of polio in the early 1960s (now showing all the signs of being an environmental affliction[29]), the many specialists trained exclusively in virology to combat the condition dropped their investigations and began to concentrate their efforts on the search for the cure for cancer. And of course, being virologists, all sought the virus that must surely lurk behind one of mankind's biggest killers. Any

---

[28] *Chicago Tribune*, "Scientific Panel Accuses Gallo of Recklessness," 27th March 1992
[29] Ransom, Steven, *Wake Up To Health...* op. cit.

26

notions cancer might be a toxic, metabolic, nutritional or environmentally-based disease were given short shrift.[30] Twas a virus and a virus only they hunted, nothing else considered. Gallo himself later remarked: *"Sometimes we virologists have a virus in search of a disease."*[31]

As we shall see, the narrow ambitions of the virus-hunting fraternity have produced some highly embarrassing and costly medical research failures. This is particularly true of the research commissioned by Congress for Richard Nixon's 1971 War on Cancer, the NCI announcing that same year that a vaccine against cancer would be available by 1976.[32] The dominant power the virus establishment wields and its disconcerting ability to get things badly wrong on occasions is highlighted most succinctly by South African barrister Anthony Brink:

> *"As we've all seen, when these oracles mumble and the press trumpets blare, the entire world eagerly gobbles up every word without demur. How many fake health crises have they delivered still-born into the popular consciousness? Take the idle herpes scare in the 70s, the phantom syphilis epidemic of the 30s and 40s, the great swine flu fiasco and that shining emblem of medical idiocy, the pellagra plague in the first four decades of this century, treating the people with arsenic and ruthless quarantine, which turned out to be plain malnutrition among the politically awkward droves of poor whites in [America's] Deep South industrial towns.*

> *We need contagious epidemics to fight. Even imagined ones. They're tremendously psychologically useful. Germ theory so dominates contemporary medicine that it seeks germs everywhere, the more virulent the better, and especially if they can be linked to our culture's great taboos - sex and death. Anything to avoid facing up to unappealing political realities like widespread chronic under-nourishment among a*

---

[30] **Day, Phillip** *Cancer: Why We're Still Dying to Know the Truth*, Credence Publications, 2004 (available through credence.org)

[31] **Maggiore, Christine** *What If Everything You Thought You Knew About AIDS Was Wrong?* AFFA Publications, 1999

[32] *In These Times*, 8-15th August 1992

shameful number of our countrymen as the time-honoured and common-sense cause of broken health."[33]

Regular intakes of nutritious food? Whoever heard of such a thing? A sensible prescription lost in our overall reverence for the pharmaceutically-driven medical model, itself intent on blaming viruses for most of man's ills.

When a disease fails to perform to a given pattern, it is understandably important the medical establishment is seen by the general populace to be in control of the situation and fully understanding of the disease in all its complexities. It was virologist Carlton Guidachek who first put forward the notion of the slow virus - that an invader could gain entrance to the body, hide up and strike, even years later. Bryan Ellison comments:

"A few virologists in the early sixties simply invented the notion of the slow virus, [a concept] which was actually awarded the Nobel Prize in 1976. Of course, once the concept of slow viruses had come to be accepted, it was possible to blame conceivably any disease on a virus, no matter how uninfectious the disease was....."[34]

Although sounding quite plausible to the laity and even to some medical experts, the idea of the slow virus was eventually consigned to the scrap-heap. Science has shown the chief causes of disease are not dominated by the virus, but by metabolic/nutritional imbalances and ongoing toxicities which affect a person's immunity.[35] Micro-organisms as disease pathogens are opportunistic. The weaker the immune system due to poor diet, lack of hydration and environmental toxicity, the greater the likelihood of ill-health from them.[36]

Yet agencies around the world, such as the CDC and the EIS, daily shape our understanding of health and disease. In a discussion on 'shaped' awareness and preconceived ideas, Noam Chomsky, Professor of Linguistics and Philosophy at the Massachusetts Institute of Technology, stated that:

---

33 **Brink, Anthony,** *The Pope of AIDS,* http://www.virusmyth.com/aids/data/abpope.htm
34 **Ellison, Bryan,** "Rethinking AIDS" interview, March 1994, www.rethinkingaids.com
35 **Day, Phillip** *Health Wars,* Credence Publications, 2002
36 Ransom, Steven, *Wake up to Health...* op. cit.

28

"Hundreds of billions of dollars are spent every year to control the public mind."[37]

Subliminally or otherwise, vast sums of vested-interest money influence our attitudes towards illness today. Bryan Ellison reports:

"By the time AIDS came along, the virus hunters controlled all the reins of power in the biomedical research establishments, and so naturally they dominated the research on AIDS. The very first person to describe AIDS cases - Michael Gottlieb in Los Angeles describing five homosexual men with pneumocystis carinii pneumonia - himself was already suggesting that it was caused by the herpes-type virus, cytomegalovirus. [Such] was the result of the virus hunters being in a dominant position in the establishment."[38]

There was no choice in the matter. Until proven otherwise, any new and emerging disease from the early sixties onwards was first and foremost considered viral in nature. And that was also true for some of the well-established diseases, especially cancer.

In the early 1970s, Robert Gallo was working out of laboratories in Bethesda, Maryland, under the wing of the National Cancer Institute, and reporting to the immensely powerful Litton Bionetics. Gallo, a fully trained virologist, had been set a specific brief. Steven S Hall, author of *Commotion in the Blood*, says this of Gallo's early calling:

"Gallo set the research agenda, did the hiring and ran the lab meetings. Every lab has an overriding mission and Gallo's was no exception. Like many virologists, Gallo had been looking for a human virus believed to cause several forms of human cancer..."[39]

Gallo was considering the possibility of a particularly nasty virus, a virus hidden deep perhaps, but a virus he believed existed and could be detected - the virus most likely responsible for the dreaded leukaemia.

---

[37]*Continuum Magazine*, October 1996. Today the NIH annual expenditure is in excess of $10 billion (*Rethinking AIDS* interview).

[38] Ellison, Brian, op. cit.

[39] **Hall, Stephen S** *A Commotion In The Blood*, Little, Brown and Co. 1997

Leukaemia is the umbrella term to denote the unrestricted growth of under-developed, 'rogue', immune-system white blood cells (leukocytes). In failing to mature properly, they create greater and greater numbers of themselves until they crowd out the healthy blood cells, bringing the immune system to a kind of leukaemic gridlock. In their attempt to validate the 'leukaemia as virus' hypothesis, Gallo's lab technicians would obtain the cancerous leukaemia cells and concentrate primarily on trying to manufacture a 'culture' in which the cancerous cells might live. This would then allow the researchers time to study the cells, in order to try and identify any attacking virus.[40]

As a point of interest, more prized than isolating any virus, the virologists' Holy Grail was independently to create in these cultures the infamous killer T-cells. Just as the alchemist pursues the life force, the 'fifth essence' (*quintessence*), and the astrophysicist the single-line equation explaining the existence of universe, so the virologist dreams of creating test-tube T-cells – those unique and incredibly complex fighters in our immune system. (*"Having such killers at our beck and call would surely then make it possible for us to manipulate them, train them even and then direct them to destroy any invading cancerous cells."*) Discovering the recipe for promoting the growth of the T-cell was an ongoing pursuit. And creating the 'culture' in which the cells might grow was, and still is, time-consuming and expensive. The laboratory beakers containing Gallo's precious and painstakingly prepared cultures were all meticulously labelled and kept refrigerated at the necessary low temperature.

And then, in late 1974, after almost three years of experimentation, a leukaemic virus was apparently isolated, which Gallo named Human

---

[40] Leukaemia viewed as a fungal infection provoking reactions from the immune system? So say a number of specialists: Meinolf Karthaus MD saw how different children with leukaemia went into remission after the administration of a triple antifungal cocktail for their 'secondary' fungal infections (Karthaus, M, *Treatment of fungal infections led to leukaemia remissions*. 28th September 1999). Mark Bielski recorded in 1997 that leukaemia, whether acute or chronic, was connected with the bowel yeast *candida albicans* (Bielski M, Boyd, W, *Introduction to Medical Science*, Lea & Febiger, Philadelphia, PA, 1997). Half a century ago, Dr J Walter Wilson stated: *"It has been established that histoplasmosis [fungal infections] and leukaemia, Hodgkin's disease, lymphosarcoma, and sarcoidosis are found to be coexistent much more frequently than is statistically justifiable by coincidence."* (Wilson, JW, *Clinical and Immunological Aspects of Fungus Diseases*, Charles C. Thomas, Springfield, IL, 1957). Milton White MD was fully convinced of the fungal/cancer connection after he had detected, using the proper isolation techniques, fungal spores in every sample of cancer tissue he studied.

Leukaemia 23 (HL23V). Gallo immediately reported the discovery to the local scientific community, and submitted a paper on the isolated virus to *Science* which was published in January 1975. Newspapers were quick to report on Gallo's remarkable achievement, but his peers were even quicker to question his claims, asking what culture he was using, how he had prepared it and how he had gone about his experiments. Gallo hedged and would not reveal the chemistry of his culture, nor would he share the exact manner in which his virus had been isolated - only that it had. Concerning the validation of scientific claims, Geoff Watts, author of *Pleasing the Patient*, reminds us of traditional scientific methodology:

"Researchers are required not only to publish their findings, but also to describe their method in sufficient detail to allow others to repeat the work. Indeed the repeatability of an experiment is one of the criteria by which scientists judge the claims of their peers." [41]

Gallo's habitual reluctance to conform to this sensible scientific methodology served only to anger his professional colleagues. Their questions became more forcefully posed: *"Where's the leukaemia virus, Dr Gallo? And how did you preserve the cells?"*

With pressure mounting on Gallo to produce the necessary evidence to support his 'discovery', suddenly... a calamity! One morning lab workers arrived to find that the refrigerator containing the supposed leukaemia virus and the precious 'cultures' had been mysteriously unplugged. Any evidence of the HL23V, supposedly preserved in the secret 'culture', known only as WHE, had now been ruined. Says Gallo of this unfortunate but quite timely disaster:

"We were screwed. We were only able to say, 'Honest, we had it!' and prove it to nobody." [42]

Popular medical literature of the day however makes no mention of these 'minor' irregularities along the way, and credits Gallo with all the 'leukaemia breakthrough' headlines. It was Robert Gallagher, a technician at Gallo's lab during this period, who later stated that they hadn't *actually* wrapped their hands around an *actual* virus; rather they had inferred its presence based on a number of intricate

---

[41] **Watts, Geoff** *Pleasing the Patient*, Faber and Faber, 1992
[42] Hall, Stephen S, op. cit.

virological predictions.[43] Exactly the same species of 'virtual truth' can be found propping up much of what we know as quantum physics. Anyone wishing for direct evidence that various, exotically named particles such as quarks, nuons and gluons, actually exist are quite breezily quoted Heisenberg's Uncertainty Principle. *"One can estimate where the particle might be going and where it might have been, but not actually where it is."* That, in laymen's terms, is the central tenet of particle physics. The virtual existence of the quark and the massive funding to track it down bears uncanny resemblance to the chemokines and cytokines rearing their virtual heads in the blood sciences of today - equally exotic and authoritative in name as the quark family, but equally elusive to the rational, enquiring eye and mind. Similarly, in the case of Gallo's HL23V, the overriding question: *"Was there ever really a virus in the first place?"*

And what about that secret 'culture' known only as WHE? Gallo certainly exercised prudence in not expanding on its exact make-up. The initials stand for 'whole human embryo'. Aborted whole foetuses, developed no further than the first trimester (3 months), had various cell extractions performed upon them, the extracted cells forming the base composite for the melted HL23V. Readers comforting themselves that foetuses not exceeding the first three months are probably just underdeveloped cell matter may be shocked to discover otherwise, as the following extract from "Love Your Unborn Neighbour" reveals:

"By the sixth week from fertilisation, tiny fingers appear, followed within days by toes. At the same time the eyes develop the lens and retina and the eyelids begin to appear. Brainwaves can also be detected. At seven weeks the child has its own fingerprints, the outer ear is present and the inner ear, with its hearing and balancing mechanisms, is well established. At twelve weeks the child's features become more defined. The unborn baby can open or close the lips, wrinkle the forehead, raise the eyebrows and turn the head. The baby's sex is easy to determine, the baby measures about 90 mm and weighs 45 g and she is also sensitive to touch."[44]

---

43 Ibid.
44 *New Scientist*, "Earliest Feelings Help to Develop the Senses," 7th May 1987. Quoted in *Love Your Unborn Neighbour*, SPUC Publications, London, 1994

Three years' lucrative funding and thousands of man-hours later and finally, a virus existing only by the word of Dr Gallo, now melted. With his reputation severely dented, and Gallo still insistent that he had isolated said leukaemic micro-organism, the Maryland virologist immediately began scouring the labs for a cell specialist, someone with the necessary qualifications to resurrect his battered HL23V program. Steve Hall recounts:

> *"It would not be exaggerating to characterize the mood in the lab as scientifically based hysteria. And into this dark environment of desperation, suspicion and frantic scientific scrambling arrived Doris Ann Morgan..."* [45]

With a PhD in Biochemical Genetics, Doris Morgan joined Gallo from Litton Bionetics where she had held the post of senior scientist in cell biology. Working alongside Frank Ruscetti, her brief from Gallo was *"Get me that HL23!"* Steven Hall again:

> *"Ruscetti's tack was to test every known bone marrow cell line and as many embryos as possible to see if he could scare up the same factor that had disappeared in the great refrigerator meltdown, and he did a prodigious amount of work. Before he finally stopped looking he had tested close to 250 cell types, all failures.*
>
> *Morgan took a different tack. She decided to stick with the existing system of growing leukaemic cells and see if she couldn't tinker with the conditions enough to nudge the cells into expanded growth. While working in Houston she had managed to keep a number of white blood cells taken from mice, known as granulocytes, in test tubes for up to 3 weeks, which at the time, was considered a phenomenally long out-of-body experience for a blood cell. The leukaemic cells Gallo studied were also granulocytic, also of myeloid (bone marrow) origin. Perhaps Morgan could tweak the system a bit."* [46]

And in March 1975, after much tweaking, Morgan noticed the appearance of cells apparently not seen before. Could they be the hallowed T-cells, the Holy Grail of immuno-biology? Said Gallo at the

---

[45] Hall, Stephen S, op. cit.
[46] Ibid.

33

time: *"My God, this is important! But we've gotta be sure we're right."*[47]

Gallo soon began informing his peers that his lab had discovered the recipe for T-cell growth culture. His peers abruptly sat up. This was a massive step towards the elusive cure for leukaemia, and for the war against cancer in general. The administration of a strain of this factor in the patient could promote an absolute proliferation of killer T-cells, that would in turn make short shrift of any cancerous cells. This time Gallo did share his recipe for human T-cell growth factor with the scientific community, submitting his research for full publication in *Science*, March 1976. Gallo subsequently received hundreds of calls from immunologists, complaining that they couldn't get the growth factor to work. Says Ruscetti, *"They were saying we were crazy, but this was only because they didn't really want to accept it."* [48]

Another dead end. But Gallo, impervious to the scepticism of his peers, sensed that Morgan's discovery was going to be big, and he calculatedly made a phone call upstairs. Stephen Hall again:

> *"Given the personalities of Gallo and Ruscetti, it's just one of those things in human dynamics. They saw the significance of it; this was Nobel Prize stuff. Those personalities never concerned themselves with personal aspects, just with the scientific problem, and Doris got left in the dust. Finally, on 23rd January 1978, Phillip Markham from Litton Bionetics informed Morgan in a letter that her job would be terminated."* [49]

Morgan was being moved on. Asked if Gallo ever treated her badly, Morgan's only regret was that Gallo had taken all the credit for the discovery of the special factor, which, perhaps for Morgan, was a blessing in disguise. Gallo's growth factor, instead of being rightfully discarded, was adopted by Steve Rosenberg, and its name changed in 1979 to Interleukin 2, IL2 for short. Rosenberg, who would later become Ronald Reagan's cancer surgeon, took IL2 to new and dizzy heights. IL2 was fêted as a 'cancer breakthrough' on the front cover of

---

[47] Ibid.
[48] Ibid.
[49] Ibid.

Fortune magazine on 25th November 1985 and Rosenberg was awarded the $100,000 Armand Hammer cancer prize the same year for his work.

Anyone wishing to embark on a study of the long history of 'cancer breakthroughs' will find the exercise a very sobering one. The NCI cancer vaccine, promised for 1976, has, of course, failed to materialise. And when traced with any objectivity, the history of IL2's 'effectiveness' in treating cancer is a horrendous litany of medical disaster. Almost every patient treated with IL2 suffered fever, malaise, nausea or vomiting, diarrhoea, sharp drops in blood pressure, skin rashes, breathing difficulties, liver abnormalities and irregularities in blood chemistry. Rosenberg himself details a number of horrifying case histories, and one in particular where the administration of IL2 had precipitated amongst other things, vomiting, swollen joints, lung fluid and 'vascular leak syndrome', where blood would ooze through the vessel walls and collect under the skin.[50] Reading between the lines, it is evident that many a hapless patient died of his oncologist.

Charles G Moertel, a renowned and respected physician at that time, delivered the following opinion on the benefits of Interleukin 2 in the *Journal of the American Medical Association (JAMA)*, 12th December 1986.

"The treatment itself is an awesome experience, usually requiring weeks of hospitalisation, much of which must be spent in intensive care if the patient is to survive the devastating toxic reactions. In short, IL2 is associated with unacceptably severe toxicity and astronomical cost. This is not balanced by any persuasive evidence of true net therapeutic gain. IL2 would not seem to merit further application in the compassionate management of patients with cancer."

And today, the Chiron Corporation, pharmaceutical manufacturers and suppliers of Interleukin 2, state on their web page that *"...many people are leading normal lives because of IL2."* Credence has requested details from Chiron Corporation on the specific manner in which people have been helped by IL2. To date there has been no reply.

---

[50] **Rosenberg, Steven** *The Transformed Cell,* Putnam, New York: 1992

In reality, Doris Morgan's much vaunted IL2, remembered only as Gallo's discovery, has proven to be yet another dead end in a history of dead ends for our senior virologist. And he never won the Nobel Prize either. And what of Gallo's credentials to date? Anthony Brink is brief and dismissive about the early days of 'the Pope of AIDS':

"Gallo's disgraceful behaviour in relation to his AIDS research was no first. Had he not ascended to such power and influence within the federal health bureaucracy, it is likely his claims to have found a single infectious cause for the disparate diseases grouped together as AIDS in the early 1980s would have been laughed out of court.

After all, this was the bright spark who, with almost as much fanfare as that at his flash-bulb popping HIV press announcement, had loudly touted his discovery of what he claimed to be the first identified human retrovirus, HL23V, in the mid 1970s. After another look, this exciting find turned out to be nothing of the kind, just another accidental laboratory artefact. His laboratory hadn't done the most basic controls. To his great embarrassment, Gallo had to retract his claims, and HL23V then modestly retired as a virus from the scientific lexicon."[51]

And what of Gallo's team? What of their credentials? A brief trawl through the records reveals that Syed Zaki Salahuddin, one of Gallo's closest lab associates, was convicted of using Gallo's laboratory credit card to purchase supplies from the NIH central stores; supplies which he then spirited out in order to set up his own research laboratory. Having established his own lab, Salahuddin then installed his wife as director. Running alongside this venture, Salahuddin also arranged for various 'private interest' items to be manufactured, all within Gallo's own laboratory, which were then sold to outside competitors.[52] Dr Dharam Ablashi, a fellow worker at Gallo's laboratory, was recruited as a sales rep for this clandestine outfit. Salahuddin was ordered to repay $12,000 and complete 1,750 hours community service. Salahuddin was also one of the principal authors of the early papers announcing the discovery of an HIV. Gallo's second-in-command at the lab, Prem

---

51 Brink, Anthony, op. cit.
52 **Oostram, Neenyah** *New York Native*, 14th August 1989, issue #330

Sarin, would later find himself on trial for directing $25,000 into his own account which should have been spent hiring a lab technician. Sarin was equally involved in the early papers on the 'discovery' of HIV.[53] In his "Lab Rat" article, Seth Roberts summarises the early years thus:

"Gallo's lab has been described by past and present employees as a 'den of thieves' and as being 'full of mediocrities'. In its quantity of intrigue and capricious purges, it resembles a 'medieval Italian town', says one former employee. He adds, 'I'm surprised somebody hasn't killed someone there.'

Without AIDS, Gallo would have been simply another grasping, over-productive, under-scrupulous scientist. Dozens of awards, hundreds of papers, thousands of tantrums, a vast phone bill, a ringside seat at the discovery of IL2 and HTLV1, and a handful of derailed careers - that would have been the Gallo legacy. AIDS, however, gave him the chance to really make a difference."[54]

And 'make a difference' he did. IL2 was becoming a fading memory for Gallo. It was now the early 1980s, and Gallo's attention was becoming increasingly diverted towards Gottlieb's up-and-coming, but as yet unnamed AIDS syndrome. But just prior to Gallo's full pursuit of the virus that *'must surely lie at the heart of AIDS'*, another startling claim was made by some members of his team. In 1980, Frank Ruscetti and fellow biologist Bernard Poiesz apparently isolated the very first human cancer retrovirus, naming it Human T-cell Leukaemia Virus or HTLV1 for short. The 'discovery' of the cancer retrovirus (a generalised description of this interesting little entity being, *"I can't see it under the microscope, and you can't see it either. But if Gallo's lab tells us there's one there, then what reason do we have to disbelieve them?"*) has subsequently precipitated massive injections of cash into virus labs the world over. It will come as no surprise to the reader that yet again, HTLV1 has proven to be just another of those 'Gallo lab discoveries' that no-one has yet been able independently to verify. This fact does

---

53 Shenton, Joan, op. cit.
54 *Rethinking AIDS* Homepage, December 1999

not stop Robin McKie, science editor for the *Observer* newspaper, from writing:

"Once a contender for the Nobel prize, for discovering the first human cancer-causing virus, Gallo...." etc, etc. [55]

But it was to be one artefact in particular, the elusive HIV, which would prove to be the most destructive 'quark' in the history of immunology.

1983 was the beginning of Robert Gallo's public ascendancy into the AIDS debate. The following chronology traces the key events leading up to Gallo's world-wide announcement of his 'discovery' of HIV and that 'HIV was probably the sole cause of AIDS'.

In May 1983, fellow virus hunter Luc Montagnier from the Pasteur Institute, Paris, trustingly submits a paper to Robert Gallo, outlining what Montagnier believes to be a new type of virus. Gallo senses that Montagnier may be on to something and edits the paper in such a manner that the reader would concur that the Montagnier virus is a member of the same family as Gallo's HTLV1 (leukaemia) virus. The ensuing paper conveniently bolsters Gallo's 'discovery', regardless of the fact that HTLV1 had been completely discredited.

In July 1983, Gallo receives a shipment of factor for inspection, which Montagnier states contains his virus, named Lymphadenopathy-associated Virus or LAV. Montagnier believes that this is the virus which may lie at the heart of AIDS.

On 14th September 1983, unaware of the growing US interest in his findings, Montagnier lectures on the blood test he has developed, which can apparently detect certain antibodies in the blood - antibodies that might indicate the presence of his virus, and hence, the onset of AIDS.

On 15th September 1983, Montagnier files for a UK patent on his potentially lucrative AIDS blood test. Throughout all of these proceedings, Gallo has been in attendance at a number of meetings

---

[55] **McKie, Robin** *Observer Newspapers*, "Resurrection of the AIDS Pioneer," 22nd December 1996

where the technicalities of Montagnier's virus and its supporting science are intimately discussed. These and other factors would later add weight to accusations that Gallo was attempting to plagiarise and then 'cash in' on Montagnier's work.

On 22nd November 1983, after close observation of Montagnier's potentially momentous discovery, Gallo announces that his lab too has isolated certain particles, which might also be the AIDS virus. Not surprisingly though, an independent analysis of the samples submitted by Gallo for verification produced no trace of a virus. To counter these embarrassing findings, Gallo's lab almost immediately announces the discovery of yet another virus, which is named HTLVIII. Gallo states that this is most definitely the much sought-after AIDS virus. A subsequent enquiry to establish the actual existence of Gallo's HTLVIII (later renamed HIV) determines that yet again, Gallo had failed to isolate any virus. Roche Laboratories found no trace of HTLVIII in the ten samples submitted to them.

On 12th March 1984, despite the fact that Gallo's HTLVIII does not apparently exist, James Curran from the CDC meets with Gallo, and tells him that the blood test procedure that Gallo has been working on confirms the presence of Gallo's HTLVIII virus in blood samples of suspected AIDS patients. In other words, Gallo claims discovery of a virus, and then claims a method to detect the virus. This 'full-circle' scenario is then given the official stamp of approval by a close colleague in an influential position. More respectably translated, the Centers for Disease Control have just informed the National Institutes of Health and the National Cancer Institute that everything is satisfactory. Gallo's two inventions will go on to 'confirm' to the waiting world that the epidemic known as AIDS is viral. Says Gallo later: *"In Curran's view, we had determined the cause of AIDS."*[56]

In the same month, Gallo's well-timed letter to the *Lancet* is published, telling of his 'struggle' to isolate Montagnier's LAV, the virus that Montagnier believed was responsible for AIDS.[57] And indeed, several years later, Montagnier would confess that his own lab had

---

[56] History of key events, 11th August 1986. Robert Gallo's sworn declaration.
[57] *Lancet,* 5th March 1984

never actually isolated the virus known as LAV, according to the standard rules for isolation.[58]

On 23rd April 1984, Heckler introduces Gallo to the world. That same day, Gallo submits his blood test kit for a US patent. Anthony Brink dryly comments:

> *"In cravenly seeking the endorsement of Big American Science, Montagnier naively left his keys in the ignition, and the next thing it was gone. Gallo resprayed Montagnier's LAV as HTLVIII. It was later renamed HIV on the basis of Gallo's claims, without proof to warrant its fearsome title."*[59]

In short, at that Washington press conference which proclaimed the discovery of the vicious virus probably causing AIDS, there was no virus.

On 29th May 1985, Gallo's patent on his own blood test is granted. Montagnier's patent is still pending at this time. (Montagnier's patent was never granted.)

In December 1992, Robert Gallo is indicted for scientific fraud by the Office of Research Integrity, a supervisory department of the National Institutes of Health (NIH), based on his declaration that he had discovered HIV. Anthony Brink comments:

> *"Having sneaked through a patent application on the blood test, thus guaranteeing him a fortune in royalties, Gallo went on to publish four papers in the prestigious if dowdy journal* Science *two weeks later. Then the trouble started: an exuberant international dispute over who stole the fake diamonds. For Gallo, this was the Paula trouble that led to Monica."*[60]

And fake diamonds they were too. For the habit of *inferring* the presence of a virus without actually being able to lay hands on one is a habit not solely confined to the Gallo labs. To loyal readers of *The*

---

58 Q. *"Could it be anything else than a retrovirus?"* A: *"No, well... after all, yes. We did not purify."* Extract from an interview between Luc Montagnier and Djamel Tahi. "Did Montagnier Discover HIV?", *Continuum* Vol 5, No 2, January 1998

59 Brink, Anthony, op. cit.

60 Ibid.

National Enquirer, Montagnier's money-spinning LAV may well be alive and well (along with Elvis and assorted bullet-headed extra-terrestrials). To the rational enquirer however, Montagnier's LAV remains elusive to this day. The scandalous use of 'inferred' photography in modern-day science and the blatantly false imagery produced is discussed in more detail later.

Montagnier was incensed when he learned of Gallo's televised announcement. He believed that Gallo had quite simply stolen his virus and would now reap the rewards. Montagnier was not going to forego his cut. Branching away from the usual loose laboratory rules for verification, Montagnier pressed for definite proof that his share of the expected proceeds would be 'isolated', verified and then visibly transferred into his own bank account. He wasn't going to rely on Gallo only inferring that this would soon take place. An indistinct photograph of Montagnier's share of the proceedings would not suffice in this instance.

The subsequent wranglings between Gallo's laboratory and the Pasteur Institute and between the French and US governments became increasingly acrimonious, with accusations of scientific plagiarism and 'inexplicable' cross-contamination of evidence. Presidents Reagan and Chirac persuaded Montagnier and Gallo to meet up to sort out their differences. They emerged from their meeting in a Frankfurt hotel, agreeing to share the royalties on the blood testing kits, which, by 1994, would amount to $35,000,000.[61] Whether or not Montagnier has ever forgiven Robert Gallo for exhibiting a photograph of Montagnier's unsubstantiated 'virus' at that Washington press conference, claiming it as his own, will probably never be known.

So where was Montagnier's virus at that press conference? Where was Gallo's virus? In truth, on that spring day in April 1984, there was actually no virus to show the world. This of course did not hinder proceedings. The show had gathered unstoppable momentum. Re-enforced with the full backing of the American medical, political and scientific establishments, a photograph of someone else's *virtual* virus, no virus of his own, and a lucrative patent application at the back of his mind, Dr Robert Gallo braced himself to enter the world's stage.

---

[61] Shenton, Joan, op. cit.

Brushing down his suit, he entered the whirring, flashing arena of the National Academy of Sciences auditorium, announced a major breakthrough in the battle against AIDS, and quite unabashedly soaked up every last bit of the worship the world bestowed upon him.

MANUFACTURING A THEORY

Who needs rules, anyway?

The Emperor's New Clothes: Many years ago lived an emperor, who thought so much of new clothes that he spent all his money in order to obtain them. One day two swindlers came to his city and declared they could manufacture the finest cloth to be imagined. Their colours and patterns, they said, were not only exceptionally beautiful, but the clothes made of their material possessed the wonderful quality of being invisible to any man who was unfit for his office or unpardonably stupid.

"That must be wonderful cloth," thought the emperor. "I must have this cloth woven for me without delay." Advancing a large sum of money to the swindlers, he requested they set to work immediately. The swindlers set up two looms, and pretended to be very hard at work. They asked for the finest silk and the most precious gold-cloth; all they were given, they secreted away, working at the empty looms till late at night.

"I should very much like to know how they are getting on with the cloth," thought the emperor. But he felt rather uneasy when he remembered that he who was not fit for his office or unpardonably stupid could not see it. Personally, he was of the opinion that he had little to fear, yet he thought it advisable to send somebody else first to see how matters stood.

So he sent one of his ministers. The good old minister went into the room where the swindlers sat before the empty looms. "Heaven preserve us!" he thought, and opened his eyes wide, "I cannot see anything at all!" But he did not say so. Pointing to the empty looms, both swindlers requested the minister to come near, asking him to admire the exquisite pattern and the beautiful colours. "Oh dear," he thought. "Can I be so stupid? I cannot say that I am unable to see the cloth!" The minister praised the weavers and exclaimed, "What a beautiful pattern! What brilliant colours! I shall tell the emperor that I like the cloth very much!"

The swindlers worked about in the air with big scissors, and sewed with needles without thread. "The emperor's new suit is ready now," they said at last. The emperor and all his ministers came into the hall. The swindlers raised their arms as if they held something in their hands and said: "These are the trousers! This is the coat! And here is the cloak! They are all as light as a cobweb, and feel as if one has nothing at all upon the body; but that is just the beauty of them."

"Indeed!" said all the courtiers. But they could not see anything, for there was nothing to be seen. The emperor undressed, and the swindlers pretended to put the new suit upon him. "I am ready," said the emperor. "Does not my suit fit me marvellously?" The emperor marched in the procession and all who saw him exclaimed: "Indeed, the emperor's new suit is incomparable! What a long train he has! How well it fits him!" Nobody wished to let others know that he could see nothing, for then he would have been unfit for his office or unpardonably stupid. Never were the emperor's clothes more admired.

Suddenly, amongst the gathered onlookers, a lone voice was heard. "But father, the emperor is naked! He has nothing on at all!" exclaimed a little child. "Good heavens! Listen to the voice of the innocent child," said the father, one whispering to the other what the child had said. And very soon did the whole people cry, "He is naked! The emperor is naked! He has nothing on at all!" This made a deep impression upon the emperor, for it seemed to him that they were right; but he thought to himself, "Now I must bear up to the end." And so it was that the king walked with still greater dignity before the crowd. And with full ceremony did his courtiers carry the train of his garments, the garments that did not exist.

* * * * *

After Gallo's 1984 press conference, the world witnessed the AIDS establishment commencing its pursuit of HIV with a single-mindedness that bordered on religious obsession. HIV became THE world threat - no longer a shadowy, ephemeral enemy. According to the Gallo camp, HIV was now a proven virus with its own pathology, biochemistry, and one heck of an impressive name. Human Immunodeficiency Virus was now officially Public Enemy No. 1.

After the historic announcement, the amount of artillery the CDC and other health organisations wheeled up to the battlefront to face HIV was awesome. The public was certainly impressed with the apparent high level of science being brought to bear on AIDS. After all, if two presidents had to meet just to adjudicate the row over who discovered HIV, this whole thing had to be for real.[62] The problem was, dissident researchers also visited the front-line to peer curiously at mankind's new virus enemy for the first time. They were at first surprised and then unnerved to find a naked emperor facing them. While there were vague 'photographs' of something referred to as HIV, no one could produce any scientific, definitive proof that the virus had been successfully isolated and catalogued in an acceptable scientific manner, surely not an unreasonable demand. Yet the more visible dispute going on that spring over who had first claim to the discovery of the supposed HIV (Gallo or Montagnier?) adeptly masked the more pertinent question of whether the virus existed at all.

Dr Kary Mullis, Nobel Prize winner for his invention of the Polymerase Chain Reaction (PCR), writes as follows:

> *"In 1988 I found myself writing a report on our progress for an HIV project, sponsored by the National Institutes of Health, when I found that I did not have the scientific reference for a statement I had just written: "HIV is the probable cause of AIDS". I turned to the virologist at the next desk, a reliable and competent fellow, and asked him for the reference. He said I didn't need one. I disagreed. While it's true that certain scientific discoveries are so well established that their sources are no longer referenced in the contemporary literature, that didn't seem to be the case with the HIV/AIDS connection.*

> *Of course, this simple reference had to be out there somewhere. There had to be a published paper, or perhaps several of them, which, taken together, indicated that HIV was the probable cause of AIDS. There just had to be. I was going to a lot of meetings as part of my job. I got in the habit of approaching anyone who gave a talk about AIDS and asking*

---

[62] *Newsweek*, "The End of a Scientific Feud", 25th July 1994

him or her what reference I should quote for that increasingly problematic statement, "HIV is the probable cause of AIDS".

After ten or fifteen meetings over a couple of years, I was getting pretty upset when no one could cite the reference. I didn't like the ugly conclusion that was forming in my mind: that the entire campaign against a disease increasingly regarded as a 20th century Black Plague was based on a hypothesis whose origins no one could recall. That defied both scientific and common sense. Later I discovered why I was having so much trouble finding the references that linked HIV to AIDS. There weren't any."[63]

And later...

"10,000 people in the world now specialize in HIV. None has any interest in the possibility that HIV doesn't cause AIDS, because if it doesn't, their expertise is useless."[64]

What disturbed Mullis was that all known and accepted, scientific investigative techniques had so far failed to prove one single aspect of the existence of HIV.

Professor Beverly E Griffin is Director and Professor of Virology at the Royal Postgraduate Medical School in London. In May 1990, Griffin stated in Nature:

"It would be irresponsible to produce guidelines on AIDS until an infectious micro-organism is identified and the means by which it causes disease are understood."

What Professor Griffin was diplomatically highlighting was that six years after Gallo made his HIV=AIDS announcement on prime-time television, a single infectious micro-organism that causes all AIDS-defining diseases had still to be identified. *Continuum*, a quarterly magazine campaigning against the fraudulent HIV=AIDS hypothesis, offered a cash reward for any proper, no-nonsense evidence for the existence of HIV. A further offer from The Huw Christie Memorial Foundation of $100,000 has also been made known to the establishment. To date, both these rewards remain uncollected.

---

[63] **Mullis, Kary** Foreword to *Inventing the AIDS Virus,* Duesberg, P, Regnery Publishing, 1997
[64] **Hodgkinson, Neville** *Sunday Times of London,* "Experts Mount Startling Challenge to AIDS Orthodoxy," 26th April 1992

Neville Hodgkinson, a former science and medical correspondent for the *London Times*, was at the forefront of breaking the AIDS story as it unfolded in the mid-1980s. He remembers:

"There was never really to my mind, and I have looked at this very closely now, evidence of a new virus actually being isolated.... I think, in that second half of the 1980s, it was a great story and we took it on board as a kind of public health emergency too. And that's a danger with any group of professionals, whether they are media workers or scientists, to get too close to the sort of propagandising that happened with AIDS. We lost our sense of judgement, I'm afraid, on this issue, because we felt that sense of fear and urgency. It was like a war and for too many of us in those circumstances, critical judgement went out of the window." [65]

Another way in which the 'AIDS as virus' theory can be called into question is by employing Koch's Postulates. These are a simple set of rules to which the medical profession generally adhere, in their attempts to identify pathogenic illness. Koch stated that three main factors must exist in order to determine that the micro-organism under scrutiny is the primary cause of the disease being observed:

1) *"...it must be present in all cases of a specific disease..."* As we will learn, there are many patients diagnosed with AIDS who do not test positive for 'HIV'.[66]

2) *"...inoculations of its pure culture must produce the same disease in animals..."* All efforts to produce AIDS by inoculation of an 'HIV culture' have failed. No pure HIV culture has ever been produced.

3) *"...and from these it must be obtained in pure cultures and propagated."* i.e. any virus or pathogen must be isolated and observed. To date, this has never been accomplished with the entity known as HIV.

When pressed on these matters, Harold Jaffe, the senior AIDS and HIV investigator at the CDC, and Professor Robin Weiss, a British AIDS researcher, both argued:

---

[65] *AIDS: A Second Opinion*, a video documentary, Gary Null & Associates, PO Box 918, Planetarium Station, New York, NY 10024 USA Tel: (212) 799-1246 Fax: (212) 769-3566

[66] US CDC report of AIDS cases without the presence of HIV - December 1992

"It seems bizarre that anyone should demand strict adherence to these unreconstructed postulates 100 years after their proposition." [67]

Gallo too saw no problem dismissing one of science's time-tested, primary check and balance systems:

"Rules were needed then, and can be helpful now, but not if they are too blindly followed. Robert Koch, a great microbiologist, has suffered from a malady that affects many other great men: he has been taken too literally and too seriously for too long." [68]

Koch's Postulates have remained one of the primary benchmarks for the germ theorists for over a century. But now, because they do not fit the HIV profile, they are apparently not to be *"taken too literally and too seriously...."* While a complete critique of germ and virus theory is beyond the remit of this book, the latest Credence title *Wake Up To Health in the 21st Century* reveals the many weaknesses in today's conventional 'infectious disease' thinking, and contains important information on the crucial, yet much ignored role played by the environment in so many of our so-called 'infectious' diseases.

Journalist John Lauritsen became intrigued with the arguments put forward by those opposed to the HIV theory of AIDS. In preparing for an interview with AIDS dissenter, Professor Peter Duesberg, a retrovirologist renowned for asserting that HIV does not cause AIDS, Lauritsen decided to do some groundwork. He telephoned the CDC and NIH to interview officials concerning HIV. Finally getting in touch with the National Cancer Institute's press officer, Lauritsen demanded definitive proof that HIV caused AIDS. She could not give an answer and postponed the call until the following day when the persistent Lauritsen confronted her again. He was read a hastily prepared response. When this failed to address his arguments, Lauritsen quizzed her about HIV not meeting the criteria for infectious disease, as demarked in Koch's postulates. Not having heard of Koch's Postulates, the press officer asked when they were formulated. On being told they

---

[67] *In These Times*, 5th August 1992

[68] **Gallo, Robert C** *Virus Hunting - AIDS, Cancer, and the Human Retrovirus: A Story of Scientific Discovery*, Basic Books, New York, 1991

had been in existence for about 100 years, she replied: *"Oh, well then, would you say that those apply now?"* [69]

Professor Duesberg is concerned at the low level of science surrounding Gallo's investigations into HIV. His reservations prompted him to state:

"If you think a virus is the cause of AIDS, do a control without it. To do a control is the first thing you teach undergraduates. But it hasn't been done. The epidemiology of AIDS is a pile of anecdotal stories selected to fit the virus-AIDS hypothesis. People don't bother to check the details of popular dogma or consensus views." [70]

With HIV undetectable and AIDS not conforming to infectious disease patterns, could this disease be in any more disarray? Unfortunately, yes. Another anomaly in the AIDS equation was that a number of people diagnosed as 'HIV negative' were being documented as suffering from symptoms identical to those who were deemed HIV positive.

Upon discovery that AIDS was being diagnosed in patients who were HIV negative, Project AIDS International (PAI), a Los Angeles-based AIDS research organisation, attempted several times to clarify this seeming incongruity with the Centers for Diseases Control. CDC at first explained that these cases had different viral causes, but later, after being quizzed repeatedly by PAI chairman Jeremy Selvey, the government agency then tried to deny any knowledge of such cases. [71] Even though this issue was clearly of major importance to public health, PAI was cautioned by CDC that these findings were not for general broadcast. [72]

After continued pressure from Project AIDS International, the CDC finally submitted documentation of at least 30 cases of HIV-free AIDS. By 31st December 1992, the CDC had reported 97 such cases. These were to be the tip of the iceberg. Later in *Science*, Peter

---

[69] **Lauritsen, John** Notes on conversations with CDC/NCI personnel, 11th - 12th June 1987
[70] Maggiore, Christine, op. cit.
[71] **Selvey, Jeremy** *Public Information Dossier and Report to the United Nations*, 15th March 1993. PAI, 8033 Sunset Blvd #2640, Los Angeles CA 90046 USA
[72] Ibid.

Duesberg would report over 2,000 cases of HIV-free AIDS in existence.[73] Since 1985, many other cases of HIV-free AIDS have been reported. Reflecting also on the absurdity of HIV=AIDS when there are so many HIV-free AIDS patients in evidence, Robert Root-Bernstein, Associate Professor of Physiology at Michigan State University, declared:

> "On the existence of HIV-free AIDS, it's time to re-evaluate the HIV/AIDS hypothesis."[74]

In 1992, serious questions were raised by the Office of Research Integrity (a department of the National Institutes of Health), concerning Robert Gallo's possible involvement in scientific fraud. He came under the spotlight primarily as a result of his declaration that he had discovered HIV. Up until 1994, Robert Gallo remained under investigation by the United States Congress on various other charges of scientific impropriety. But today he is back in the fold, reinstated at the forefront of AIDS research in the United States.

By the end of the 1980s, Gallo's well-reported lack of laboratory ethics was beginning to concern other scientists around the world. Upon publicly questioning his old friend Gallo's HIV hypothesis in a paper published in *Cancer Research*, Duesberg's laboratory at Berkeley had its funding suspended.[75] Journalist Frank Prescott notes that during this period, Duesberg remained unruffled and stuck to his guns:

> "HIV does not cause AIDS," the scientist would tirelessly repeat. "The point that everyone is missing is that all those original papers have been found fraudulent... The HIV hypothesis was based on those papers."[76]

Despite his long-standing reputation as an outspoken critic of AIDS being caused by an infectious virus, Duesberg the retrovirologist is nevertheless still mounting arguments for the existence of HIV, but attributing to it only harmless, retrovirus-like qualities.[77] A more prosaic description of HIV retrovirology could be '*convincing*

---

[73] **Duesberg, Peter H** *Science*, September 1992
[74] Selvey, Jeremy, op. cit.
[75] *Cancer Research*, Vol 47, pp.1199-1220, 1st March 1987
[76] **Prescott, Frank** *"At Last. The Proof Sex and HIV Are Not the Real Causes of AIDS"* *Perceptions* magazine, Summer 1994
[77] Duesberg, Peter H, *Inventing....* op. cit. pp.175-178, 335, 338

terminology supporting the search for a biological entity supposedly lurking inside yet another biological entity, neither of those entities yet proven to exist'. Hardly the most exact of sciences. We must recall, though, that it was Robert Gallo who laid claim to the first human retrovirus 'discovery'. Both Gallo and Duesberg were 'retro-colleagues' in the early 1970s, and for Duesberg, the retrovirus remains a reality. However, for all the years Duesberg has spent relentlessly pursuing and 'inferring' the presence of the HI retrovirus, so far he has not persuaded this enigmatic little snipe to put in even the briefest appearance. What then is one to make of the 'inferred' science of retrovirology?

In his commentary on the ease with which fundamental error can become established 'scientific truth', W Deutscher's succinct statement more than adequately applies to Peter Duesberg's chosen profession:

> *"We concentrate on consistency without much concern of what it is we are being consistent about, or whether we are consistently right or wrong. As a consequence, we have been learning a great deal about how to follow an incorrect course with the maximum of precision."*[78]

Duesberg and other retrovirologists continue to validate their calling and justify pursuit of a missing retrovirus, telling us that the necessary proof is just around the next lucratively funded corner. This is simply not acceptable, says Dr Stefan Lanka:

> *"Why do 'HIV'-virologists never subject their viruses to the same generally accepted standard techniques of molecular biology as all other virologists and biologists do?"*[79]

And further:

> *"Such evidence up till now has never been produced for HIV. No photograph of an isolated HIV particle has ever been published. No control experiments as mentioned have been published to date. What has been shown are photographs of virus-like particles in cell cultures, but none of isolated viruses,*

---

[78] **Deutscher, W** University of Manchester Institute of Science & Technology course handout, 1994
[79] **Lanka, Stefan** *HIV: Reality or Artefact?*
http://www.virusmyth.com/aids/index/slanka.htm

let alone a structure within the human body having the shape ascribed to HIV. What the whole world has seen are models representing HIV with dish aerials, said to be receptors with which the virus attaches itself to cells." [80]

Thus we find ourselves in an ever-expanding No-Man's Land; that gulf separating 'virtual truth' from sensible science. The Emperor's new virus has been spun from an empty loom. Donald Gould, the former editor of *New Scientist*, warns of the dangers we invite by going that one step further and admiring the cut of the Emperor's cloth:

"Why not make the most of what the non-conformists have to offer and to hell with uncharitable logic? There is, I suggest, a powerful reason for rejecting this superficially attractive option. Truth is a fundamental value. If we accept uncritical thinking in one area of our lives for the sake of convenience or because of the popular appeal of a seductive myth and the short-term comfort to be gained by believing in the unbelievable, or because a false answer lets us pretend we are completely coping with a painful problem we haven't truly tackled, then we are all the more likely to adopt the same strategy in other situations; from dealing with the family, to managing the national economy, and from chairing the parish council to handling arsenals of nuclear weapons. The result is likely to be unhappy and stands a decent chance of proving a disaster. Irrational beliefs are always dangerously corrupting, even when they only relate to the cause and cure of piles." [81]

Duesberg is often cited as one the most respected and qualified heroes to champion the AIDS dissident cause. But the fact he believes HIV exists (albeit citing it as harmless) is a confusing position for those looking for intellectual consistency in the HIV debate. Karl Krafeld, president of the organisation Science, Medicine and Human Rights, believes Duesberg could be doing more harm than good. Krafeld has a history of being an awkward thorn in the side of the establishment. In 1989 he received two prison warrants for disclosure of corruption in financial services and for revealing that the German government was concealing information pertinent to human rights. In commenting on

---

[80] Lanka, Stefan, op. cit.
[81] **Gould, Donald** *The Black and White Medicine Show*, Hamilton, 1985

Duesberg's role in perpetuating the general belief in HIV, Krafeld makes the following observations:

"In their fight over who discovered HIV, Montagnier and Gallo promoted the retrovirus construct in a roundabout way. Duesberg publicly claimed the 'Missing Virus' award even after several scientists, including Dr Lanka, had published beyond reasonable doubt that there was never any such discovery. Acting thus, was Duesberg mindless of the fact that with his collaboration, millions of people would remain scared to death and continue dying?

If in future Duesberg does not want to be named in the same breath as Gallo and Montagnier, he has to present biological proofs, according to the fullest standards of biology, for the existences of retroviruses and HIV before he speaks about them, or claims 'HIV is harmless.' If this is not possible, he must then concur that belief in them is a psycho-product, an idea and biological error. A scientist who wants to be respected must be able and willing to escape the influence of his own psycho-mechanisms. With AIDS and HIV, lives are at risk. Lies and scientific slop work are unacceptable."[82]

Dr Robert Willner, author of *Deadly Deception: The Proof that Sex and HIV Absolutely Do Not Cause AIDS*, was another HIV=AIDS dissident up until his death from a heart attack aged 67. So determined was Dr Willner to prove to the world that AIDS was not spread sexually or through blood contamination, that he stunned the nation of Spain in 1993 by inoculating himself on TV with the blood of Pedro Tocino, a haemophiliac said to be HIV positive. The footage was broadcast in several European countries. Encouraged by the coverage he was receiving, Willner repeated his performance with different patients in front of the cameras of ABC and NBC. Said Willner:

"I have vowed that, if necessary I will go on injecting myself with the blood of ANY HIV positive person in every city of the world until this genocide is stopped. AIDS is the greatest fraud in medical history, and the perpetrators of this crime are raking in billions of dollars from it while hundreds

---

[82] **Krafeld, Karl** *Inventing the AIDS Virus?* Continuum. Vol 5. No 1, 1997

of thousands of innocent people are being murdered with the deadly drug AZT." [83]

Perhaps predictably, no US network reported this dramatic news on national television.[84] Up until his death, Dr Willner remained 'HIV-negative' in spite of constant testing and constant skin-pricking with supposedly HIV-infected blood.[85]

Dr Harvey Bialy, editor of *Bio/Technology*, made his views about the HIV hypothesis very frankly known as far back as spring 1992 in Britain's *Sunday Times*:

"The [HIV] hypothesis has become all things to all people. It violates everything we previously knew about virus disease, and allows any kind of therapy, any kind of research, to generate research bucks. What kind of science continues to place all its marbles, all its faith, all its research dollars, in such a theory? The answer I keep coming back to is that it has nothing to do with science; the reasons are all unscientific. We have taken sex and equated it with death, and into that mixture we have thrown money. What an ugly stew." [86]

And Professor Gordon Stewart, from the Public Health University of Glasgow in the UK, has noted:

"Nobody wants to look at the facts.... I've sent countless letters to medical journals.... they simply ignore them. The fact is, this whole heterosexual AIDS thing is a hoax." [87]

Nevertheless, the orthodox medical establishment is not about to have 'Project HIV' derailed quite so easily. The ultimate, twin heresy of the AIDS orthodoxy remains to this day:

---

[83] **Ashwell, David**, *Oxygen: The Source Of Life*, at www.shambhallah.com.au/AIDS.html

[84] See Part 2 for an examination into the role of the media in AIDS.

[85] **Willner, Robert** *Deadly Deception*, Peltec Publishing Co., 4400 N Federal Highway, #210, Boca Raton, FL 33431 USA

[86] Hodgkinson, Neville, *Sunday Times of London*, op. cit. pp.12-13

[87] AIDS Day Hypocrisy, The Health Supreme Network at http://www.newmediaexplorer.org/sepp/2003/12/01/aids_day_hypocrisy_why_fall_for_the_propaganda.htm

- Questioning the HIV=AIDS hypothesis
- Calling into doubt the infectious nature of AIDS

The reality is that since 1984, over 100,000 papers have been published on HIV, yet, with all the accepted methods available in biochemistry today, there is still no definitive proof that AIDS is infectious; that HIV causes AIDS; or that HIV even exists to be photographed. As anti-HIV activist Michael Verney-Elliott acerbically declared: *"Congratulations. From the people who didn't bring you the virus that causes cancer, it's the virus that doesn't cause AIDS."*[88]

Steve Connor, former medical correspondent for the UK's *Independent* newspaper, penned an article on the existence of HIV, and supported it with a front-page photograph of something referred to as HIV, where the 'virus particles' had been highlighted in luminous green for his 500,000-plus readership. Connor was contacted by Credence researchers on this matter. He was reminded that this colouring-in technique was actually standard *'inferred presence only'* practice in HIV virology. Since HIV had never been isolated, and was therefore invisible, it naturally followed that a luminous green overcoat was a vital addition, in order to help make its 'presence' known.

Credence asked Connor why he had not mentioned or explained the colouring-in technique in his article. Connor did not answer any of our questions, replying only that our line of argument was unconventional and most offensive to the many, many thousands who had so far died of AIDS. Connor, himself an author of a book on HIV=AIDS, stated further that our questioning him on this matter also flew in the face of the overwhelming evidence that HIV had been isolated. *"Those who question the HIV hypothesis,"* Mr Connor told us, *"also argue that the earth is flat."*[89]

AIDS dissident writer Alex Russell, son of film director Ken Russell, worked for a number of years at *Continuum* magazine, a publication devoted to examining the AIDS/HIV debate from all angles. On a

---

[88] Maggiore, Christine, op. cit.

[89] **Ransom, Steven** Personal telephone conversation with Steven Connor on 21st December 1999 in regard to Mr Connor's article dated 16th December 1999

number of occasions, Russell had reason to write to the Press Complaints Commission concerning HIV journalism, in particular, alleged inaccuracies in the writings of Connor:

"I would like to warn The Press Complaints Commission that Steve Connor is a well-known 'HIV' propagandist and will use highly emotive rhetoric to defend his 'HIV' credo. When it comes to reporting on 'HIV', he is not a critical, disinterested, or objective journalist but a fundamentalist defending his fanatical 'HIV' faith. Yet in a court of law, Steve Connor could not prove that 'HIV' exists.

I ask the Commission to take up my complaint against the editor of The Independent and Steve Connor for misleading their readership with this fraudulent [coloured-in] image. I have written three letters to the editor of The Independent, a) asking him to reconsider publishing my original letter, which was not published, b) to publish the letter in the correspondence pages, which was not done, and c) to ask the editor why he has not responded to my complaint. I look forward to hearing from the PCC in due course. Alex Russell, Assistant Editor, Continuum magazine."

Steve Connor is one of hundreds of journalists responsible for perpetrating the unproven HIV hypothesis. In an article from the UK's *Daily Telegraph*, dated Wednesday 20th September 2000, science editor Roger Highfield provided another fake photograph of the supposed HIV, his convincing caption reading *'Culprit: the AIDS virus..'* The glowing golf ball-type image was credited to the London Science Photo Library. This made the task of confirming the veracity (or otherwise) of Highfield's HIV picture relatively simple.

Upon our phoning the library, picture editor Justin Hobson stated:

"Oh yes, that was one of a number of computer-generated artists' impressions of what the AIDS virus might look like. In Highfield's article you are not seeing the real thing, it's only an impression. In fact we had another call from a scientist who was also concerned that the image was quite misleading. We

supplied *Highfield with a number of images, but he specified he wanted a computer graphic."* [90]

So who is the culprit in this instance? Surely, it is not a glowing, computer-enhanced golf ball, but *Telegraph Newspapers*. It is also interesting to note that, for some time now, the *Telegraph's* science department has been in possession of well-documented and very newsworthy contrary information on the subject of AIDS and HIV, none of which seems to be making any appearance in the paper. Suppression of vital facts, conflicting interests, and the role of the media in the AIDS debate are explored in more detail in a later chapter.

In an interview for *Zenger* magazine, Dr Lanka recounts his course of action when he discovered that there was actually no evidence for the existence of HIV:

"I was afraid of speaking about this with my friends and family. They would think I was absolutely crazy. So for a long time, I studied virology, from the end to the beginning, from the beginning to the end, to be absolutely sure that there was no such thing as HIV.... I realised that the whole group of viruses to which HIV is said to belong, the retroviruses - as well as other viruses which are claimed to be very dangerous - in fact do not exist at all." [91]

Lanka's personal quest to get to the heart of a matter (in this case, proof for the existence of HIV), serves as a reminder to us all that truth is not always presented on a plate. There are times when we must accept the responsibility to make that truth-seeking journey for ourselves. On the science supporting HIV, Martin Walker, author of *Dirty Medicine* stated:

"Had Gallo presented his theory in a reputable scientific journal rather than the Washington Press conference, his proposal would have been tested by his peers. A focused, centralised authority which had responsibility for evaluating scientific knowledge would have made a judgement, its clinical

---

[90] Telephone conversation with Steven Ransom
[91] *Zenger*, December 1998, p.7

basis would have been replicated and a dialectic process would have hopefully forged the truth.

As it was, there was no proving, no dialectic process, no clinical proof, no biological proof, no peer review, no open public critique. Gallo's idea was passed down in tablets of stone. HIV was found the guilty party without any kind of trial or search for the truth.... The idea that HIV is the cause of AIDS-associated illnesses is just that – an idea. There is even now no evidence, but only supposition to support it." [92]

Dr Valendar F Turner, a Fellow of the Royal Australasian College of Surgeons, has long been arguing against the HIV=AIDS hypothesis. On being asked in an interview to expand on his statement that not one antibody-positive person in the world is infected with HIV, he replied:

"No one has yet proved the existence of HIV using the proper method, based on the definition of a virus, as discussed at length at the 1973 Pasteur Institute meeting.... [93] *No research group has ever presented evidence for the existence of HIV according to the proper rules."* [94]

Fellow colleague of Turner, Eleni Papadopulos-Eleopulos is a bio-physicist at the Royal Perth Hospital in Australia. She has long proclaimed the falsity of HIV=AIDS.

"What nobody can deny is that HIV has never been accorded reality according to the correct definition [of a virus].... *Instead everybody's opted for a set of non-specific criteria and appear to imagine that if you put all these together, they must somehow metamorphose into the right answer.... In our view the greatest single obstacle to understanding and solving AIDS is HIV."* [95]

---

[92] **Walker, Martin** *Continuum* "A Seller's Market," Vol 5, No 1, October 1997

[93] **Sinoussi F, Mendiola L, Chermann, JC** "Purification and partial differentiation of the particles of murine sarcoma virus (MSV) according to their sedimentation rates in sucrose density gradients." *Spectra*, 1973; pp.225-235.

[94] **Turner, Valendar** "Do Antibody Tests Prove HIV Infection?", *Continuum*, Vol 5, No 2, December 1997

[95] Eleopulos and Johnson Interview, "Is HIV the cause of AIDS?" *Continuum*, Vol 5, No 1, October 1997

Here, Eleopulos and her colleagues are arguing that it is the use of the term 'HIV' itself that is the obstacle. Alex Russell adds body to this argument by stating:

"HIV imprinting has become subconsciously internalised on such a global scale that people will not be able to accept the brute reality that HIV does not exist." [96]

It was physicist Carl Popper who, in his defence of guarding the rules for logical argument, stated that no one can ever say there is no such thing as a white crow. One can only state that, *"To date, and according to my experience, I have not yet seen a white crow."* Whilst there is certain merit in this line of cautious argument, this approach has wreaked considerable damage to the valuable role played by definitive common sense. At what point does the crowd finally admit the emperor is naked? Eleopulos, Lanka, Turner, Krafeld and Russell are to be congratulated for taking an absolute position in the HIV debate.

Now, if the virus *does* exist, let's gather all the dissident dignitaries around the table and take a good look at the little critter. For the HIV-propagandists, surely now is the time for them to produce the necessary evidence, or publicly retract their position.

It is at this point in the AIDS story that we must now unavoidably head towards much bleaker terrain. What has perhaps been a gradual and somewhat uncomfortable downward slope for the reader who is new to this information on HIV/AIDS, now precipitates into a steep and horrifying descent, as the full implications of an HIV positive diagnosis are examined. One day, a normal everyday individual; the next, an abrupt HIV positive diagnosis and the death sentence is passed. And all it takes to know for sure is Robert Gallo's patented 'AIDS test'.

---

[96] "HIV Does Not Exist", *Positive Nation*, January 1998

POSITIVELY NEGATIVE

Examining the 'AIDS test'

"Have you considered an 'AIDS test'...?" Those two words instil only fear. Who is not aware that an HIV-positive diagnosis is synonymous with a suspended death sentence? In reality, the term 'AIDS test' is fraudulently misleading. There is not, nor ever has been, a 'test for AIDS'. Neither of course has there ever been a successful 'test for HIV' - the virus that not only has never been proven to cause AIDS, but, ever more disconcertingly, never seems to put in an appearance. What can be said with absolute certainty, however, is this. The ELISA and Western Blot tests are generating enormous incomes around the world for their respective manufacturers.

These two tests, we are told, identify HIV antibodies that have been created by a person's immune system in response to 'HIV invasion'. This statement is nonsense, and dangerous nonsense, as we shall discover. So what are these tests – the ELISA and the Western Blot - and how are they supposed to work?

The ELISA (Enzyme-Linked, Immuno-Absorbent Assay) and Western Blot tests are designed to highlight the presence of the supposed HIV, not by identifying the virus itself, but by identifying the presence of antibodies in the blood, allegedly unique to, and stimulated by the virus. The only real difference between the two tests is that the ELISA is supposed to measure antibody activity as a whole, whereas the Western Blot measures reactions to separate proteins supposedly making up the virus. As a result of this claim, the Western Blot method is deemed by most in the AIDS industry to be more specific than the ELISA test, and will often be used to confirm a positive ELISA test.[97] But, as we shall discover, all the diagnostic methods employed by the recognised laboratories are far from specific.

To carry out the test, the clinician introduces a foreign protein (antigen) into the blood sample and then monitors the blood for any signs of unique activity as the antigen meets up with the immune system's antibodies. And it is here that we immediately encounter the

---

[97] **Lake, Douglas** *The Biology Project*, University of Arizona School of Medicine

first hurdle. Introducing a foreign body into the bloodstream will always provoke a response from the immune system, the foreign presence releasing killer blood cells to combat the invading germ. This is what our immune system has been designed to do. The problem is that no antibody is ever specific to any one disease - a fact that has been widely known in science for a number of years. The ELISA and Western Blot tests are both marketed as being highly specific and accurate in identifying the presence of HIV antibodies in a person's body, but, as Christine Maggiore explains:

> "Both tests are non-specific to HIV antibodies and are highly inaccurate. Non-specific means that these tests respond to a great number of non-HIV antibodies, microbes, bacteria and other conditions that are often found in the blood of normal, healthy people. A reaction to any one of these other antibodies and conditions will result in an HIV-positive diagnosis. A simple illness like a cold or the flu can cause a positive reading on an HIV test. A flu shot or other vaccine can also create positive results. Having or having had herpes or hepatitis may produce a positive test, as can a vaccination for hepatitis B. Exposure to diseases such as tuberculosis and malaria commonly cause false positive results, as do the presence of tape worms and other parasites. Conditions such as alcoholism, liver disease and blood that is highly oxidated through drug use may be interpreted as the presence of HIV antibodies. Pregnancy and prior pregnancy can also cause a positive result."[98]

Yes, you read correctly. **A simple illness like a cold or flu, and even pregnancy can cause an HIV positive reading.** You could be suffering from a relatively innocuous illness, and your immune system, functioning quite normally, has detected the presence of an invader and ordered the defender blood cells into action. The activity of those perfectly healthy killers working away in the blood can then be interpreted by the 'AIDS test' and the experts administering it as indicative of the presence of the elusive HIV. **Did you know that?**

Christine Johnson of Project HEAL in Los Angeles, a voluntary organisation dedicated to exposing the myth of viral AIDS, has

---

[98] Maggiore, Christine, op. cit.

compiled and referenced some sixty different conditions that can cause a false HIV-positive reading. Some of these conditions have been included below for sober consideration.

"Naturally occurring antibodies, exposure to viral vaccine, flu, flu vaccination, tuberculosis, renal failure, hepatitis, organ transplant, haemophilia, tetanus vaccination, leprosy, alcoholic liver disease, blood transfusions, malignant cancers, proteins on the test filter papers, rheumatoid arthritis, herpes, Hepatitis B vaccination, healthy individuals as a result of poorly understood cross-reactions.... [plus forty-six others]."[99]

In the case of haemophilia and AIDS, it is Factor VIII, the man-made compound used to help in the coagulation process, that in the main has been responsible for false HIV readings.[100] Introducing this artificial agent into the bloodstream to help stem blood-flow will naturally provoke an antibody response, the immune system demonstrating it is functioning properly. These heightened levels of antibody activity are mistakenly read by the HIV test as indicative of the presence of HIV. Haemophiliacs, by the very nature of their condition, are prone to a number of life-threatening illnesses, and many do indeed die, but not from HIV.[101] The popular tabloids, of course, prefer to blare out *'HIV INFECTED BLOOD FOUND IN BLOOD BANKS MAY INFECT THOUSANDS'* rather than report the prosaic truth. Explaining the subtleties of opportunistic infection and blood-test cross-reaction does not sell newspapers.

Prior to the AIDS phenomenon, **the presence of antibodies had *never* been used as an indicator of any illness.** Yet since Gallo's HIV hypothesis was popularised, antibody testing has become *de rigeur* in the AIDS establishment as the indicator of infection, when the presence of antibodies actually denotes a normal immune system

---

[99] **Johnson, Christine**, in *Continuum*, September/October 1996

[100] Haemophiliacs lack key components that allow their blood to clot. In the 1970s-80s however, scientists developed Factor VIII, a product that contains the protein composites haemophiliacs need to restore the clotting ability they lack. Haemophiliacs are now living longer, but another problem has been widely recognised, as recorded by Professor Peter Duesberg: *"Hemophiliacs lose immune competence according to the cumulative amount of Factor VIII consumed: However, when the clotting factor is highly purified, the immune system remains healthy. Cost unfortunately bars many hemophiliacs from using purified Factor VIII. [Those] treated with commercial Factor VIII consequently develop some opportunistic, infectious diseases in the long run, particularly pneumonia and yeast infections."* (Duesberg, Peter H, *Inventing...* p.287)

[101] **Duesberg, Peter H** "Is HIV the Cause of AIDS?" *Lancet*, 346 (1995): pp.1371-1372

response to contaminants. The following extract from *Foundation News* is a glaring example:

> *"Professor Andrew McMichael in Oxford announced that 50 Nairobi prostitutes had high levels of killer T-cells in their bodies, which suggested they had been exposed to HIV. The Nairobi research was complemented by Oxford studies in Gambia which yielded similar results. Said Dr Omu Anzala: 'This was further evidence that it was the presence of T-cells which was holding the virus at bay'."* [102]

The possibility that the test kits could merely be reacting with parasites, TB bacilli, *candida albicans*, fungal conditions and other medical problems common to Africans is rarely considered by these doctors, even though the problem of inadvertent cross-reaction is common knowledge in the higher echelons of the AIDS establishment. In reality, a 'positive' reading is actually a 'false positive', the tests confirming only that the immune system is functioning satisfactorily.[103] **NO VIRUS IS ACTUALLY DETECTED, ONLY ANTIBODIES!**

The potential for false diagnosis with HIV tests has been fleetingly alluded to in mainstream publications such as *The London Times*, The European Union's *The Business*, *USA Today*, *The Telegraph* and *The Wall Street Journal*, the latter of which, on 11th January 1995, reported that the FDA were recalling HIV testing kits due to problems with high rates of 'false positives'.[104]

---

[102] *Foundation News*, Issue #34, September 1999
[103] *Bio/Technology Journal*, 11:696-707, June 1993
[104] *Wall Street Journal*, 11th January 1995, Health, page B-8

Frank Prescott, writing on behalf of Peltec Publishing in *Perceptions Magazine* in 1993, tells us:

"The London Times reports a major research group has recently proven the test for HIV to be completely invalid and 'riddled with false positives'. Malnutrition, multiple infections, having once had the flu, measles or a simple flu shot can all result in positive HIV diagnosis." [105]

This one fact alone destroys any validity of an 'AIDS test'. Yet there are many more ....

The US Food and Drug Administration also admits the 'highly specific' AIDS test has some worrying glitches, as the following *USA Today* bulletin tells us:

"People who receive gamma globulin shots for chicken pox, measles and hepatitis could test positive for HIV even if they have never been infected. The Food and Drug Administration says that a positive test could be caused by antibodies found in most of America's supply of gamma globulin. Gamma globulin is made from blood collected from thousands of donors and is routinely given to millions of people each year as temporary protection against many infectious diseases. <u>Dr Thomas Zuck of the FDA's Blood and Blood Products Division says the government didn't release the information because 'we thought it would do more harm than good.'"</u> [106] [emphasis ours]

US News & World Report had this to say on the subject on 23rd November 1987:

"With public health officials and politicians thrashing out who should be tested for HIV, the accuracy of the test itself has been nearly ignored. A study last month by Congress's Office of Technology Assessment found that HIV tests can be very inaccurate indeed. For groups at very low risk - people who don't use IV drugs or have sex with gay or bisexual men - <u>9 in 10 positive findings are called false positives, indicating infection where none exists.</u>"

The New England Journal of Medicine recorded the following:

---

[105] *Perceptions* magazine, op. cit.
[106] *USA Today*, 2nd October 1987

"The techniques of the HIV test have not been standardized, and the magnitude and consequences of inter-laboratory variations have not been measured. Its results require interpretation, and the criteria for this interpretation vary not only from lab to lab, but also from month to month."[107]

In reality, what one of the most respected medical journals in the world is diplomatically attempting to tell the reader here is that the HIV test is utterly invalid. A tacit endorsement of these sentiments comes from a surprising and unexpected source - the manufacturer's leaflet which accompanies the Western Blot (HIV) test kit itself!

"The test for the existence of antibodies against AIDS-associated virus is not diagnostic of AIDS and AIDS-like diseases. Negative tests do not exclude the possibility of contact or infection with the AIDS-associated virus. Positive tests do not prove AIDS or pre-AIDS disease status nor that these diseases will be acquired."

This from the test which is supposed to confirm the ELISA test! In other words the test kit is saying: *"Thank you for spending your money on me. In return for your considerable investment, I can predict absolutely nothing except that your blood sample contains antibodies."*

Medical researcher Dr Roberto A Giraldo is very familiar with the ELISA, Western Blot and Viral Load tests. He works at a laboratory for clinical immunology in one of the most prestigious university hospitals in New York City. When Dr Giraldo first came across the ELISA, he was surprised to learn that, to run the test, a patient's serum required diluting 400 times with a special specimen diluent. Most serological tests that search for the presence of antibodies against germs, such as those for syphilis, hepatitis A and B and the rubella virus, use neat or undiluted serum. The obvious questions facing Dr Giraldo were: What made HIV so unique that the test serum needed to be diluted 400 times? And what would happen if the patient's serum were not diluted?

Dr Giraldo ran extensive tests on blood samples that tested negative at 1:400 dilution. The same samples conducted with neat

---

[107] *New England Journal of Medicine*, 317:238-241

serum ALL showed positive. Dr Giraldo further found that if any person's blood, including his own, was tested with neat serum using the ELISA, the test came out positive! Dr Giraldo concludes that the tests are worthless, once again merely highlighting the presence of non-specific antibodies in the patient's blood serum.[108]

It is standard practice in most UK haematology and/or other blood testing laboratories to conduct at least two tests if the first test reads 'positive'. Confirmatory testing is usually carried out at any one of a number of Public Health Laboratory Service centres, for instance, across the UK. Credence Publications contacted the virus reference library at the UK's leading PHLS in Colindale, north London, to determine if they had ever been able directly to identify the presence of HIV in any of the blood samples sent to them. Was it rather the case that their blood test was designed to measure the presence of antibodies only? The representative from the lab informed us that he was not permitted to answer any of our questions, referring us instead to their press office. On asking the press office for the references that would point to HIV having been independently isolated, we were informed that of course HIV had been identified. *"The virus was isolated as far back as 1983 by Drs Gallo and Montagnier."*

Concerned at the high level of ignorance demonstrated in this reply from a leading virus laboratory, an attempt was made to speak to someone at management level at Colindale. A Mr John Parry, deputy head at the virus library, could make only vague references to papers he believed proved the existence of HIV, and he admitted that the testing procedures employed at the laboratories included ELISA, Western Blot and Polymerase Chain Reaction (PCR), and that they were not one hundred percent precise.[109]

In particular, PCR is used to measure the supposed 'viral load' of HIV, since the elusive virus itself can never be found, using traditional methods of detection such as virus culture. PCR's highly theoretical

---

[108] **Giraldo, Roberto** "Everybody Reacts Positive on the ELISA Test For HIV," *Continuum*, Vol 5, No 5, pp.8-10

[109] Polymerase Chain Reaction or PCR is another 'method' of HIV detection. PCR is invariably quoted as highly specific by those unacquainted with its true history. Neither approved nor recommended by either the FDA or the CDC, the application of this equipment in AIDS research has been described as *"...far more misleading then useful."* Maggiore, Christine, op. cit.

technique is supposed to detect fragments of genetic material in the blood that allegedly indicate the presence of HIV. The problem once again is, no proof has ever been furnished that any 'fragments' produced by PCR are peculiar to HIV, doubtless the reason the Roche PCR testing kit actually contains a warning against using PCR as a test for the presence of HIV: *"The test is not to be used as a screening test for HIV or as a diagnostic test to confirm the presence of HIV."* [110] [111]

This significant fact was pointed out to Mr Parry. During the course of the conversation, Mr Parry was also reminded that Kary Mullis, the Nobel laureate inventor of PCR, publicly referred to his own diagnostic invention as *"inappropriate for use in AIDS medicine."*[112] Startled perhaps that an ordinary member of the public actually knew what PCR stood for, was well versed on its history of unreliability, and then had the audacity to question what went on within Colindale Laboratories, Mr Parry chose to offer no further reply.[113]

The simple question remaining for the reader? Would you trust your blood sample to this methodology? The stark truth here is that a blood sample, quite falsely deemed HIV positive by the highly inaccurate ELISA test, is then sent on to Colindale and other 'specialist' laboratories to be *'confirmed as positive or otherwise'* again by ELISA and then secondarily tested in the same establishment by the equally inaccurate PCR or 'viral load'. Another glaring example of following an incorrect course with the maximum of precision. Can it really get any worse?

Yes. In the case of the Western Blot test, the positive criteria differ from continent to continent! (*see photo section*). You can be tested positive in one country, and with the same blood sample, be tested negative in another. Gene Franks, author of *Testing, Testing* states:

> *"Another reason the medical community loves diagnostic testing is that it is so wonderfully unreliable. One test leads to*

---

[110] Roche Amplicor PCR Diagnostics HIV-1 Monitor test kit pamphlet.

[111] Concerning the use of PCR in forensics, in the infamous OJ Simpson case, presiding Judge Ito allowed a Dr John Gerdes freely to testify about systemic problems with PCR and widespread cross-contamination difficulties within the lab.
www.courttv.com/casefiles/simpson/criminal/summary/week28.html

[112] Index for Free Expression. *Big Science and Little White Lies,* March 1999

[113] Credence telephone conversation with Colindale staff on 14th March 2000

another and to another. Tests are rated according to their sensitivity and specificity. Accuracy is determined by balancing specificity and sensitivity. Incredibly, some very expensive tests are less than 50% accurate.[114]

Now consider the following:

"Early civilisations were based upon the invention of agriculture and the ability to determine the proper time for planting and harvesting crops was very important. In those societies, a small group of men studied the heavens and learned how to divine the seasons from the positions of the sun, moon, planets, and stars. Instead of passing along their knowledge, they kept it to themselves and became priests who provided life and death information for society as a whole. As a result of their monopoly of vital knowledge, more and more power and wealth flowed to them and in time they formed a religion. That religion eventually became the basis of all-powerful states ruled by god-kings. In such a society, heresy was the most heinous crime imaginable, with revelation of the secrets of the religion to the masses a close second. From the vantage point of history, the motivation of these priests was obvious. They worked to achieve enormous power and luxury for themselves at the expense of the peasants. They did not work for the benefit of society as a whole."[115]

Today, we have our scientific priests thrusting upon us genetics, viral diseases and the impenetrable domain of DNA. We must not question their pronouncements. We must bow to their knowledge, nod and obey, and at the same time discard any basic tenets of logic and common sense.

Kim Marie Bannon was not aware of any of these test anomalies. Writing of her own personal experiences with the HIV establishment, Kim's 'AIDS Journey' began in 1992, following a routine health examination. Her boyfriend at the time had discovered he had a herpes sore and Kim thought it only sensible to order a check-up for herself.

---

[114] **Franks, Gene**, *Testing, Testing*, at www.purewatergazette.net/testing.htm
[115] **Retic, H, E**, "The Einstein Hoax: The Disastrous War on Common Sense" at
http://www.members.aol.com/postinglog/posting1.htm

"At the health department, I was told that since I didn't have a sore that could be cultured, they could not test me for herpes; but how would I like to have an AIDS test? They were offering it to everyone these days. I was embarrassed and confused. I felt that a refusal of this AIDS test would be tantamount to a confession of illicit drug use or promiscuity. I had heard that anyone can get AIDS, but I still felt I was in a very low risk-group. I agreed to the test and was told to come back in a week for my results. A week later and my test was positive. They told me it was just a 'screening' test, which was called an ELISA. They said I was not in any risk group, and it would most likely turn out to be negative when I was given the 'confirmatory' test. Two days later on May 1, 1992, the specialist 'confirmed' my positive diagnosis with the results of a Western Blot test. She called it 'classic'. When I got the 'confirmation', I felt my life was over." [116]

Another precious life recklessly cast onto the rocks. Ms Bannon, however, is alive and well today, currently raising finances to take the establishment to court over the baleful state of government-approved testing procedures.

Yet another hurdle the 'AIDS test' has quite disastrously failed to clear is 'The Gold Standard Test'. Christine Maggiore explains:

"HIV tests have been developed without verification by an independent 'gold standard'. In medical science, a gold standard means that viral isolation has been used as an independent means of establishing the presence or absence of a virus. This process is essential for the authentication of any diagnostic test. Without a gold standard, it is impossible for a doctor or scientist to know if a positive antibody test indicates infection or what it may indicate." [117]

Gary Null is an independent AIDS researcher whose work has taken him around the world, resulting in film documentaries, countless interviews with medical personnel, and media articles presenting his findings. Null runs his own nutrition clinic and hosts *Natural Living*

---

[116] The Kim Bannon Story, Well Aware Network, July 2004 at
http://www.robertogiraldo.com/reference/KimMarieBannon.html
[117] Maggiore, Christine, op. cit. p.42

on New York City's WBAI Radio. An excerpt from his program, broadcast on 21st March 1996, had him addressing the 'gold standard' issue:

"No one, I repeat, no one under ANY circumstances should have an HIV test. It is a fraud. A complete and total fraud. Why is it a fraud? Because there is no 'gold standard'. I have just gone all over the world trying to find the independent verification of this test. I have not found it."[118]

Of course none of the above information is shared with the patient at the point of testing. As if all this wasn't bad enough, a new form of diagnosis came into being in late 1987. The *Los Angeles Weekly* explains:

"In the 4th September issue of the Journal of the American Medical Association [JAMA], the CDC announced that a diagnosis of AIDS no longer requires an AIDS test. The government now considers you are an AIDS carrier if you suffer from any of the maladies on its new list of diseases indicative of AIDS, including such relatively common infections as herpes simplex, tuberculosis, salmonellosis and a shockingly broad 'other bacterial infections'. This broad definition will lead to countless new AIDS diagnoses - whether or not the person actually has AIDS. A major problem with the new AIDS definition is that it ignores the many environmental causes of immune suppression. Exposure to toxins, alcoholism, heavy drug use or heavy antibiotic use all can cause onset of the list of 'diseases' indicative of AIDS."[119]

And the CDC itself, in a stunning remark, conceded:

"The diagnostic criteria accepted by the AIDS surveillance case definition should not be interpreted as the standard of good medical practice."[120]

Presumptive diagnosis was born. Now the orthodoxy was able to diagnose any patient as an 'AIDS carrier' simply by looking at their lifestyle and asking whether they had any one of a handful of common symptoms from which people have been suffering for centuries. On the

---

[118] see also Maggiore, Christine, op. cit. p.5
[119] *Los Angeles Weekly*, 18th December 1987
[120] Ibid.

basis of this unscientific determination alone, tens of thousands of Americans have been given the fateful diagnosis. Seldom considered are the appalling consequences and the private grief for the individual once a positive result is announced. Iola Martin was one such person given a positive diagnosis. Here she recounts her own particularly traumatic experience at the hands of the medical establishment.

"In 1990, it was recommended that I took an HIV test because I was pregnant. The first test came back inconclusive, the second was positive. The positive result left me in total shock. I was told that I would have to decide what to do about my baby. The information I was given left me without much choice. They said there were two scenarios. I could live long enough to watch my baby die of AIDS, or I could leave my baby without a mother, when I died of AIDS, knowing that my baby would die soon after me. Believing in the death sentence I had been given, I agreed to a second trimester abortion. It was a terrible, terrible experience, and the decision haunts me to this day."

Today, ten years later, Iola is still with us. She is alive and physically well but her experience has taken its emotional toll. Iola's long-term relationship has ended: *"I was so bitter, sad and angry and caught up in the idea that I was going to die."* [121] Discovering the truth about AIDS in 1996 came too late for Iola, and far too late for her unborn child.

Celia Farber in *Impressions* Magazine recounts the following:

"In Winston Salem, North Carolina, 3-year-old Joey D was struck by a car. He suffered a fractured skull and was rushed to a nearby hospital. A week later, as Joey was recovering, some of his blood splashed on hospital workers when an IV line was being changed. Joey was given an HIV test. He tested positive, and a doctor told Joey's already traumatized mother, LaTonia, the news. Both of Joey's parents were tested negative, and LaTonia asked how this could have happened to her son.

---

[121] Maggiore, Christine, op. cit.

The doctor told LaTonia she needed to launch an investigation into her entire family and circle of friends because the child had been sexually abused. There was no other explanation, the doctor said, for the child being positive.

More testing was ordered, and LaTonia spent two days waiting, trying not to go insane. She thought about finding out who had infected her son or hurt him and "killing them." But then the second round of test results came in, and Joey was found to be HIV-negative.

LaTonia was relieved, but understandably livid. (Imagine how many lives would have been shattered in one moment had she begun accusing family members of sexual abuse!) She asked the doctor to apologize, but in keeping with HIV-related arrogance, he refused. The case was referred to the Culpepper, Virginia-based watchdog group International Coalition for Medical Justice (ICMJ).

Even some of the hospital's staff have encouraged LaTonia to contact an attorney. The hospital, meanwhile, held a press conference, where a remarkable admission was made. In her effort to clear the hospital of any wrongdoing, a hospital spokesperson announced that "... these HIV tests are not reliable; a lot of factors can skew the tests, like fever or pregnancy. Everybody knows that." [122]

The widespread acceptance of the HIV test has opened the way for all manner of calamitous, secondary effects, not always immediately obvious. Take the practical advice dispensed by Dr Patrick Dixon, a well-recognised UK voice on AIDS and HIV. Dr Dixon was at the forefront of those early AIDS doom-and-gloom statistics and his 1987 book, *The Truth About AIDS*, warned of a pandemic of massive proportions on the horizon. The opening chapter, entitled *The Extent of the Nightmare*, speculated that the UK could be witnessing 18,000 AIDS deaths a year. No such pandemic arrived, of course. The same book warned against deep kissing and suggested the pill and even sterilisation for women who had been diagnosed HIV-positive.

---

[122] **Farber, Celia,** *Positively Flawed*, Impressions Magazine, 7th June 1999

"Deep kissing, where saliva may pass from one mouth to another, is probably not a good idea. Dry kissing carries a much, much lower risk.... An infected woman should probably avoid pregnancy as there is a significant chance that any child born may also be infected. So use a second method of contraception as well, e.g. the pill, or consider sterilisation very seriously." [123]

Telephoning Dr Dixon on this matter, Credence pointed out the physiological dangers of the contraceptive pill and also asked him to comment on the medical evidence sent to him and everyone at management level within his organisation, highlighting the fallacy of the HIV test. Given the potential for such a high rate of 'false positives' (including a reaction to pregnancy), should he really be suggesting the test, let alone that women consider the irreversible sterilisation procedure?

Becoming quite angry, Dr Dixon accused us of being *flat-earthers* and has so far refused to seek ways of professionally resolving these issues. Furthermore, as of November 2004, Dr Dixon's same ghastly advice on sterilisation still has not been omitted from his updated version of *The Truth About AIDS*, stored in electronic format on his website. Perhaps if enough people e-mail him, the sterilisation advice at least will be removed. Dr Dixon has since gone on record to say SARS could be deadlier than AIDS.[124] Where is the SARS pandemic? Dr Dixon's Global Trend/Global Change website reportedly received 5.5 million hits over the last twelve-month period, so someone's listening to him. Given Dr Dixon's HIV recommendations, what are we then to make of his web-site's opening banner, *'Take hold of your future, before your future takes hold of you'*?

Saturday, 6th November 2004, in the UK county of Berkshire, 48-year-old Brian Drysdale deliberately parks his car on the rails at a rural level-crossing and waits for the London-Plymouth express train. He is killed instantly, taking with him six other lives and injuring one

[123] **Dixon, Patrick** *The Truth About AIDS*, Kingsway Publications, 1987. Dr Dixon's contention that Africa is dying ultimately of a sexually transmitted disease brought about by 'rampant trans-African truck drivers', etc., has attracted a particularly large and loyal following. The nonsensical nature of this reasoning is addressed in the second part of this book

[124] **ONE BILLION TO BE INFECTED WITH SARS WITHIN 60 WEEKS**, *Daily Record*, Wednesday 23rd April 2003 at www.indybay.org/news/2003/04/1603343.php

hundred more as the train ploughs into his car at high speed and derails. The UK's *Sunday Mirror*:

> *"Drysdale made an anguished 25-minute call to the Samaritans on his mobile phone and poured out his heart about his HIV agony. A police source said that blood tests after he died confirmed he did have the killer virus [standard media-speak for HIV]. During the conversation with the Samaritan, Drysdale told her he believed he was HIV-positive and that there was no point in going on with his life. He was asked in what way he intended to commit suicide, and he told the woman that he intended to 'go out with a bang'. The Samaritan assumed he meant by use of a shotgun or firearm. Drysdale had also been depressed over splitting up with a gay lover. The police source also revealed that small amounts of cocaine, cannabis and two ecstasy tablets were found at Drysdale's home - a Victorian terrace in East Reading. 'We don't think Drysdale was a heavy drugs user. We believe he used them for recreational purposes,' said the source."* [125]

Yes, but did he use those drugs in sufficient quantity to trigger a positive test? Had he been exposed to flu, flu vaccination, tuberculosis, renal failure, hepatitis, organ transplant, haemophilia, tetanus vaccination, leprosy, alcoholic liver disease, blood transfusions, malignant cancers, proteins on the test filter papers, rheumatoid arthritis, herpes, Hepatitis B vaccination, or a test turning positive as a result of poorly understood cross-reactions?

This is the HIV-positive diagnosis. Relationships severed, marriages called off, lives wrecked, babies aborted, social ostracism, mental torture, suicides on railway crossings... And all this before any medication has even been prescribed. The physician warns that the disease may progress, and if it does, the patient will eventually die of AIDS-related disorders. And we believe him. As we witness the withering decline of our loved ones, who among us is not persuaded that what we are seeing is death brought on by the effects of the virus?

Rarely will we consider another possibility: *AIDS by prescription.*

---

[125] UK *Sunday Mirror*, 14th November 2004

THE AIDS PHARMACY

"We are apt to shut our eyes against a painful truth, and listen to the song of the siren till she transforms us into beasts. For my part, whatever anguish of spirit it may cost, I am willing to know the whole truth, to know the worst, and provide for it." **Patrick Henry,** on the brink of the American Revolution

An individual given an HIV positive diagnosis is generally recommended 'early intervention' treatment with the drug Azidothymidine (AZT) and/or other AIDS-related medications. The AIDS physician suggests this course of action because this is what he has been taught to do. The theory runs that 'early pharmaceutical intervention' reduces the rate at which HIV spreads, thus raising the levels of immune function T-cells, which then do battle with the supposed virus, and thus delay the onset of AIDS-related diseases in the patient.

Let us now trace what happens to that individual, who maybe feels a little run down, and who has decided to go to the doctor. We'll call him Chris. Perhaps Chris belongs to one of the AIDS risk groups popularised by an emotionally charged media (active multi-partner, fast-track hetero/homosexual and/or drug user). Perhaps his tiredness and flu-like symptoms have worryingly coincided with his having recently returned from a trip abroad. Perhaps his tiredness and flu-like symptoms are just that - flu. Either way, through previous conversations, Chris's doctor is aware of the AIDS-type risk categories being presented in this instance, and he advises Chris to get tested for HIV.

But Chris is not aware of the truth concerning AIDS or the HIV tests. He has only been told that HIV is an incredibly volatile viral agent capable of spreading easily through bodily fluids and through the transfer of blood products. So Chris takes the highly unspecific 'HIV test', and after two weeks of inner turmoil waiting for the result, he is told he has 'the virus.' As Joan Shenton says:

"The inexorable death sentence – 'you have ten years at most' pronounced by doctors on young men and women, has led to some of the most intense human suffering imaginable. It has broken up families, alienated individuals from their communities and led to psychological death and suicide." [126]

Looking quite unwell through the stress of it all, Chris is now recommended one of two courses of action:

- Early intervention treatment with anti-viral therapy (AZT, ddI, ddC, d4T, etc.)... *or*
- Go home untreated and come back when AIDS symptoms start to manifest.

Chris decides on early intervention with AZT - after all, his doctor knows best and this is modern medicine. Had Chris elected not to have AZT to begin with, but to go home and wait for the AIDS symptoms to manifest, he would not have long to wait before starting to notice a number of physical symptoms. That is because Chris is already showing signs of illness through stress alone. He has been persuaded by his doctor and a relentless media into watching for the common symptoms of AIDS. These indicators are 'something like flu', diarrhoea and pronounced fatigue. Notice that these are also psychosomatic symptoms, each of which can be brought on simply by the worry of being HIV positive and thus 'prone to AIDS'. [127]

Gary Null has studied in detail the correlation between receiving bad news (a 'positive' result) and the onset of ill-health. Says Null:

"I've looked at all the literature on psycho-neuro-immunology and I have seen an abundant series of articles that show that if you give a person some bad news, all the quantitative measurements of immune function - natural killer cells, T-cells, phagocytes etc - go down. In a matter of hours, the entire immune system can become depressed. Now

---

[126] Shenton, Joan, op. cit.

[127] **Brown, George** *Life Events and Illness*, Guildford Press, 1999. Assembles examples of findings where the LEDS (Life Events and Difficulties Schedule) is used to examine the onset of a range of disorders. In consultation with GPs and related healthcare professionals, Steven Ransom has compiled a list of over 70 conditions that can manifest as a direct result of life stresses. Details available from Credence Publications.

give them bad news that is only going to get worse and you're putting that person's psycho-neurological immune system into a tailspin."[128]

Chris has not opted to go home and wait. Having received the equivalent of a verbal death sentence and now not feeling well at all, Chris has decided on the doctor's suggestion of early intervention treatment with AZT.

So what is AZT? Dissident AIDS researcher and author Christine Maggiore introduces us to this widely prescribed AIDS drug.

"AZT is not a new drug. It was not created for the treatment of AIDS and is not an anti-viral. AZT is a chemical compound that was developed - and abandoned - over 30 years ago as a chemotherapy treatment for cancer. Many cancer patients do not survive chemotherapy due to its destructive effects on the immune system. Because of the damage it causes, chemotherapy is never used as a prevention and is only administered for very limited amounts of time.

Since cancer is made of persistently growing cells, AZT was designed to prevent formation of new cells.... In 1964, experiments with AZT on mice with cancer showed that AZT was so effective in destroying healthy growing cells that the mice died of extreme toxicity. As a result, AZT was shelved and no patent was ever filed."[129]

It has been reported by Project AIDS International that Richard Beltz, the creator of AZT, called for the abandonment of this drug because 1) its extreme toxicity made it unsuitable for any chemotherapy - even short term, and 2) it was carcinogenic (cancer causing) at any dose. [130] [131]

Barrister Anthony Brink remarks:

"In truth, AZT makes you feel like you're dying. That's because on AZT you are. How can a deadly cell toxin

[128] **Null, Gary**, *Zenger*, August 1997
[129] Maggiore, Christine, op. cit.
[130] Selvey, Jeremy, op. cit. p.7
[131] **Cohen, S S** *New England Journal of Medicine*, 317 (1987): 629

conceivably make you feel better as it finishes you, by stopping your cells from dividing, by ending this vital process that distinguishes living things from dead things? Not for nothing does AZT come with a skull and cross-bones label when packaged for laboratory use." [132]

And indeed that is the case. With a skull and cross-bones on the outer label (see photo section), and a reminder to wear *suitable protective clothing when handling,* the inner contents of the AZT packaging include the following side-effects advisory notice:

WHOLE BODY: abdominal pain, back pain, body odour, chest pain, chills, edema of the lip, fever, flu symptoms, hyperalgesia.

CARDIOVASCULAR: syncope, vasodilation.

GASTROINTESTINAL: bleeding gums, constipation, diarrhoea, dysphagia, edema of the tongue, eructation, flatulence, mouth ulcer, rectal haemorrhage.

HAEMIC AND LYMPHATIC: lymphadenopathy.

MUSCULOSKELETAL: arthralgia, muscle spasm, tremor, twitch.

NERVOUS: anxiety, confusion, depression, dizziness, emotional lability, loss of mental acuity, nervousness, paresthesia, somnolence, vertigo.

RESPIRATORY: cough, dyspnea, epistaxis, hoarseness, pharyngitis, rhinitis, sinusitis.

SKIN: rash, sweat, urticaria.

SPECIAL SENSES: amblyopia, hearing loss, photophobia, taste perversion.

UROGENITAL: dysuria, polyuria, urinary frequency, urinary hesitancy.

Dr Stefan Lanka has this to say:

"...The use of AZT and other 'anti-retrovirals', which are supposed to target HIV replication, but actually kill cells indiscriminately (and ultimately the whole body), must be stopped immediately. It is especially distressing to note that AZT and its analogues preferentially attack those cells which

---

[132] **Brink, Anthony,** *AZT and Heavenly Remedies,* Rethinking AIDS Homepage: www.rethinkingaids.com

divide most rapidly, namely cells in the intestines causing diarrhoea and malabsorption of food, and in bone marrow, ironically, the primary production site for cells of the immune system." [133]

The horrific toxicity of AZT brings on the symptoms of AIDS: diarrhoea, malabsorption of food, leading to rapid weight loss and immune deficiency disorders. This, of course, has led some doctors to maintain the dosage of AZT or even increase it in the patient, believing the medication 'isn't working' and more is required. This, in turn, accelerates the degradation of the patient. More AZT is given. The patient relapses further, and so on, down the slippery slope to death. More disturbingly, while most cancer chemotherapy agents are only administered to the patient for a strictly limited period of time in view of their toxicity, AZT is prescribed until the end.

Chris is now quite literally dying. In being prescribed AZT, Chris is receiving white capsules with a blue band. Chris hasn't been told about the protective clothing worn in the AZT labs. He's read the side-effects insert, but he's resolved to fight his dreadful 'illness' with the strongest medicine the doctors have got.

Chris will not live much longer. Now his doctor advises that his dosage be increased to attempt to combat the ravaging effects of the HIV, now apparently evidencing itself so markedly. Chris agrees to the increased dose. And when Chris eventually dies of liver and heart damage, malnutrition and dramatic weight loss through internal haemorrhaging and other complications, his family will mourn the passing of a dearly loved husband, father or son who was brave to the very end, but who had, to the uninitiated, finally succumbed to the deadly HIV.

But Chris did not die of HIV/AIDS. Chris's death was by prescription.

In exactly this manner, thousands upon thousands of men and women have been persuaded to take AZT, a drug believed by the more

---

[133] Lanka, Stefan, op. cit. Also **Lauritsen, John** *Poison by Prescription: The AZT Story,* Asklepios, New York, 1990. Also **Lauritsen, John** *The AIDS War. Propaganda, Profiteering and Genocide from the Medical-Industrial Complex,* Asklepios, New York, 1993

discerning in the scientific community to be the leading cause of AIDS in the Western world. Researcher Newly Abbott remonstrates:

"AIDS is truly an iatrogenic disaster of the primary magnitude. By 'iatrogenic', we mean that clinical AIDS is a syndrome that is primarily being caused in the Western world now by doctors and their medicine. I'm not sure what's more terrifying, that this state of affairs continues to exist at all in spite of all the obvious evidence, or that the English language actually has a word for it."[134]

Despite this catastrophic history, GlaxoSmithKline (GSK) rises defiantly in defence of the positive benefits of its most infamous product. In fact, AZT's information leaflet, incongruously titled *Positive Benefits*, states *"... there are no life-threatening side-effects associated with zidovudine [AZT]."* GSK further cites numerous studies to substantiate its claims that AZT both *"prolongs life"* and *"enhances its quality"*. The problem is, the only studies that appear to demonstrate these *"positive benefits"* are the studies funded, either directly or indirectly, by the GSK's Wellcome Foundation.[135] As we shall see, independent studies conducted on AZT paints an entirely different picture.[136]

How is it that such a drug can ever be prescribed today? Serendipity. Twenty years after AZT was shelved as an unusable poison, HIV was the talk of the medical establishment after Gallo's press conference. The emergence of the phenomenon of immune suppression known as AIDS presented an incredible opportunity for someone to come up with a lucrative, new drug to combat the supposed guilty virus.

David Barry, GSK's (Wellcome's) erstwhile chief researcher in the United States, was a man who knew a golden opportunity when he saw one. Barry had a number of advantages working for him. He knew US FDA drug approval procedures after having worked at the federal agency during the 1970s as a virologist. Barry's main advantage, however, was that he worked for the Wellcome Foundation, whose

---

[134] **Abbott, N** "AIDS - Examining the Politics of Medical Genocide," a special report. Sydney Australia, 1994
[135] Project AIDS International, Public Information Dossier, 15th March 1993. p.9
[136] **Hamilton et al**. VA Study 1990. Also, CDC unreleased study 1990

unusual non-profit charity status enabled the corporation to donate large sums of tax-free grant money to strategic institutions throughout government, universities and the corporate world.[137] Wellcome thus had many grateful and influential friends.

David Barry turned his attention to the company archives in the early 1980s in search of previously rejected compounds. The race was on for an AIDS drug, there was no time to research a new substance from scratch, endure the interminable FDA approval procedures and expect to be first into the new and wide-open AIDS market. Barry knew if he succeeded in locating a suitable *existing* substance, Wellcome would save millions in research and development money in addition to being perfectly positioned to corner sales.

Barry selected a group of drugs and forwarded them to his friend, Dani Bolognesi, a professor at North Carolina's Duke University and a former colleague. Bolognesi tested the substances in his lab to see if any proved to demonstrate an ability to halt viral cell multiplication. One drug, codenamed Compound S, was wildly successful. Bolognesi wasted no time in sending his approval back to Barry for Compound S, or, as the archive tag in Barry's office would later identify it, AZT.[138]

Bolognesi subsequently referred David Barry to Sam Broder, the man in charge of Robert Gallo's laboratory at the National Cancer Institute. Barry and Wellcome needed the clout the new 'Pope of AIDS', Robert Gallo, was able to bring to bear to get AZT through the FDA approval procedure.[139] Barry duly sent Sam Broder a sample of Compound S in late 1984. The drug's ability to interrupt cell multiplication impressed Broder right away. Broder was later to become known in research circles as 'Mr AZT', such was his new-found fervour for the drug.

Barry and Broder were the right men at the right time for AZT, Bruce Nussbaum recalls:

---

[137] Duesberg, Peter H, *Inventing...* op. cit. p.310

[138] Ibid, p.311

[139] **Nussbaum, Bruce** *Good Intentions: How Big Business, Politics, and Medicine are Corrupting the Fight Against AIDS*, Atlantic Monthly Press, 1990

"David Barry was the puppet master, and his favourite marionette was Sam Broder. While Broder was charging around promoting AZT at the National Institutes of Health, Barry was working quietly behind the scenes, orchestrating a whole panoply of actors who would ensure the drug's ultimate, commercial success." [140]

Broder hurried AZT through its Phase 1 trials. Unprecedented FDA co-operation was extended because of the extreme pressure being brought to bear on the US government by pro-medication AIDS activist groups determined to see a drug onto the market as quickly as possible. Duesberg records what was happening in these hurriedly approved AZT trials:

"Sixty-six AZT recipients suffered 'severe' nausea... as compared to twenty-five in the placebo group. All AZT users saw their muscles waste away, while only three placebo recipients suffered this symptom. And a full thirty in the AZT group survived only with multiple blood transfusions to replace their poisoned blood cells, compared to five similar cases among the placebo users." [141]

A follow-up study shattered anyone's illusions that AZT was in any way beneficial when all the patients were put on the drug. An unacceptable rate of fatalities prompted urgent calls for the trials to be stopped. Bruce Nussbaum again:

"A move to stop the trial began immediately. The toxicity of AZT was proving to be extremely high, much higher than indicated by Sam Broder's safety trials. PIs [Principal Investigators] began to worry that AZT was killing bone marrow cells so fast that patients would quickly come down with aplastic anemia, a murderous disease. This was terrifying to many PIs. "There was enormous pressure to stop," recalls Broder. "People said, 'My God, what's going on? We're getting these anemias. What's going on?' We never saw this level of anemia before." [142]

---

[140] Nussbaum, Bruce, op. cit. Also **Wyatt, EA** "Rushing to Judgment," *Barron's*, 15th August 1994, p.23-27

[141] Duesberg, Peter H, *Inventing...* op. cit. p.317

[142] Nussbaum, Bruce, op. cit.

Unknown to Broder however, another disastrously unscientific situation was developing. Some of the patients, completely sold on media rumours of AZT's miracle healing powers with AIDS, were determined to get their hands on the drug and forget the placebo. Discussions among the patients began, with some tasting another's medication. Some of the placebo group, unknown to the investigators, began taking AZT, further corrupting any blinding value the trials would have had in determining the effectiveness of the drug. Also, some of the AZT recipients simply were not able to complete their courses of AZT due to the drug's extreme side-effects. Margaret Fischl, who headed up the study, admitted:

"Drug therapy was temporarily discontinued or the frequency of doses decreased... if severe adverse reactions were noted. The study medication was withdrawn if unacceptable toxic effects or a [cancer] requiring therapy developed."[143]

Here Fischl blatantly admits that doctors knew all along who was using AZT. So much for the double-blind, placebo-controlled trial. Christine Maggiore records other trials, not funded by Wellcome, which were producing a similar worrying picture:

"A multitude of independent studies, including the Concorde study - the largest (1,749 subjects) and longest (three years in duration) - concluded that AZT increases T-cell counts only moderately and briefly without improving health (clinical status), and that it does not delay the onset of AIDS indicator diseases.[144]

Following recommendations for 'early intervention', one third to one half of those who take AZT begin treatment before manifesting any symptoms of AIDS,[145] *although independent studies have shown that AZT actually accelerates clinical decline and decreases quality of life, at times even causing death before any AIDS defining illnesses appear - an*

[143] **Fischl et al** The AZT Collaborative Working Group, "Efficacy of Azidothymidine", 185-191
[144] *Lancet* 343:871, Concorde Coordinating Committee
[145] *British Medical Journal*, 15th July 1995, p.156-158 (49%); *Science Magazine*, 24th February 1995, p.1080 (34%)

occurrence officially described as 'death without any preceding AIDS-defining event.'" [146] [147]

British and French scientists organised what became known as the Concorde study in 1991. The purpose of the three-year study was to test whether AZT prevented the onset of AIDS indicator diseases in HIV positive but otherwise symptomless individuals, as compared with those who were already demonstrating the onset of AIDS. Evidently as the study progressed, arguments between the scientists erupted over whether to continue the trials in view of the appalling toxic attrition they were witnessing. They nervously agreed to continue.

After three years, the researchers published their results. Their indictment of AZT was total. The death rate in the AZT group who were taking the drug to avoid developing AIDS was 25% higher than the control group.[148] Then again, some of those who survived could no longer stand the nausea, vomiting and anemia, so they flushed their AZT capsules down the toilet.[149] The day before this news was reported in England, Professor Tony Pinching, director of immunology at St Bartholomew's Hospital, London, went on record in the *Daily Telegraph*, warning HIV positive, symptomless individuals that they would be better off without drug therapy. Not surprisingly, the *Concorde* report also clearly showed that AZT did not halt the development of AIDS.[150]

Even Jerome Groopman, one of the participating scientists, had serious doubts about the humanitarian nature and efficacy of AZT. He gave it to 14 patients in his Boston hospital on a compassionate basis. Three months later, only three were still able to take AZT. *"We found it nearly impossible to keep patients on the drug,"* Groopman admitted.[151]

Gay historian and AIDS dissident John Lauritsen was incensed:

[146] *JAMA* 260:3009, 1998; *New England Journal of Medicine* 326:437, 1992
[147] Maggiore, Christine, op. cit.
[148] **Seligman, et al.** "Concorde: MRC/ANRS Randomized Double-Blind Control Trial."
[149] **Hodgkinson, Neville** "The Cure that Failed." *London Sunday Times*, 4th April 1993
[150] **Pallot, Peter** "HIV Carriers Advised to Stop Their Treatment," *Daily Telegraph*, 3rd April 1993
[151] **Kolata, G** "Imminent Marketing of AZT Raises Problems," *Science*, 235 (1987): 1462-1463

"The multi-center clinical trials of AZT are perhaps the sloppiest and most poorly controlled trials ever to serve as the basis for an FDA licensing approval.... Because mortality was not an intended endpoint, causes of death were never verified. Despite this, and a frightening record of toxicity, the FDA approved AZT in record time, granting a treatment IND [investigational new drug] in less than five days and full pharmaceutical licensing in less than six months." [152]

Dr Joseph Sonnabend, an American AIDS researcher, had this to say about AZT:

"It is beyond belief. I don't know what to do. I'm ashamed of my colleagues. I'm embarrassed. This is such shoddy science. It's hard to believe nobody's protesting. Damned cowards! The name of the game is to protect your grants. Don't open your mouth. It's all about money. It's grounds for just following the party line and not being critical when there are obvious financial and political forces that are driving this." [153]

And Dr Harvey Bialy, molecular biologist and science editor of *Bio/Technology*, states:

"I'm stunned by the low quality of science surrounding AIDS research. I'm horrified by the widespread use of AZT, not just because it is toxic, but because the claims of efficacy are false. I can't see how this drug can be doing anything other than making people extremely sick." [154]

Another alarming trend noticed was that longer-term treatment with AZT brought on lymphoma (a type of cancer) in around half of the patients.[155] Incredibly, even then, the virus-hunting lobby rushed to defend the drug, declaring that patients were living longer on AZT and therefore merely stood a higher, statistical risk of developing cancer! [156] Dr Sonnabend filed a report with the Food & Drug Administration

---

[152] Lauritsen, John, op. cit.

[153] Quote recorded by **Jeremy Selvey**, PAI Archives.

[154] Project AIDS International, Public Information Dossier, op. cit.

[155] **Pluda et al.** "Development of Non-Hodgkin Lymphoma in a Cohort of Patients with Severe Immunodeficiency Virus (HIV) Infection on Long-Term, Anti-Viral Therapy." *Ann. Intern. Med.*, 113 (1990): 276-282

[156] Ibid.

questioning the criteria and basis for the licensing of AZT. He never received a reply either from the FDA or from Burroughs-Wellcome. [157]

In spite of these and other drug trial fiascos, the Food & Drug Administration approved AZT as an anti-retroviral treatment for AIDS. Once approval was granted, AZT became THE AIDS drug, and demand for the expensive and exclusive substance grew so fierce, Wellcome was hard pressed to supply the quota.

Despite the widely reported failures, Wellcome's income from AZT very quickly became the envy of its counterparts. Soon, other drug giants began vying for a piece of Wellcome's AIDS pie. Hoffman La-Roche produced dideoxycytidine (ddC) and Bristol-Myers Squibb marketed its version, known as ddI. During testing, ddI was found capable of destroying nerves throughout the body and causing fatal damage to the pancreas,[158] something not even AZT was reported to do. Doctors began experimenting with ddI, giving it to patients who were unable to tolerate AZT.[159] Many patients inexplicably died during these unofficial trials, but once again, the FDA was able to staunch the inevitable flood of complaints.

AZT (Retrovir) and its derivatives are still prescribed with reckless abandon. But, just as the turbulent history surrounding the UK's Windscale nuclear power plant necessitated a politically expedient name-change to Sellafield, Wellcome and other manufacturers are now giving their window display a fresh new look. At the 1996 Conference on Retroviruses and Opportunistic Infections, a new generation of AIDS drugs known as 'protease inhibitors' was launched. Protease inhibitors, or 'combo cocktails', are said to enhance dramatically the effects of AZT and ddI. Since then, drug companies have been pushing the 'latest, great news' on AIDS, stridently insisting that their cocktails be taken, like margaritas, in large doses for life, yet in the small print stating *"...the long-term effects of protease inhibitors are unknown."*[160] Christine Maggiore explains the drug companies' continued psychological conditioning of their vulnerable patients:

---

[157] **Sonnabend, JA** "Report on MultiCenter Study of AZT to FDA", 1987
[158] Merck Index
[159] Lauritsen, John, *AIDS War*, op. cit.
[160] Wording on the Merck protease inhibitor product, Crixivan.

"The absolute compliance required for protease treatment is a popular subject of news reports and AIDS organization seminars. Patients are required to pop 30 to 50 pills a day on a 24-hour-a-day schedule - some taken with food, some on an empty stomach. Patients are warned that if they do not rigorously adhere to the strict protocol schedule, their virus will mutate into new, drug resistant strains."[161]

Drug company Merck muscled to the front in getting FDA approval for its protease inhibitor cocktail drug, Crixivan. Such was the hype surrounding the AIDS scare, the drug received FDA approval in just 42 days. Christine Maggiore again:

"Crixivan's FDA approval broke a 72-day record for the fastest approval in FDA history, previously set by the protease inhibitor Ritonavir. Newsday articles noting the toxic effects of these drugs - diarrhea, nausea, fungal infections, bloody urine, kidney stones, weakness, headaches and liver inflammation requiring "doctor visits and additional medicines" - were ignored by AIDS organizations, who pressured the FDA for fast-track approval.[162]Recently reported side-effects include CMV retinitis, diabetes, liver failure, 'buffalo humps' (large fat deposits at the base of the neck), acute kidney failure, acute pancreatitis, grade four diarrhea and sudden death."[163]

Protease inhibitors have been wildly successful in one area however - breathing new life into the AIDS industry and increasing the cash-flow further. The US has traditionally dominated the HIV market in terms of sales and as of October 2004, is the largest market

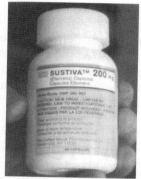

"My Nightmare on Anti-HIV Therapy" - On the second day of treatment, one young man became confused and scared. He began to hear strange, non-existent sounds which were the start of a series of hallucinations. *"I couldn't find my way home. I couldn't remember how to put a record on or how to use a computer."* He was taking Efavirenz, Abacavir and d4T. Within 48 hours of stopping the drugs, everything returned to normal. (*Positive Nation Magazine.* "The Crazy Beat of Those Combo's", January 2000)

---

[161] Maggiore, Christine, op. cit. p.17

[162] *Newsday Magazine*, 30th January 1996

[163] *Lancet*, 1st June 1997. Vol.349, p.1745; *Philadelphia Inquirer*, Associated Press Report, 13th June 1997; *Rolling Stone Magazine*, "Special Report: Dr David Ho and the Lazarus Equation", 6th March 1997; *The Valley Advocate*, "The Big 'Tease", 20th February 1997

87

in terms of antiretroviral sales, accounting for 62% ($6.7 billion).[164] Now that is a lot of money. Drug companies are promoting their protease inhibitors in an orgy of marketing excess. Billboards and magazines advise 'AIDS-infected positives' to *"be smart about HIV"* by *"hitting early and hard"* with the new generation of AIDS wonder cocktails.

Straight Up is a glossy African AIDS community magazine promoting the latest 'breakthroughs' in the war against AIDS. Featured in one section is a double-spread on alternative treatments for HIV positive sufferers, including the highly favoured homoeopathy. The basis of homoeopathy's alleged curative powers is to administer to the patient minute doses of the main aggravating agent, thus conforming to the principle of 'like cures like'. Where, one might legitimately ask, does the homoeopath obtain his minute quantities of HIV?[165] Alongside other questionable, alternative treatments, the magazine also included several full-page adverts from the pharmaceutical industry:

"Stay Strong... HIV Care" - Glaxo Wellcome
"Celebration of Life..." and
"Investing in Your Future" - Pharmacia & Upjohn
"The Tide is Turning in HIV Therapy" - Boehringer Ingelheim
"In HIV Therapy, There is Hope... We're Working on It"...Merck, Sharp & Dohme[166]

The fresh and healthy promises, a central feature of these multi-million-pound PR campaigns, mask the ugly, clinical reality concerning these drugs. And what is the ugly, clinical reality? It is that protease inhibitors have been a dismal failure from the very start. Merck actually delayed marketing their own protease inhibitors for four years because the drugs were killing their laboratory animals.[167] This

---

[164] Inpharm.com at http://www.inpharm.com/External/InpH/1,2580,1-3-128917-0-inp_intelligence_art-0-248892,00.html

[165] **Ransom, Steven** *Homoeopathy, What Are We Swallowing?* Credence Publications, 1999. An examination of fraudulent practices and charlatanism dominating the movement known as 'alternative health'.

[166] All advertisements from *Straight Up*, Axiom Publishers, London: December 1999

[167] *Dayton Daily News, New York Times*, August 1997. Quoted in *Continuum* Magazine, Vol 5, No 1, October 1997. The National AIDS Manual reports that Efavirenz causes abnormalities in animal offspring and therefore should not be taken during pregnancy. Psychological changes in

ethically controversial data was not made known to those people taking part in the protease inhibitor trials. Little wonder the *New York Times* reported that *"...unexpected deaths amongst human protease inhibitor consumers are rising."* [168] Even Dr Michael Saag, a paid consultant for AZT's manufacturer GlaxoSmithKline and other pharmaceutical corporations, confesses that the cocktail dam holding back AIDS is already springing serious leaks:

"Failures [with Highly Active Anti-Retroviral Therapy (HAART)] *are occurring right and left,"* Saag confides. *"[Doctors] should expect failure with whatever* [HAART cocktail they] *first use. We should plan on it. We should prepare for it. Clinicians should expect failure."* [169]

Fellow protease expert Dr David Rasnick is equally dismissive. For Rasnick, the press ecstasy and back-slapping over the release of protease inhibitors recalled the previous euphoria over AZT.

"Once again, all we have are researchers talking to reporters about incomplete studies that haven't been scrutinized by the scientific review process. And the researchers involved are funded by the companies that make the drugs in question. There is no justification for the claims coming from these sources, particularly when we have seen it all before [with AZT]." [170]

Gallo too, in a break from his usual upbeat tradition, stated that *"... these drugs are toxic... The longer you take the drugs, the greater the toxicity."* [171]

One would imagine that an organisation such as The AIDS Treatment Project would take the comments of Saag, Rasnick and Gallo into consideration before dispensing their advice to the HIV-positive community. Sadly, this is not the case. In their leaflets entitled *An Introduction to Combination Therapy* and *Changing Treatment,*

---

the first four weeks with Efavirenz can include euphoria, vivid dreams, psychotic episodes and suicidal thoughts. *Anti-HIV Drugs*, NAM Publications, first edition, 1999.

[168] *Dayton Daily News*, August 1997, op. cit.

[169] *Esquire Magazine*, April 1999

[170] Maggiore, Christine, op. cit. p.20

[171] Maggiore, Christine, op. cit. p.18

there are numerous warnings to adhere strictly to the regime and not miss medication times:

"Use a pill beeper or alarm watch to set dose times.... If you are going away for a few days, take extra drugs.... If you have been taking all your drugs at the right time, but you have not had a very good response, you may need a drug concentration test. The £25.00 test will check to see if you are absorbing enough of the drugs.... The chance to return to the luxury of a drug-free period can help improve adherence to the regimen.... It is always safer to use a stronger combination than a weak one...." [172] [emphasis ours]

Stephen Rogers recounts his nightmare encounter with protease inhibitors. Heralded as the Wonder Drug and possible cure for AIDS, Stephen was recommended to take part in a clinical trial for one of the new protease inhibitor products, Saquinavir.[173] Stephen's account has been necessarily condensed, but the thrust of his story is self-evident:

"These new protease inhibitors are marvellous." said my consultant. "Pretty soon everyone will be on them." My trial consisted of AZT, ddl, and Saquinavir. During the first year, I needed a blood transfusion. During the second year I developed a mild attack of shingles and I became affected by the condition Lypodistrophy, with changes in my body shape and veins of the lower limb beginning to protrude and the skin on my thighs becoming more transluscent.[174] My medication was changed to Ritonavir.[175] My doctor brushed aside my concerns that some people had died of liver failure through this drug.

The first two weeks brought no side-effects and then... the onslaught. Numbing and tingling in the lips, lethargy,

---

[172] ATP Guides to 'Combination Therapy', August 1999, and 'Changing Treatment', July 1999

[173] *New York Times*, 16th May 1999, contains a report on their ten-month investigation into drug companies offering large payments to doctors to recruit patients into testing experimental drugs. Top recruiters can earn $1,000,000 per annum. Says Dr David Shimm of the Ethics Committee at Porter Adventist Hospital, Denver: *"Doctors are enticing and cajoling patients who are in no position to resist, and who do not see a dual agent with divided loyalties."*

[174] *New York Times*, 5th February 1998: *"Paunches, buffalo humps, puffy cheeks and other unusual accumulations of fat are changing the body-shape of many people taking combination therapy."*

[175] Incidence of severe liver damage amongst patients taking Ritonavir was five times higher than among those taking other drugs. *Journal of the American Medical Association*, 5th January 2000

insomnia, crippling stomach cramps and chronic diarrhoea. My doctor then reintroduced Saquinavir, alongside the Ritonavir. I developed a skin abscess, which swelled to the size of a golf ball. My doctor tried to blame it on my sexual pursuits.... My clinic appointments were now a torture, occurring every two to four weeks. I began to feel more like a lab rat than a person. The mountain of pills and capsules I had in my hand now filled me with dread. Each time before taking them I would pause and think: 'These drugs are killing me.' I felt confused and frightened. The organisations set up to help people like me had become no more than shadow puppets, projecting the image of living longer and better on combination therapy, but with no actual substance to their claim.

And so, instead of accepting the situation as many do, I began a relentless quest for the truth and began asking lots of questions. When I learned the Viral Load Test is highly inaccurate, my fear turned to anger at being duped. I made a decision to stop taking the drugs." [176]

Amazingly, Saquinavir was declared a 'Millennium Product' by the Millennium Design Council. Exhibited in the failed, now-dismantled Millennium Dome at Greenwich, London, and included in exhibitions in schools and colleges across the UK, a jubilant spokesperson for Roche, the manufacturers of Saquinavir, said, "We are proud that Saquinavir's contribution to anti-HIV therapy has been recognised and delighted that it has received this award." [177]

Stephen believes he is alive today largely as a result of ceasing his 'award-winning' medication. AIDS establishment critic Dr Jens Jerndal notes:

"If statistics show that AIDS sufferers live longer now than they used to, do not let yourself be lulled into believing that this is due to scientific advances in treating AIDS. There are two reasons: One is that when AZT [and its derivatives] was first introduced, very high doses were prescribed, which finished off the patients quite fast, usually in 1 - 3 years.

[176] **Rogers, Stephen** *Continuum*, Vol 5, No 5, December 1998
[177] UK *Gay Times*, June 1999

Eventually it was decided to reduce the recommended doses given, with the result that the patients now stay alive longer. So they do not live longer because they get better medicines. They live longer because they get less of the medicines. The other reason is simply that many AIDS patients secretly go for alternative and holistic treatments instead of drugs, or combine the two, and thus manage to escape or postpone their death sentences."[178]

There are now too many medical case histories which bear out the fact that the body (as in Stephen's case) demonstrates a remarkable ability to recover from many of the illnesses we are witnessing today when one exchanges toxic medicines for a sensible lifestyle and sound nutritional regime.[179] More information on this subject can be found in later chapters.

But for those diagnosed with AIDS, things can get confusing when it comes to recovery programs, for there are now a huge number of treatments on offer that fall outside the orthodox camp, many of which appear quite valid. *But are they?* Would they stand or would they fall, if exposed to the same critical, impartial examination levelled at AZT and its derivatives? While critical deconstructions of orthodox AIDS treatments exist in abundance (and quite rightly so), it is apparent that little room is given to critiquing coherently the many inadequate, alternative therapies existing today, posing as *bona fide* AIDS treatments. Unfortunately, vehement defence of inadequate treatments is rife in both camps. Alex Russell again:

"It seems to me to be quite dishonest that the dissident AIDS movement can be so all-dismissive of the conventional poisons and yet so all-embracing of alternative hocus-pocus. One is a 'conventional' poison for the body, another can quite easily be an 'alternative' poison for the mind. The horrors we have witnessed over the years in the history of AIDS and HIV stem just as much from entrenched scientific error as they do

---

[178] **Dr Jens Jerndal**, *'AIDS - the Facts and the Cure'* bulletin, November 2000

[179] **Day, Phillip,** *Health Wars*, Credence Publications, 2001 A critical examination of current conventional healthcare wisdom, its generally damaging effects upon today's health and well-being, and how, despite this veritable abundance of unhealthy medical error in our midst, it is possible to avoid major disease killers using simple, straightforward techniques (available through Credence at www.credence.org).

from a painfully obvious inability to think rationally and coherently."[180]

The skepticism Stephen showed towards more up-to-date medicalised nonsense - the viral load theory - was also not unfounded. Viral load is a relatively recent hypothesis proposing that HIV is replicating in the body at least one billion times a day, thus increasing a patient's 'viral load', eventually leading to their death. Kary Mullis's Polymerase Chain Reaction (PCR) is once again wheeled out to measure the 'load' of a virus no-one can seem to find. AIDS journalist, Christine Johnson explains:

"If a meaningful amount of HIV were present, the time-honoured laboratory techniques should be able to find it. They can't. Now we need not only PCR, but continuous modifications and improvements on PCR, in order to try to find HIV.

This is how the idea of 'viral load' came about, inspired by two spates of scientific papers that claimed HIV is busily replicating by the billions: initially, papers claiming HIV was 'hiding in the lymph nodes',[181] *and more recently, the Ho and Wei papers.*[182] *The latter studies attempted to measure 'viral load' at a given point, after which 'antiviral' drugs were administered to the patient. The drugs were supposed to prevent replication of any new HIV, and the viral load would decrease accordingly. However, within a few days, the remaining virus would mutate into a form resistant to the drugs, and in a few weeks the viral load would return to its pre-treatment levels. Applying a mathematical formula to this dynamic, the rate at which the virus replicates was allegedly determined.*

---

[180] Russell, Alex. Personal correspondence, 26th November 2000

[181] **Embretson J, Zupancic M, Ribas JL, et al.** "Massive covert infection of helper T lymphocytes and macrophages by HIV during the incubation period of AIDS," *Nature*, 362:359-362, 1992; **Pantaleo G, Graziosi C, Demarest J, et al.** "HIV infection is active and progressive in lymphoid tissue during the clinically latent stage of disease," *Nature*, 362:355-358, 1993

[182] **Ho DD, Neumann AU, Perelson AS, et al.** "Rapid turnover of plasma virions and CD4 lymphocytes in HIV-1 infection," *Nature*, 373:123-126, 1995; **Wei X, Ghosh SK, Taylor ME, et al.** "Viral dynamics in human immunodeficiency virus type 1 infection," *Nature*, 373:117-122, 1995

Hence was born what I call 'Dr. Ho's Kitchen Sink Theory'. According to Ho, billions of copies of HIV are being made every day, which infect billions of T4-cells. These T-cells are destroyed not by HIV, but by the immune system. They are replenished every day, but over the years, the immune system loses ground and HIV finally wins.... It is most important to note that the viral load studies all rely completely on PCR and related techniques, already discredited [as accurate methods of determining HIV infection]."[183]

Nevertheless, drug researchers and their pharmaceutical companies have used 'viral load' as a fresh new vehicle upon which to launch further cocktails to combat this 'vicious, new replicating danger.' The AIDS Treatment Project again:

"Several billion new HIV infected cells are produced in an HIV positive person every day."[184]

Just like a blockbuster Hollywood thriller, it seems that AIDS, the phantom virus phenomenon of the 20th and 21st centuries, has a way of regularly 'upping the ante'. Following hot-on-the-heels of the public health scare that new antibiotic-resistant, opportunistic superbugs are stalking the planet (inspiring unforgettable tabloid headlines such as "Killer Bug Ate My Face"[185]), AIDS researchers are now predicting and promoting a new drug-resistant AIDS epidemic, which is set to engulf us 'very soon'. The following headline is a good example:

THE BEST AIDS DRUGS ARE STILL NOT GOOD ENOUGH - *Scientists at Jefferson Medical College have found evidence for the first time of actively replicating HIV in the bloodstream of patients taking the most powerful anti-AIDS virus drugs available. Scientists knew that the combination of drugs known as HAART, highly active anti-retroviral therapy, did not eradicate the AIDS virus, <u>despite the fact that the virus could not be detected by conventional means in the patient's</u>*

---

[183] Johnson, Christine, "Viral Load and the PCR", *Continuum*, November 2001; for a more complete explanation of the problems with PCR and 'viral load', please see http://www.virusmyth.net/aids/data/chjtests5.htmwww.virusmyth.net

[184] ATP Guides to 'Combination Therapy', August 1999, and 'Changing Treatment', July 1999

[185] In June 1994, British tabloids fanned fears in England with headlines such as 'Eaten Alive', and 'Killer Bug Ate my Face'. The stories tell of a 'deadly, flesh-eating bacteria' that had killed 11 people in England and Wales in 1994. These fears spread to the United States, where it was reported that a handful of cases and at least two deaths had occurred that same year.

blood [emphasis ours]. *But they thought that the drugs had at least arrested the virus from replicating. No-one had been able to find active virus in the blood of patients still on the drugs.... until now. Roger J Pomerantz, MD, professor of medicine, biochemistry and molecular pharmacology, etc. etc....."* [186]

The only measurable contribution which this report (and the many similar to it) has made to the debate on AIDS is to crank up the public fear-factor. As a direct result of this fear-mongering, health officials and legislators in the US have increasing freedom to call for compulsory treatment laws for 'HIV-positive' persons, to protect a vulnerable public from a new and potent AZT-resistant AIDS horror. [187]

And in the UK, London's Enfield and Haringey Health Authorities have reached their target to screen 80% of their expectant mothers for HIV by 2004. [188] In their misguided attempts to guard the health of all expectant mothers in their area, do Enfield and Haringey have any idea of the horrors they are unwittingly calling down upon the innocents in their care? *A healthy, young expectant mother who has just recovered from flu is coincidentally advised to take the ELISA test...?* Christine Maggiore again:

> *"The effects of the drugs on the mother include muscle deterioration, severe anemia, nerve damage, liver and kidney damage, diarrhoea, dementia and seizures. The effects of these drugs on the developing fetus include deformities, and other birth defects, spontaneous abortions and the need for therapeutic abortions of severely damaged fetuses. In many states today, children who test HIV positive risk being removed from their homes by the welfare agencies or public health services if the parents do not agree to give them treatment with AZT or other pharmaceuticals."* [189]

It is at this point in the story of AIDS that the enormity of the charge of negligent homicide can now be examined in its proper

---

[186] Jefferson Medical College, 11th November 1999

[187] *Continuum*, Vol 4, No 4, 1996. *"Health officials in San Francisco want to identify everyone who is HIV+ and force them to have drug therapy... City's health director Sandra Hernandez believes this measure 'has potential for curtailing the further spread of the HIV epidemic.'"*; also, New York Native Issue, 15th July 1996. p.691

[188] Enfield & Haringey Health Authority, *Sexual Health Promotion*, Winter 1999

[189] Maggiore, Christine, op cit. p.14

context. An expectant mother who tests positive for HIV through cross-reactions, is then advised to begin 'anti-viral' treatment with AZT or similar drugs as soon as possible *"...For the benefit of your baby, Mrs Smith."* Mother and child then have every likelihood of going on to die a slow and agonising death.

A study in *The Lancet* gives tacit admission that administering protease inhibitors to children can, as with adults, cause skin and bone abnormalities such as the infamous 'buffalo humps'.[190] Writing in defence of these hump-causing, toxic 'medicines', Tim Horn and Linda Grinberg of *Act Up Golden Gate Writers Pool* scorned the notion that these drugs had bypassed all the normal tried and tested procedures. They went on to state that many people were alive as a result of these drugs. Credence wrote to Horn and Grinberg, asking them to supply further evidence that people's lives had been saved. To date there has been no reply. Horn and Grinberg's wholly unsubstantiated quote *"Tell that to those whose lives were spared..."* [191] will no doubt be used to support further ill-researched and pharmaceutically funded articles in defence of protease inhibitors.

Those more conversant with the AIDS debate know very well the dangers of these medications. *People Magazine*, dated 5th October 1998, carries an article about Maine, USA housewife Valerie Emerson whose two children, Tia and Nikolas, were diagnosed as 'carrying HIV'. Her three-year-old daughter Tia was put on AZT and subsequently died in 1997. After ten weeks of AZT treatment, Mrs Emerson saw Nikolas go *"...from being a little boy who was active to being a little boy who lay on the floor and cried."* The article continues:

> *"She took Nikolas off AZT last fall, but by March two doctors advised Emerson, a welfare mother, to begin treating her son with an aggressive new 'cocktail' of drugs that included AZT to combat HIV-related symptoms. She refused. Officials from Maine's Department of Human Services accused her of endangering her child's health and began legal proceedings to take custody of Nikolas.... On 14th September, after a four-month legal struggle, a district judge in Newport, Maine, upheld her right to determine her son's treatment...."*

[190] **Vigano, Allesandra et al** *Lancet*, 352:1905, 12th December 1998
[191] **Horn, Grinberg** *HAART Sick Hoax,* Act Up Golden Gate Writers Pool, 24th February 2000

The August 1999 edition of the widely read *Positive Treatment News*, an ATP publication, contains a variety of information for HIV-positive women and pregnancy. Alongside snippets such as *'Sperm washing in the UK – significantly reducing the risk of mother or baby becoming HIV positive...'* and *'...if you're going into hospital, remember to pack your drugs into your hospital bag'*, an interview was included with Dr Karen Beckerman, who manages HIV-positive women through their pregnancy at the Bay Area Perinatal AIDS Center in San Francisco. Among the drugs used at the centre are the old favourites Saquinavir, Ritonavir, AZT, ddl and d4T. On being asked what effects anti-retrovirals might have on fertility, Dr Beckerman replied: *"I think they enhance it. Women feel better, they're healthier, they start thinking long-term."* and on her preference for the latest protease inhibitors, Beckerman stated *"I have to be honest with you, I have a special fondness for d4T. Many years hence, it may prove to be a better drug than AZT."*[192] In what capacity *better*?

ATP openly declare their publications are copyright-free, and that readers may photocopy and distribute material as they wish. In the face of the evidence against the efficacy of AZT and its derivatives, disseminating Beckerman's statements might seem unbelievably irresponsible. Consider the following report, one of several warnings to doctors in the treatment of expectant mothers.

"In pregnant women treated with AZT at a hospital in India, Kumar et al. report a shocking number of therapeutic and spontaneous abortions, and of the live births, a number of grotesque birth defects included holes in the chest, abnormal indentations at the base of the spine, misplaced ears, mis-shapen faces, heart defects, extra digits and albinism."[193]

In the September 2001 issue of *Mothering Magazine*, Neville Hodgkinson's "Poisoning our Babies – The Dangers of AZT" read:

"Increasing the number of drugs used in pregnancy increases the risk to the baby. In New York, an HIV-negative baby whose positive mother received AZT and two other anti-virals was born with congestive heart failure secondary to profound, life-threatening

---

[192] *Positive Treatment News*, August 1999

[193] **Kumar et al.**, *Journal of Acquired Immune Deficiency Syndromes*, 7:1034-9, 1994

anaemia. Doctors said the cause was suppression of the baby's bone marrow by one or more of the antiretroviral agents administered to the mother. AZT damage to bone marrow can be long-lasting as well."

And in the UK, a 'Mum on the Run' story was blazoned across the pages of several nationals in late August 1999. The mother had been diagnosed HIV-positive in 1992 after submitting to an ELISA test. On discovering her 'HIV-positive' status, Camden Council in north London applied to the High Court under the 1989 Children's Act to have the mother's perfectly healthy five-month-old baby girl tested for HIV. The council had taken this unprecedented action because the mother had so far refused their requests, herself knowing full well the true nature of AIDS and AIDS 'medicines'.

The case took on added emotional force when, in July 1999, the British government announced plans to include HIV testing in all routine ante-natal examinations *"...in a bid to reduce the UK's exceptionally high transmission rates from mother to child."* [194] In the belief that if the child tested positive she would need the best care and medical intervention, High Court Justice Wilson declared the baby had 'a right to life' and announced *"I order the test."* Both parents and their baby subsequently vanished, unwilling to submit to the authorities, to the fundamentally flawed test, or to the horrors of AIDS anti-viral therapy.

Project AIDS International's chairman Jeremy Selvey commented thus on the widely-established practice of prescribing deadly chemicals to babies who inadvertently triggered a 'positive AIDS test':

> *"The practice of treating HIV-positive infants with AZT based on 1) tests with questionable accuracy such as the ELISA and Western Blot, and/or 2) presumptive diagnosis when no clinical illness is present - is* <u>*murder*</u>*. Murder as used here means 'the introduction of a known toxic substance that ultimately results in the infant's premature death.'"* [195]

---

[194] *The Guardian*, 27th August 1999
[195] Selvey, Jeremy, op. cit. p.8

It is for the above reasons that Camden Council is unable to trace the whereabouts of mother, father and child. In keeping with the words of Patrick Henry, no matter the anguish of spirit, Mum and Dad had purposed to discover the truth about AIDS some time ago. They disappeared because they know the worst. They wished to avoid their infant's premature death at the hands of state legislation. But who will now provide for them?

London's *Evening Standard* ran the following headline:

CALL TO TEST ALL MOTHERS AS LONDON HEADS HIV BABY LEAGUE - *All pregnant women should be tested for HIV, particularly in London where more babies are born with the virus than the rest of Britain, experts have warned.... Dr Walters, a senior lecturer in paediatrics and infectious diseases at St Mary's Hospital in Paddington, said, "One of the advantages of testing pregnant women is that we are able to offer them healthcare <u>before they become very ill</u>."*[196] [emphasis ours]

Katrine is another 'mum on the run', determined at all costs to evade conventional 'AIDS healthcare'. Whilst in Africa in 1996, Katrine contracted malaria. On her return home to the US, a doctor took a blood sample and went on to perform an AIDS test without her permission. As a result, and despite the doctor knowing that she was suffering from malaria (one of the many diseases which can give rise to a false positive HIV diagnosis), the doctor nevertheless pronounced Katrine an official AIDS case. Katrine had recently given birth to a baby boy. As a result, both Katrine and her husband vanished with their baby in order to avoid the highly dangerous conventional AIDS healthcare being forced upon them by the US Child Protection Services.

"Although I planned to deliver at home with a midwife, I asked what would happen if I gave birth at hospital. The answer – 12 hours of intravenously fed AZT, a caesarean and formulae-feeding for the baby with AZT liquid – sealed my decision to stay out of the system.... The CPS questioned my mother and said they would notify the police if she did not reveal my whereabouts.... Ten days after our baby was born

---

[196] *Evening Standard*, 24th November 1999

at a friend's house, my husband and I packed up our entire lives and fled the state for good. We left behind a home, careers, friends and family. This is what we have to do to keep our son off toxic AIDS drugs, and to ensure that he receives the vital nourishment and immune protection through breast-feeding. As I write this, we have no idea where we are going or what we will do, but at least our son is healthy and in our care. Katrine. Somewhere in America." [197]

And what of the effects of AIDS drugs on a mother unaware of the dangers of AZT and its derivatives, trying also to cope with lively school children? The following news item from *Observer Online* is one of many altruistic and well-meaning reports, where neither the reporter nor the sufferer have any idea of the deadly truth that can now be read between the lines. Once again, we are witnessing another needless tragedy unfolding:

MOM WITH AIDS by GIGI ANDERS, Staff Writer
– RALEIGH - Matthew and Jonathan, who resemble young McCauley Culkins, must fend for themselves this morning. Their mother's alarm clock went off at 6, as did theirs, but she's too sick to get up with them and make breakfast. More often than not, that's the case. There's a loud crash. Suddenly, their sleepy mother, Nicole, appears in the doorway in a long, white T-shirt and bare feet. The 33-year old has long, blonde hair and an ivory complexion, with reddish spots across her pale arms and strange, pink squiggles on her hands.

"Are you OK, Mama?" Matthew asks, appraising her. "Your eyes are as red as a rabbit's."

"I'm just real tired, honey. I'll be fine."

From the doorway Nicole watches them run off. She waits to make sure they don't return for something they've forgotten. Now she can begin her ritual, the ultimate secret she keeps from her children. Taking a glass of orange juice into her bedroom, Nicole locks the door. She reaches under a bench and produces a locked metal box. She sits cross-legged on her king-size water-bed and unlocks it. There is a mini-pharmacy inside

---

[197] Maggiore, Christine, *"What if Everything..."* 4th Edition, 1999

that box, 25 plastic orange bottles and tiny vials that contain the pills she must take every day to stay alive.... When she's too sick to make their meals, Nicole tells her sons she has a bad cold or feels run down. They seem to accept it. Nicole says she doesn't want to burden them with the truth, especially since her time with them may be short. The red spots explain the truth, [which is] kept at a lawyer's office, along with a will." [198]

Credence Publications has contacted the reporter in this instance and supplied the necessary information, which we hope will find its way to Nicole.

Another disturbing account of AIDS 'medicine' abuse is recounted by journalist Liam Scheff who, in 1997, discovered a particularly horrific situation taking place in the Incarnation Children's Center in New York. Shockingly, the events taking place there did not reach the mainstream press until August 2004. The children, from poor Hispanic or African-American backgrounds, had mothers who were using drugs. Predictably, HIV tests produced cross-reactive, positive results. Various pharmaceutical companies, including GlaxoSmithKline, Pfizer and Biocene, seized the opportunity to use these children as guinea-pigs for clinical trials at the home. Scheff takes up the story:

"The kids are given AZT, protease inhibitors, etc, as well as experimental drugs, or drugs in experimental combinations. When the children refuse the drugs, they're force-fed. If the kids continue to refuse, they're given surgery to implant a plastic tube through their abdomen into their stomach. The drugs are then injected directly into their stomachs - no refusing. This year a six-year-old and a twelve-year-old child had strokes because of the drugs. The twelve-year-old went blind. They both died shortly after. The children walk around in various states of deformation and retardation because of life-long exposure to AZT and protease inhibitors.

Parents who refuse to give their children the drugs are labelled 'incompetent' by the city/state agency. The children are removed from parental custody and remanded to ICC. I've written an extensive story about this, which consists of an

---

[198] *Mom with AIDS,* Gigi Anders, 8th January 1999, *News and Observer* online. www.newasandobserver.com

interview with a mother of two children at Incarnation, as well as the administering doctor at the place, who blithely confirms the practice of cutting these children open so they can be drugged.

This is a horrible, grotesque story. But it's real, it's happening now. I've been there, I've seen it, and I'm sick to death being the only one who knows about it. I don't have an outlet yet, and I'm wondering if you can help put the story out there - web, local underground papers, any friendly, or at least not-unfriendly outlet. I certainly want everybody who is aware of the problem with the AIDS diagnosis to know that this is going on." [199]

And for exactly this reason, Scheff's story has been included here. A November 2004 update on this story is featured on the Josef Hasselberger Health Supreme website and reveals some interesting information. Scheff again:

"So why were infants at ICC getting AZT? Weren't there better solutions? ICC seemed to think so. From their published history: "Early in the epidemic, HIV disease of childhood was considered to be a down-hill course leading to death. But in the late 1980's, before AZT was available, many very ill children admitted to ICC got dramatically better with proper nurturing and high-quality medical and nursing care." I wrote about this in the New York Press in July, 2004. I haven't seen anything on it in the New York Times. But, of course, the chief writer on HIV at the NY Times is (and has been for over 20 years) a man named Lawrence Altman. And Lawrence Altman can't write stuff like this, even if he wants to.

You see, Altman is a former graduate of the CDC - the organization that makes the rules for how HIV patients are treated and diagnosed in this country. So, of course, Altman's hands are tied. [The NYT strap-line] 'All the News That's Fit to Print' suddenly has a very clear, very unpleasant meaning. Next time you see the headline 'New AIDS Drugs for Africa' or 'Noble Doctors Try New Drugs on Orphans', what will you

[199] Posted to Credence ,18th December 2003, as part of a discussion forum at http://health.groups.yahoo.com/group/AIDSsoc/messages

think? Will you ask yourself what's behind it? If you want to find out, you'll have to dig a little."[200]

The Incarnation Children's Centre aside, there are a great number of genuinely caring and compassionate conventional 'AIDS care' organisations who literally have no idea what effect their pharmaceutical ministrations are having on those in their care. The following text was used to support the photograph of Ida (see photo section). Credence contacted Ida's care agency to request the possibility of being supplied with further details. The love and concern the carers had for Ida were self-evident and beyond question. Their moving tribute to Ida reads as follows:

"After a year of gradual decline, Ida Janel left her physical body on 2nd January 1997 at 12:02 am. We lost our sweet Ida to a myriad of systemic failures, toxic shock, respiratory failure and heart failure all brought on by that vicious virus, HIV." [201]

Was it a vicious virus which finally caused Ida to leave her physical body? Or was it not the case that Ida died of toxic shock through AIDS medications, albeit innocently dripped into her little body, every bedside action being carried out with the best of intention? A copy of *The Truth About HIV* has been sent to Ida's carers.

Christine Maggiore runs the *Alive and Well* website. State medicine determined Christine was HIV-positive some fifteen years ago. Having enjoyed great health by staying off all AIDS medications and also giving birth to two healthy children, Christine actively campaigns against HIV industry injustice, and her site includes many testimonies, such as the one below, from those who likewise have refused their HIV 'medications'.

"In 1996, the AIDS drug cocktails came out and there was such elation, almost hysteria. The new tests were great, the new drugs were great, and everybody was living longer. It was the first good thing to happen in AIDS in the last 15 years. I bought into all the glowing media reports and decided to

---

[200] Orphanage Toxic Drugs, Health Supreme Update, 5th November 2004 at http://www.newmediaexplorer.org/sepp/2004/11/05/azt_nevirapine_children_in_new_york_o rphanage_given_toxic_drugs.htm
[201] www.thebody.com/loel poor

take the drugs. For a while, I didn't have any side-effects except that my cholesterol[202] was rising. After about nine months on the treatments, I started to gain weight, but I looked thinner because my face was getting gaunt. I developed an extended belly, my cheekbones sunk in, and my arms started to waste away. The first time I'd ever felt sick since testing positive was a direct result of taking the medication.

I got more information about the drugs through HEAL Toronto, and after speaking with Christine Maggiore one year into the drugs, I decided to quit them. Since then, I've had no problems at all and everything in my body is back to normal. My doctor was annoyed at first, but ultimately he supported my decision. I feel great these days and haven't looked back. I don't go to the gym, but I have a dog and I walk him to the park every day. I tell myself at least once a day that my body is healthy and I'm going to live a long and happy life."[203]

Hippocrates stated, "First, do no harm to the body." The Hippocratic Oath binds all doctors with this most fundamental axiom. Furthermore, the 18th World Medical Assembly in Helsinki, Finland, convened in June 1964, binds physicians with the words, "...the health of my patient shall be my first consideration." The American Medical Association, the British Medical Association and other medical authorities worldwide are signatories to this declaration. What then is one to make of the murderous quackery practised in AIDS medicine today? Of HIV-positive mothers, hunted down and compelled to submit their child to 'an AIDS test', then told upon receiving a 'positive' result, "You are harming your child's right to life by refusing treatment for their life-threatening illness"?

There is no doubt that extreme drug toxicity brings on the very symptoms of AIDS itself. But this is by no means the whole story. AZT, the first AIDS drug, did not hit the market until 1987. So what was wasting and killing young, homosexual men (and as we shall discover, heterosexual men and women also) for at least six years prior to that? To answer this question, let us return to America's beautiful West

---

[202] Another sham test, supporting a £$multi-billion 'necessary-pill-for-health' industry'. Please visit The Cholesterol Myths at www.curezone.com/art/read.asp?ID=63&db=6&Co=13
[203] http://questionaids.com/index.php?page=survival

Coast city of San Francisco, where the story of Acquired Immune Deficiency Syndrome had its 20th century genesis....

ANNIHILATING THE
ANNIHILATORS

examining the sexual 'link' to AIDS

"If I could take any one thing out of my life, it wouldn't be AIDS. I really didn't have a life before AIDS." Former prostitute, drug addict and convicted felon Cyndi Potete, founder of Positive Voices.

As has already been noted, it was Dr Friedman-Kein who brought a wider attention to the emergence of *'a rapidly fatal form of cancer'* being diagnosed in those first 41 men. Dr Friedman-Kein's *New York Times* article continues as follows:

"The reporting doctors said most cases involved homosexual men who have had multiple and frequent sexual encounters with different partners, as many as ten sexual encounters a night, up to four times a week. Many of the patients had also been treated for viral infections such as herpes, Hepatitis B, as well as parasitic infections such as amebiasis and giardiasis. Many patients also reported that they had used drugs such as amyl nitrites and LSD to heighten sexual pleasure." [204]

A valid question being asked by those opposed to the 'AIDS as virus' hypothesis was this: How much damage was being wrought on the human immune system by choosing to indulge in such extreme behaviour, let alone the additional effects a rumoured AIDS virus might be having?

Joan Shenton sheds light on some of the less publicised details of life in most city/suburban gay communities in the 1980s.

"In some New York and San Francisco bathhouses, clients were offered a tray as they entered, replete with a range of antibiotic cocktails to take as an aperitif, supposedly to help protect against the soup of sexually transmissible

---

[204] *New York Times*, 3rd July 1981

infections waiting inside. Backrooms were to be found in most capital cities across America and Europe. These were the special areas in popular gay bars where patrons could indulge in wild, promiscuous sex involving sado-masochism and all the most excessive forms of gay sex. The sexual activity was of such intensity that drugs were needed to fuel it. At the height of bathhouse and backroom activity, more than seventy different chemical stimulants or depressants were commonly used by the dedicated 'fast-tracker'. Backrooms usually had very low lighting or were pitch black to facilitate anonymity. Before the visit to the backroom or the bathhouse often came the disco where other dangers lay."[205]

Cathy Kay, RN, Director of National Healthcare Advocates, reveals that, from a hygiene perspective alone, the more extreme homosexual practices can invite all manner of health-related dangers:

"Sodomy... the ingestion of one another's feces; urinating on one another, it's called 'golden showers', and 'rimming' where they lick one another's rectums. These are things that people really don't realise are going on, but it's all part of the behavioural lifestyle that can go along with homosexuality."[206]

Sean and Andrew, both former homosexuals and AIDS patients, had this to say about their former lifestyles:

Sean: *"When I first moved to the city, I was very naïve. But after a couple of years of seeing these things happen in bathhouses, it just gave me the creeps. After a while I knew this was abnormal. 23-year-olds with colostomy bags? Everyone in San Francisco that I knew was getting into this sado-masochism. It was like a spiral funnel. Everyone was gravitating towards this intense sex."*[207]

Andrew: *"I was aware of something deeply disturbing going on* [within the gay scene]. *I came to realise we were being manipulated in a spiritual fashion by forces beyond our control, which had as their goal our death. Gays know that*

---

[205] Shenton, Joan, op. cit.

[206] *Gay Rights, Special Rights*, a video documentary, Jeremiah Films, PO Box 1710, Hemet, CA 92546 USA.

[207] Ibid.

107

promiscuous sex in communities such as San Francisco and Los Angeles is a death sentence, but far from responding to our natural instinct for self-preservation and survival by changing our lifestyles to avoid this miserable death, we are driven by these forces to indulge in it with ever increasing abandon."[208]

And today, Celia Farber writes of bare-backing, or 'conscious, unprotected, unsafe sex' - a sexual pursuit that has had its devotees for years.

"The idea is to unapologetically do it raw. In the most hardcore circles, it goes even further. Here HIV-infected semen [if you believe it is infected] is itself eroticised and the ultimate erotic bond is for one man to infect another – consciously. Equated with breeding, some men going as far as to select the man who will father their HIV.... This has less than nothing to do with dangerous dissident movements and everything to do with basic human lust and rage."[209]

The casualness of sex, both homosexual and heterosexual, was adopted without question by many in the 1970s' younger generation - the decade of 'new-found sexual liberation'. Heterosexual promiscuity and its little-mentioned place in AIDS history is explored a little later in this chapter. For the homosexual, abandoned forms of sexual expression were the cornerstone of the 1970s' gay rights movement. Gay Lib epitomised a new lifestyle, which ran counter to one of mankind's most enduring taboos. It offered a daring new sexual freedom to all who would reach out and grasp it. Phillip Gefter's recollections of times spent on New York's notorious Fire Island at the height of the gay liberation movement of the 1970s succinctly capture the mood of the period:

"The Ice Palace was the most fabulous disco I'd ever been to - two thousand writhing, drugged, beautiful bodies on the dance floor. By 6am we were outside across the pool dancing under the stars as the sun was coming up. And I believed at this moment in time that we were having more fun than anybody in the history of civilisation had ever had. The sexual

---

[208] Day, Phillip, personal notes.
[209] **Farber, Celia** *Continuum*, Vol 5, No 5, December 1998. See also transcript of Radio 4 'PM News,' 28th February 2000

tension, the drugs, the music and the sun coming up created a special kind of thrill and excitement. I can remember the sexual meeting ground known as the 'enchanted forest'. On one occasion on our way back from the Ice Palace at seven in the morning, there were these four men naked. We watched them. They just kind of reached out and grabbed us and drew us in."[210]

The Vietnam era witnessed a huge increase in recreational drug consumption among the younger generation. Justice Department figures reveal that the Drug Enforcement Agency confiscated 9,000 kilograms of cocaine in 1980, compared with 100,000 kilograms in 1990. The National Institute on Drug Abuse also reported that 5,000,000 people were using nitrite inhalants at least once a week.[211] Readily available street narcotics, such as cocaine, heroin, amphetamines and the new nitrite inhalants, such as the party drug 'poppers', were now being used to heighten sexual pleasure. With the maximum of hard drug-taking, chronic antibiotic use and the minimum of consideration being given to the body's basic needs, such as a sensible diet and regular sleep patterns, Howard Rosenman, another active member of San Francisco's gay community, recalls similar days of reckless excess:

"Between 1972 and 1983, we had a group in California, about fifty of us, partying at Nando Scarffioti's house, production designer for The Last Emperor. At the beginning we would buy a gram of coke and split it between all of us for the entire weekend: just one little toot at the very beginning. By the time the parties were over we would be consuming 6 oz of cocaine a weekend and every other drug known to man. Of those fifty there are six that are still alive - everybody else is dead."[212]

During the 1970s and early 1980s, Gary Null spent hours interviewing literally hundreds of promiscuous hetero- and homosexuals, witnessing firsthand the effects of their relentless lifestyle:

[210] **Kaiser, Charles**, *Gay Metropolis*, Phoenix Press, 1997

[211] **Duesberg, Peter H** "The Role of Drugs in the Origin of AIDS", *Biomed. & Pharmacotherapy*, Vol 46, 1992

[212] Kaiser, Charles, op. cit.

"I went to the baths, to the night-clubs and I would hang out and interview people. I knew people who were partying ten hours a night, seven nights a week, for two or three years straight. There were two guys who lived nearby, and I spoke to them on a regular basis when I was out there. I watched them physically deteriorate. In less than six months, I saw them go from being really masculine and pumped-up bodybuilders to just shells, emaciated... I found only two percent of people were doing it because they wanted to hurt themselves. Most of them just loved what they were doing. It was just like taking a kid and putting him in a candy shop. They wanted to eat everything in there, and the fact that they were going to get sick - well, you know '...the sickness will pass, let's keep gorging!'"[213]

Journalist and historian John Lauritsen has investigated and written about AIDS for over 20 years. In an interview with *The Weekly Dig*, Lauritsen stated:

"There was a marvellous sense of freedom for gay men in the early 70s. These were strong, healthy, young men who suddenly had this tremendous freedom offered to them. Using a lot of drugs and having a lot of sex was part of that freedom. I lived in New York from 63 to 95; I was there, right in the heart of it. I lived around the corner from an extremely popular gay club called The Saint where there was a drug schedule. Someone would say, "Now it's time for ecstasy, now it's time for crystal, now it's time for Special K," and hundreds to a couple thousand guys would all do drugs at the same time. This went on all evening. They mixed this with alcohol through the course of the long, long night. A drug called 'poppers' was used constantly, because it was cheap and legal....

At gay discothèques, men shuffled around in a daze, holding their poppers bottles under their nose. The acrid odor of poppers was synonymous with gay gathering places. Poppers are an extraordinarily toxic drug. They cause brain damage from strokes, severe skin burns and heart failure. They suppress the immune system and damage the lungs.

---

[213] Null, Gary, *Zenger*, op. cit.

They've caused death from a single use. They're such an effective poison that they've been used to commit suicide and murder. By the end of the '70s, some of the healthy young men weren't looking so young and healthy. They were worn out. Their faces were gray. They looked prematurely old. I remember going to a party in the late '70s and being shocked to see how many men were gravely ill." [214]

From the outset, there were medical scientists who were seriously considering whether it was the accumulation of drugs, antibiotics, poor sleep and diet that was responsible for such fatal immune system depression.[215] Witness Professor Duesberg, writing in 1992, seeking to wrench the AIDS establishment back to reason:

"Hardly anybody can remember that only ten years ago AIDS was still considered by many scientists as a collection of diseases acquired by consumption of recreational drugs. Since nearly all early AIDS patients were either male homosexuals who were using nitrite and ethylchloride inhalants, cocaine, heroin, amphetamines, LSD and other drugs as sex stimulants, or were heterosexuals injecting cocaine and heroin intravenously, early AIDS researchers named these drugs as the causes of AIDS.[216] Drugs seemed to be the most plausible explanation for the near-perfect restriction of AIDS to these risk groups because drug consumption is their most specific, common denominator. This original drug-AIDS hypothesis is called <u>the lifestyle hypothesis.</u>" [217] [218] [emphasis ours]

214 **Scheff, Liam,** "The Gay Plague", *The Weekly Dig,* May 2003 at http://www.weeklydig.com/dig/content/3499.aspx
215 **Kaslow, RA, et al** "No Evidence for a Role of Alcohol or Other Psychoactive Drugs In Accelerating Immunodeficiency in HIV-1-Positive Individuals", *JAMA,* 261 (1989): pp.3424-3429; **Weiss, R and H Jaffe,** "Duesberg, HIV and AIDS", *Nature* (London), p.345 (1990)
216 **Marmor, M. et al** "Risk Factors for Kaposi's Sarcoma in Homosexual Men," *Lancet,* i (1982): pp.1083-1087; **Jaffe, HW, et al** "National Case-Control Study of Kaposi's Sarcoma and *Pneumocystis Carinii* Pneumonia in Homosexual Men: Part 1, Epidemiological Results," *Ann. Intern. Med.,* 99 (1983) pp.145-151; **Haverkos, HW, et al** "Disease Manifestation Among Homosexual Men with AIDS: A Possible Role of Nitrites in Kaposi's Sarcoma," *Journal of Sex. Trans. Dis.,* 12 (1985) 203-208; **Newell, GR, et al** "Volatile Nitrites: Use and Adverse Effects Related to the Current Epidemic of the Acquired Immune Deficiency Syndrome," *Preventative Med.,* 14 (1985b): pp.81-91
217 **Oppenheimer, GM** "Causes, Cases, and Cohorts: The Role of Epidemiology in the Historical Construction of AIDS," *AIDS: The Making of a Chronic Disease,* Berkeley, Calif: University of California Press, 1992: pp.49-83

Duesberg explains that, with AIDS, the First World is witnessing the long-term effects of drug abuse now becoming evident in those sections of the population which chronically abuse these substances:

"The key to the drug hypothesis is that only long-term consumption causes irreversible AIDS-defining diseases. Occasional or short-term recreational drug use causes reversible diseases or no diseases at all. Toxicity of drugs is first a function of how much is taken at any given time."[219]

And this observation from Gary Null, interviewed in 1997 on the longer-term effects of continual excess:

"There are consequences. Every action begets a reaction, and the reaction of a lot of the heterosexuals who participated in the revolution is that they are very sick today, just as the gays who participated in that revolution are very sick, unless they have detoxified and changed their lives, then they're OK. But the majority have not done so, so they linger in this disease limbo. Nobody knows what they have or why they have it. But I've been on top of this a long time and that's how I see it."[220]

Duesberg points out that no one has a problem accepting that it can take twenty years of smoking to acquire irreversible lung cancer or emphysema, or twenty years of hard drinking to acquire irreversible liver cirrhosis:

"Consider a grace period of about ten years to achieve the [drug] dosage needed to cause irreversible disease, and you can date the origin of AIDS in 1981 as a consequence of the drug use epidemic that started in America in the late 1960s during the Vietnam War.... Since 1987, AZT and other [similar drugs] have been added to the list of toxic drugs consumed by AIDS patients and those at risk from AIDS. AZT is now prescribed to about 200,000 HIV positives world-wide."[221]

The AIDS problem has been immeasurably worsened, Professor Duesberg contends, by medical orthodoxy's dismissal of the cumulative evidence which demonstrates that it can take about ten years of

[218] Duesberg, Peter H, *Inventing...* op. cit. pp.410-411
[219] Duesberg, Peter H, *Inventing...* op. cit. pp.411-412
[220] Null, Gary, *Zenger*, op. cit.
[221] Duesberg, Peter H, *Inventing...* op. cit. p.420

nitrites, heroin, amphetamines, or cocaine to develop AIDS through toxic load. Further, that it can take potentially less than a year of the much more toxic drugs, such as AZT, to cause AIDS by prescription. [222]

"The untold price of frequent drug use is the cumulative toxicity that builds up over a lifetime, causing irreversible damage," Duesberg concludes. [223]

As mentioned, the idea that heavy recreational drug consumption could, in itself, be the cause of AIDS is not a new one and was originally held by the medical establishment prior to discarding it in favour of the more profitable advent of Gallo's 'virus' in 1984.[224] But the serious champions of the drug hypothesis, like Duesberg, have been consistent in publishing hard evidence in medical journals that cumulative drug toxicity, brought on by long-term drug consumption (either recreational or pharmaceutical), has been the obvious culprit with Western AIDS all along. Although the dangers of drug overdoses are widely known, street narcotics have surprisingly been viewed by the orthodoxy as <u>illegal</u> rather than <u>toxic</u>, *Science* even stating *"...heroin is a blessedly untoxic drug"* provided that it is *"injected with a clean needle."*[225]

Ten years after this toxic onslaught struck the Western nations and institutionalised itself into the fabric of society, AIDS incidences (cases of chronic immune suppression) went from a few dozen cases in 1981 to about 100,000 in 1993.[226] Duesberg believes the AIDS establishment's dogmatic support of HIV and its unwillingness to investigate the drug/AIDS connection can be viewed either as markedly incompetent or calculatedly dismissive of the evidence. The great majority of American and European homosexuals today inhale nitrites on a regular basis, yet, he states, there exists *not one study* that measures the long-term effects of these substances either on animals

---

[222] **Duesberg, Peter H** "How Much Longer Can We Afford the AIDS Virus Monopoly?" *AIDS: Virus or Drug-Induced?* Genetica: 1996

[223] Duesberg, Peter H, *Inventing...* op. cit. pp.411-412

[224] **Kaslow, RA, et al** "No Evidence for a Role of Alcohol or Other Psychoactive Drugs In Accelerating Immunodeficiency in HIV-1-Positive Individuals", *JAMA*, 261 (1989): pp.3424-3429; **Weiss, R and H Jaffe**, "Duesberg, HIV and AIDS", *Nature* (London), p.345 (1990)

[225] **Cohen, J** "The Duesberg Phenomenon: Duesberg and Other Voices," *Science*, 266 (1994a): pp.1642-1649

[226] Centers for Disease Control and Prevention, "US HIV and AIDS Cases Reported Through June 1994", 1-27

or humans. Duesberg's exhaustive supply of the evidence over ten years leads him to file the following dramatic conclusion:

> *"All AIDS diseases in America and Europe that exceed their long-established, normal backgrounds are caused by the long-term consumption of recreational drugs and by AZT and its analogs.[227] The correct hypothesis of AIDS must 1) explain why a [single] agent is a plausible cause of one or all of the thirty fatal AIDS diseases and 2) predict all clinical... aspects of AIDS. The drug hypothesis meets these criteria to the letter, but the HIV hypothesis does not."[228]*

Later in his report in the *New York Times*, Dr Friedman-Kein stated that he had personally tested 9 of those initial 41 victims, remarking that in each case he had found *"...severe defects in their immunological systems, severe malfunction of the T and B cell lymphocytes which have important roles in fighting infections and cancer."[229]*

Dr Paul Brand introduces us to the importance of the immune system as our body's first line of defence against hostile microbiological invasion. In his book, *The Forever Feast*, he explores some of the amazing aspects of a human's in-built army of infection fighters:

> *"I must share just one facet of the skills of the T lymphocytes, because I get excited at the ingenuity that must have gone into their design, and because I'm so happy to have these little guys on my side when I am sick. My T lymphocytes concentrate in places where most germs try to get into the body. It is never very long before an invading germ meets a T lymphocyte.*
>
> *The first, wonderful thing is that the lymphocyte knows at once that this living cell is not 'one of us', it is an enemy. The next wonderful thing is what it does. It inspects the enemy cell and takes a template or pattern of its surface, noting*

---

[227] **Duesberg, Peter H** "AIDS Epidemiology: Inconsistencies with Human Immunodeficiency Virus and with Infectious Disease," *Proc. Natl. Acad. Sci.*, USA 88 (1991)

[228] Duesberg, Peter H, *Inventing...* op. cit. p.414

[229] *New York Times*, 3rd July 1981

especially the weak points. Then our friend runs back to the factory where new cells are made and announces the emergency: "An enemy has entered the body and is rapidly multiplying. We have to manufacture antibodies of exactly this shape, so the enemy will be killed and no other cell will be harmed. An older lymphocyte may hurry up at this point and tell the factory that the shape of the needed antibodies is exactly the size as was used a year ago, when there was a brief war in the body during the flu season. Therefore there is no need to repeat the time-consuming preparation of the prototype antibodies - we already have them. All that is needed is to rush into mass production." [230]

Lennart Nilsson, author of *The Body Victorious*, writes:

"Suddenly the site of injury and infection, previously so peaceful, is transformed into a battlefield on which the body's armed forces hurl themselves repeatedly at the encroaching micro-organisms, crushing and annihilating them. No one is pardoned, no prisoners are taken... All these events take place in a microscopic world where nothing, neither the body's cells nor the micro-organisms that assail them, measures more than a few thousandths of a millimetre across." [231]

So what was really happening to these men with their severely malfunctioning T and B cell lymphocytes? Were those men, diagnosed with AIDS-related symptoms, really suffering from a new and exotic killer virus? Would it not be more reasonable to propose that they were suffering the effects of destroying their personal little army of infection annihilators through persistent sexual infection, hard drugs, poor diet, little or no sleep and an enormous array of immuno-suppressant antibiotics? Had their annihilators quite literally been annihilated? They were certainly finding themselves unable to combat even the most minor of illnesses – illnesses that in normal circumstances should have posed no threat to the body at all.

Some in the active gay scene were asking themselves the same questions and began calling for abstention from certain meeting places and forms of particularly dangerous sexual behaviour. Dan William, a

[230] **Brand, Paul** *The Forever Feast*, Monarch Publications, 1994
[231] **Nilsson, Lennart** *The Body Victorious*, Faber, 1987

prominent New York doctor and himself a homosexual, suggested that bathhouses be required to post warning signs about the epidemic and of the dangers of promiscuous sex. His suggestions were angrily rejected by most in the community, and William was accused of being *"a monogamist and a scaremonger."*[232]

While there was a definite resistance to giving up a lifestyle that many gay men found both compulsory and necessary to their identity, there were other reasons why calls for moderation in homosexual behaviour were rejected. Gallo's announcement brought relief to more than a few in the gay community since it provided a 'no-blame' hypothesis for AIDS. The new virus tag was readily accepted, and those previously advocating restraint in extreme sexual practices, indiscriminate drug-consumption and 'high-revving' lifestyles were now dismissed. Less focus on lifestyle was necessary, it was simply a virus. Joan Shenton again:

> *"Once HIV was accepted as the cause of AIDS by the majority of gay men, a certain sense of relief entered their lives. They had seen many of their lovers and closest friends waste away before their eyes. Now they could grieve for them, knowing that HIV, this strange novel virus said to come from Africa, had caused the death of their loved one, perhaps after one 'unlucky' sexual encounter. Nothing to do with the fact that the friend or loved one had probably been sniffing nitrites on the dance floor; or taking any one of fifty different 'recreational' chemical drugs night after night for years; might have had hundreds of sexual partners in a year; might have stopped eating and sleeping properly; and might have been taking antibiotics all year round for recurring syphilis, gonorrhoea and hepatitis. No, the friend or loved one had definitely died of HIV. Anyone challenging the accepted cause of death was deeply resented and quickly labelled 'homophobic'."*[233]

No mysterious, sexually spread virus is necessary to explain the catastrophic health failures being witnessed in these gay men. The link between marked ill-health and irresponsible lifestyle is obvious. In the

232 Shilts, Randy, op. cit.
233 Shenton, Joan, op. cit.

Dr Robert Gallo of the National Institutes of Health, who made the 1984 historic global announcement that HIV was the probable cause of AIDS

Peter H Duesberg, professor of molecular and cell biology at the University of California at Berkeley, has been at the heart of the 'dissident' movement, declaring the fraudulence of the HIV=AIDS hypothesis

Dr Luc Montagnier of the Pasteur Institute, Paris (above), and Dr Robert Gallo were the most high-profile and foremost exponents of 'viral' AIDS, an unproven notion that is used to terrify millions of men, women and children around the world.

Dr Stefan Lanka is an uncompromising scientific leader in the struggle against the HIV theory of AIDS. His published research in 1994 astounded many, declaring that HIV does not exist

Eddie, (deceased)
Eddie, a dancer, was prescribed AZT on being diagnosed 'HIV positive'. The above picture was taken at the point of his diagnosis and at the beginning of his chosen mission – to keep a photo-journal of his 'illness'. It was Eddie's wish that these images might serve in some way to educate a future generation, and call for more research into AIDS. Posthumously, Eddie's wish has been fulfilled.

Eddie, 13 months after beginning AZT. Experiencing malabsorption of food and a host of opportunistic infections, he died soon after, weighing just sixty pounds.

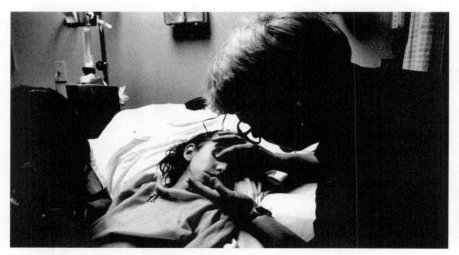

The death of a 12 year old girl. Establishment medicine says that she died of AIDS. More and more doctors and AIDS researchers however are stating that tragedies like these are being caused by the very drugs used to fight the elusive 'HIV'.

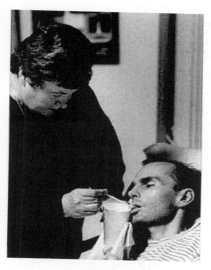

Deceased

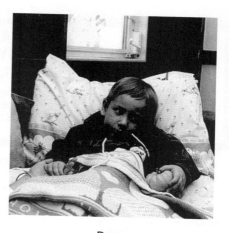

- Danny -
Deceased

Loving Ministrations
should carry no condemnation

- Ida -
Deceased

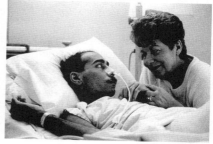

- Eddie -
Deceased

SIGMA

TOXIC
Toxic by inhalation, in contact with skin and if swallowed. Target organ(s): Blood Bone marrow. If you feel unwell, seek medical advice (show the label where possible). Wear suitable protective clothing.

3'-AZIDO-3'-DEOXY-THYMIDINE
(AZT; Azidothymidine)   *(30516-87-1)*

Desiccate
Store at less
than 0°C

$C_{10}H_{11}N_5O_4$ FW 267.2
Purity 99% (HPLC)
For laboratory use only. Not for drug, household or other uses.

AZT label. This label has appeared on bottles containing as little as 25 milligrams, a small fraction (1/20th – 1/50th) of a patient's daily described dose. (*Physicians Desk Reference*, 1994, p.324)

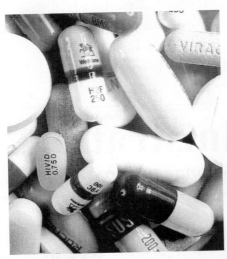

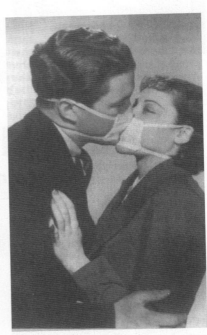

A selection of AIDS drugs including AZT, seen here bearing the Wellcome trademark. AZT was originally pioneered as a chemotherapy agent in the 1960s by Dr Richard Beltz, whose studies led him to shelve the drug as an unusable poison. This very same substance was brought out of retirement years later by Wellcome and patented as the new AIDS wonder drug

Everybody's at risk... A poignant illustration highlighting the hysteria the world has suffered at the hands of HIV propaganda

"Although no one knows what the long-term effects of protease inhibitors will be, I'm certainly pleased... my doctor prepared me for the common side-effects – feeling weak or tired, vomiting, diarrhea, loss of appetite, abdominal pain, taste disturbance, numbness in the hands, feet or around the lips, headache and dizziness." – Abbott Laboratories advert for AIDS drug Ritonavir

HOW TO BE POSITIVE IN ONE COUNTRY AND NEGATIVE IN ANOTHER

WESTERN BLOT "VIRUS" PROTEINS	AFRICA	AUSTRALIA	UNITED KINGDOM	USA CDC 1	USA CDC 2	USA FDA	USA RED CROSS
ENV gene: p160, p120, p41	ANY TWO		ONE OR MORE	p120/p160* &p41	p120/p160* OR p41	ONE OR MORE	ONE OR MORE
POL gene: p68, p53, p32		OPTIONAL ANY THREE		p31**		p32	ANY ONE
GAG gene: p55, p40, p24, p18				p24		p24	ANY ONE

Dr Roberto A Giraldo works at a laboratory of clinical immunology in one of the most prestigious university hospitals in New York. He has worked extensively with the ELISA, Western Blot and Viral Load tests. His disturbing conclusion is that everybody reacts positive on the ELISA when their *undiluted* serum is used - the standard medical practice for serological testing

The Jody Wells Memorial Prize

£1,000 Reward
MISSING VIRUS!

Blind romantics still believe HIV causes AIDS. But if 'HIV' has never been isolated, what is AIDS?

Never isolated? So what? So a cash prize of £1,000 is offered to the first person finding one scientific paper establishing HIV actually exists.

If you can prove isolation, £1,000 is yours. In cash. In public. Standard criteria for structural isolation apply.

We bet you'll be surprised to discover the truth.

CONTINUUM
CHANGING THE WAY WE THINK ABOUT AIDS

One of many challenges to the AIDS establishment to furnish empirical proof for the existence of their virus, HIV. This advertisement is from the UK magazine *Continuum*, a publication long dedicated to exposing the scientific and medical frauds surrounding HIV and Acquired Immune Deficiency Syndrome (AIDS)

Stephen Rogers quit protease inhibitor 'combo cocktails' after recognising that the drugs were causing the very symptoms of AIDS

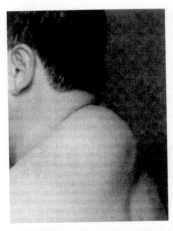

'Buffalo Humps', fatty deposits appearing around the base of the neck and across the shoulders. These are just one of the many side effects that can be experienced by those prescribed the 'exciting new range' of protease inhibitor drugs.

Diagnosed HIV positive in 1991, and pictured here with her son, author **Christine Maggiore** says: *"Life came to a grinding halt. I bought a wedding ring to ward off potential suitors. A year or so into my diagnosis, I found a caring doctor who urged me to take another test. Further testing produced a positive followed by a negative and another positive.*
In my search for more information, I became more and more convinced that AIDS research had jumped on a bandwagon that was headed in the wrong direction. In the seven years since receiving my death sentence, I have gone from frightened victim to AIDS activist to HIV dissident to spokesperson for new views about HIV and AIDS. Although my HIV status has been decidedly positive for the last five years, I enjoy abundant good health and live without pharmaceutical treatments or fear of AIDS."

debate on AIDS however, this common sense approach to cause and effect has been largely ignored. The fact that A (the ill health and/or death of a loved one) is believed to be the result of B, (the 'strange, novel virus') whilst taking no account of other factors, C, is the curse that bedevils analytic thought in AIDS 'science' today. Commenting on the need for intellectual rigour when seeking to establish cause and effect, Geoff Watts, presenter of 'Medicine Now' says:

> *"Another trap for the unwary lies in the failure to distinguish between association and causation. The fact that two things repeatedly happen at the same time doesn't mean that one is necessarily the consequence of the other. Both may be the result of some third event of which the observer is unaware."* [234]

That other factor 'C', or third event, which coherently explains the immuno-deficient disorders seen in these men, is excessive and toxic lifestyle. This also explains why many sick individuals who choose a more healthy lifestyle and diet experience startling recoveries, and not just with AIDS. Credence researchers have witnessed and recorded many impressive recoveries from cancer, heart disease, stroke, arthritis, menopausal problems and other chronic degenerative conditions simply through the application of common-sense. More about these later.[235]

Aside from uncritical thinking, there were also those in the gay community who were quite well aware of the 'third event' lifestyle factors contributing to their friends' ill-health and death. Joan Shenton again:

> *"[Leading gay figure] and cabaret singer Michael Callen told me that when HIV came on the map, many gay leaders, though largely persuaded of the multi-factorial risk hypothesis (repeated re-infections and a fast-track, drug-associated lifestyle), took a conscious decision for political reasons to support the 'no-blame' AIDS-as-virus hypothesis."*

The enthusiastic acceptance of the virus hypothesis as an excuse to continue a dangerous lifestyle, however, was mirrored in the equally

---

[234] **Watts, Geoff** *Pleasing The Patient*, Faber and Faber, 1992
[235] **Day, Phillip** *The ABC's of Disease*, Credence Publications, 2002; also **Day, Phillip** *Cancer: Why We're Still Dying to Know the Truth*, Credence Publications, 2003

enthusiastic acceptance of the 'gay gene' some years later. In 1993, Dr Dean Hamer proposed a link between the 'X' chromosome and sexual orientation.[236] *The Wall Street Journal* immediately announced 'Research Points to Gay Gene'.[237] Overnight, the little known geneticist, who had previously restricted his experiments to mice, became a hero to gay activists. Thousands of T-shirts appeared bearing the slogan *"Thanks for the Genes, Mom"*. Hamer's homosexual gene theory progressed to become a major influence in the passing of much pro-gay legislation. Two years later, Hamer, himself openly homosexual, was under investigation by the Office of Research Integrity for selectively reporting his data, and for promoting the socio-political ramifications of his findings, rather than merely reporting the science.[238] And so, the disturbing pattern of AIDS research is seen once again. Not unsurprisingly, no one to date has yet been able to reproduce Hamer's 'gay gene' or find any trace of it.

Dr Dean Hamer

Readers may be interested to know that Hamer is currently attempting to isolate the gene suspected of influencing people to believe in God.[239] To most people, it would seem strange to believe that some folks have genetic machinery that causes them to believe in God, whereas others are barred from such belief by an accident of birth. However, in the world of the geneticist, where everything is up for grabs and little proof required or expected, Hamer's interest in isolating the God Gene appears another risible attempt to propagate science's existing 'Man-is-God' ideology. Countering Hamer's runaway theories, Mark Almond, a lecturer in modern history at Oriel College, Oxford, has this to say:

"In our age when 'Science' has achieved a God-like status, and many people are morally confused, nothing helps to sell a

[236] **Hamer, D** *Science*, "Linkage Between 'X' Chromosome and Male Sexuality," #261, July 1993
[237] *Wall St Journal*, 16th July 1993
[238] **Marshall, E** "Gay Gene Study Questioned," *Science*, #268, 1995
[239] *Today* program, BBC Radio 4 Interview with Sue McGregor, 4th May 2000. Credence contacted Hamer to confirm the God story, and learned that he is indeed soon to be releasing a book entitled *'The God Gene'*.

divergence from traditional ideas like the claim that it is scientifically justified. The official investigation into Hamer is not before time. We cannot allow the myth of the gay gene to continue, a gene which ominously suggests that science is the cause of moral behaviour."[240]

In his book *Homosexuality and the Politics of Truth*, Jeffrey Satinover argues against the genetics of homosexuality and in favour of a variety of 'nurture not nature' factors. Satinover states:

"The desire to shift to a biological basis for explaining homosexuality appeals primarily to those who seek to undermine the vast amount of clinical evidence confirming that homosexuality is significantly changeable."[241]

Michael Callen, author of *Surviving AIDS* and now deceased, confessed to having had 2,000 sexual partners by the time he was 23. In his book, Callen wrote:

"Can researchers really comprehend the dynamics of urban gay male promiscuity? The commercialisation of promiscuity and the explosion of establishments such as bathhouses, bookstores and backrooms is unique in Western history."[242]

But urban promiscuity was by no means confined to the gay community. Immune system failure as a result of rampant self-abuse was occurring in promiscuous heterosexuals also. Gary Null again:

"In 1979-1980, I was doing research on heterosexuals who were coming down with a series of illnesses, chronic fatigue, thrush, herpes, hepatitis, chronic coughs and pneumonias – no matter what time of year. Their lifestyles included lots of unprotected sex with lots of partners, lots of drink and lots of drugs. Sometimes at swingers' parties, which were all the rage at the time, you might have 15 – 20 different partners a night. You might do this three or four times a week. And, of course,

---

[240] **Almond, Mark** *Mail on Sunday,* 9th July 1995

[241] **Satinover, J** *Homosexuality and the Politics of Truth,* Baker Books, 1996. See also **Whitehead, Neil,** *My Genes Made Me Do It. A Scientific Look at Sexual Orientation,* Huntingdon House Publishers, 1999. **Horgan, J** "Limitations of Genetic Research into Human Behaviour", *Scientific American,* June 1993, pp.123-31. See also www.narth.com, National Association for Research and Therapy of Homosexuality.

[242] **Callen, Michael** *Surviving AIDS,* Harper and Row, London: 1990

you drank a lot, you took amyl nitrite, lots of lines of cocaine and smoking. These were both men and women.

The trouble is, no one wanted to hear that. We wanted to hear, we needed to hear that these people were not representative of society as a whole; that they were part of Sodom and Gomorrah, self-loathing, self-hating, self-destructive. By 1990, I had seen thousands of heterosexuals who had a virtually indistinguishable form of AIDS that had gone almost unnoticed. Nobody was looking at them, nobody was marking them as a risk factor... They're just part of the $1.3 trillion national medical bill each year. They're getting antibiotics and treatments for their individual conditions. They're virtually invisible." [243]

The findings of Null serve to reinforce the argument that in the early years, AIDS or immune system failure was not a homosexual plague, it was the plague of toxic excess, affecting all who indulged in irresponsible drug and sex lifestyles.

The rapid uptake on the idea that homosexuals were the harbingers of the dreaded AIDS in the US was no doubt influenced by the McCarthy *'queer witch-hunt'* years. In one particular political campaign in the late 1940s, thousands of leaflets were distributed to the electorate suggesting that sexual perverts were perhaps as dangerous as communists. The message vigorously encouraged a campaign to rid the government of *"queers who had lodged themselves in the tissues of bureaucracy."* [244] Soon after, the US Senate responded to the inevitable public outcry and formed a special 'pervert' committee to investigate *"the corrosive influence that homosexuals tend to have upon fellow employees. One homosexual can pollute a government office."* [245]

Attitudes such as these were surely the more corrosive in influence. The prejudices that helped shape the homosexual connection with AIDS/HIV have shrouded the more important issues of the

---

[243] Null, Gary, op. cit.

[244] **Von Hoffman, N** *Citizen Cohn. The Life and Times of Roy Cohn*, New York, Doubleday Press, 1988

[245] Von Hoffman, N, op. cit.

irresponsible and damaging lifestyles indulged in by those of either sex or sexual preference. In conversation with Joan Shenton, AIDS victim Michael Callen admitted that it was not the effects of a supposed virus, but his lifestyle that was the cause of his illness. He stated:

"It became impossible for me to pretend that the disease history was irrelevant to the fact that I was sick. It was sort of emotionally attractive to believe that it had nothing to do with any [lifestyle] choices I had made, that it was just bad luck – I'd accidentally slept with the wrong person. But once I was presented with a non-moralistic, calm, medical presentation of a multi-factorial mechanism which might account for my illness, I was never quite able to believe again that a disease of this complexity was ever going to have a single, simple [viral] cause." [246]

Countering the non-moralistic argument put forward by Callen and others, Mark Almond argues against certain human sexual behaviours, reminding us that:

"Human beings are distinguished [from animals] by their ability to act according to moral criteria. In fact most morality is about controlling natural impulses as well as unnatural ones. Morality and individual responsibility remain the basis for any civilised society." [247]

Even so, years after AIDS appeared, the queues at the bathhouses were not noticeably thinning. Increasing numbers of gay men were manifesting the symptoms of AIDS. Despite intense political and media pressure to believe otherwise, there still remained a number of medical professionals who believed the root cause of AIDS was more attributable to lifestyle than virus. In an effort to look at ways of trying to stem the rapidly growing number of AIDS cases now being reported across California, a meeting was convened at a suburban San Francisco AIDS centre between concerned doctors and several of the owners of the notorious bathhouses:

"The bathhouse owners who attended were hostile. Some had only come because they felt pressured to attend. Other proprietors couldn't be bothered to attend and simply sent

---

[246] Shenton, Joan, op. cit.
[247] Almond, Mark, op. cit.

their attorneys. After Dr Abrams had finished speaking, the owner of one of the largest bathhouses took the doctors aside and tried to reason with them. "We're both in it for the same thing," he said. "Money. We make money at one end, when they come to the baths. You make money from the other end, when they come here." Volberding, Dr Abrams' colleague, was speechless. This guy wasn't talking civil liberties, he was talking greed. The bathhouses were open, not because the owners did not understand they were spreading death, but because they were still making money."[248]

A marked unwillingness to participate in any line of questioning which might threaten a lucrative income was an attitude of mind not solely confined to the bathhouses. Intolerance to reasonable debate has been a prevalent factor in the AIDS establishment's attitude from the outset, and is alive and well in all the major AIDS organisations today.

It is said that the last recourse of a cornered politician is fervent patriotism. And there can be no doubt that in the AIDS industry today, a particularly perverse form of patriotism exists. AIDS patriotism rears its fanatical head whenever one attempts to counter the high degree of intellectual dishonesty inhabiting the AIDS debate. On many occasions Credence researchers have posed simple questions to the AIDS scientists and assorted 'AIDS politicians' - questions the latter do their best to avoid. After finding themselves cornered and seeing their inevitable entreaties to *'respect the worthiness of the AIDS calling'* falling on stony ground, these men and women resort to raising their AIDS patriotism like a shield before them - often the shield of ridicule or personal abuse directed towards those asking the legitimate questions.

This experience is by no means unique. Medical correspondent Nicholas Regush (now deceased) was founder of the Internet health magazine RedFlagsDaily and had a regular slot on ABC News, entitled *Second Opinion*. He was one of a number of journalists who had stumbled across the secretive, closed-off world of 'AIDS science'. Said Regush:

---

[248] Shilts, Randy, op. cit.

"I have worked as a medical science reporter for 30 years. I began this career at age 22. I've interviewed thousands of scientists for newspaper and magazine stories, radio and television productions, and books. I've met many scientists who at least try to keep an open and fair mind on scientific issues. I have also met many propagandists who think they're scientists. In all the time I've worked as a journalist, I've never come across a nastier group of people to interview than those propagandists who work in HIV research." [249]

Dr Kremer attempted to bring the truth about AIDS to the media as far back as 1984. He invited medical professionals and the media to his hospital to see for themselves the hepatitis patients who would test HIV+ due to blood test cross-reaction but who did not have AIDS. Stefan Lanka recounts Kremer's experience:

"Kremer informed the mass media, who went to his hospital to see for themselves in great detail. He told them all the evidence. And the very same journalists from talk shows and Der Spiegel, one of Germany's largest and most popular magazines, published just the opposite. So Kremer knew it was intentional from the very beginning. They played war. They all wanted to have a blood and sex plague contrary to the evidence he presented them. So AIDS was built upon misconceptions. He was dealing at the top political level. They told him off the record that they knew and they didn't care." [250]

AIDS is big business, and any attempt to shed light on the lies of this deceitful and self-serving industry is met with fierce, witch-hunting opposition. Today, the facts clearly demonstrate that it is choice of a toxic lifestyle, coupled with the wholly misguided pressure to submit to inaccurate blood tests and the subsequent effects of ravaging 'anti-viral' drugs, which produce the phenomenon known as AIDS in the Western world. This conforms exactly to the 'AIDS=Long-Term Drug Abuse' model, which explains why the syndrome is still chiefly restricted to its risk groups, and has not spread exponentially

---

[249] **Regush, Nicholas**, *Second Opinion*, "The HIV Party Line", www.abcnews.go.com/sections/living/secondopinion, March 2000
[250] **Lanka, Stefan**, *Zenger*, "Challenging AIDS Views," December 1998

into both males and females in the general population, as one would expect with a sexually transmitted syndrome.

AIDS in the Western world can be viewed as a smorgasbord of unproven hypotheses, greed, pride, profitable toxic pharmaceuticals and an orthodox establishment too well-heeled and entrenched in scientific error to heed the voice of reason. And how successful, as well as deadly, the deception continues to be. Today, the public widely believes:

- AIDS is a range of diseases arising from infection as a result of the virus known as HIV.
- The AIDS test is a simple and accurate method of detecting HIV.
- The virus is contracted and spread in humans through 'one-off' and/or promiscuous unprotected homo/heterosexual activity, through the sharing of intravenous drug users' contaminated needles or through contaminated blood supplies.
- Pregnant women who test positive can pass the virus on to their unborn child. HIV can also be transmitted to the baby outside of the womb through breast-feeding.
- In the West, HIV infection is spreading among women and heterosexual men and is increasing exponentially every year.
- Drugs are available to treat AIDS patients but they are very expensive. A new range of anti-HIV drugs, the 'protease inhibitors', are now believed to be more effective.
- AIDS is devastating the Third World.
- There is currently no cure for AIDS.

As far as Western AIDS is concerned, we can see that with the exception of AIDS drugs being expensive, **everything you have just read in the above summary is entirely false and has no scientific validity whatsoever.** Yet this has not stopped the AIDS juggernaut from dipping the clutch and shifting up a few gears in more recent years. This from CBS News, 23rd February 2004:

"The virus that causes AIDS [standard AIDS-speak for HIV] is spreading again in Western Europe and is rampaging through Eastern Europe and Central Asia, where it infected 250,000 people last year, a United Nations health official said Monday. Eastern Europe and Central Asia are experiencing

the fastest-growing HIV epidemic in the world, said Peter Piot, the executive director of the U.N. AIDS organization."

And this from The World Bank, dated 16th September 2004:

"The world's most rapid spread of HIV/AIDS is occurring in Eastern Europe and Central Asia, and the World Bank is raising an alarm to contain the epidemic and lessen the potential damage. In the report 'Averting AIDS Crises in Eastern Europe and Central Asia', the World Bank outlines a strategy to prevent huge socio-economic costs."

And this from the BBC dated 23rd October 2004:

*"**Asian Community Warned Over HIV** - At the moment the level of HIV among the South Asian communities in the UK is relatively small, but experts warn that, without care [i.e. drug intervention], the HIV infection trends could soon start to mirror those on the sub-continent. They warn that arranged marriages, which rarely look into the sexual history of prospective partners, and an increasing number of people having unprotected sex in India before returning home, could soon cause problems in the UK.*

Yes folks, it's official. The scary AIDS headlines are cranking up once again. Only this time, we're armed with information that can interpret the lies. Regarding the World Bank, we will examine this organisation and its dubious affiliates shortly.

Now we must turn our attention to the continent synonymous with Death by AIDS. What should we make of the reports that HIV is decimating many African nations? What of the millions apparently dying of 'HIV', where recreational lifestyle, expensive blood tests and toxic drugs cannot possibly be the primary cause? In examining these issues, we discover rational and straightforward medical and environmental reasons for the convincing appearance of an 'AIDS' pandemic Africa as well as Asia. And as our investigations continue, we sadly uncover new depths to man's inhumanity to man.

Part 2

'AFRICAN' AIDS

ON A MISSION INTO THE AFRICAN AIDS JUNGLE

Africa is now in a state of emergency comparable only to war. **BBC News, 26th September 2003** - *The executive director of UNAIDS, Dr Peter Piot, said progress was being made in the battle against HIV/AIDS in Africa but much still had to be done. Speaking in Nairobi at the end of a conference on AIDS in Africa, he singled out greater access to cheaper anti-AIDS drugs as a major challenge.*

DEATH STALKS A CONTINENT. Time Magazine, 24th November 2003 - *This is a story about AIDS in Africa. Look at the pictures. Read the words. Then, try not to care. Even as you read this, AIDS is taking lives in Sub-Saharan Africa, swallowing families, communities, hopes. So far 17 million have died. At least 25 million may follow. An intimate look at a modern curse. Visit our interactive website at http://www.time.com/time/2001/aidsinafrica/*

The Orphaned Continent, BBC Online Special, October 2004 - *AIDS kills some 6,000 people each day in Africa - more than wars, famines and floods. Millions of children are orphans, many more live with HIV or AIDS. This special report, with correspondents' despatches, key facts, audio, video and interviews, asks why the devastation continues.*

'The battle!' 'Swallowing families!' 'AIDS - the silent stalker!' 'A slow-burning tragedy.' 'Key facts.' And so the rhetoric continues.

There's an old African saying which goes: *'The African race is like a rubber ball: the harder you dash it to the ground, the higher it will rise.'* And for one reason or another, it seems at this point in history that Africa is indeed being dashed to the ground - almost mercilessly so. Can it bounce back from this present curse of AIDS?

Thankfully, the 'AIDS in Africa' situation is more about perception than reality. As we begin to unravel the vivid mythology surrounding AIDS, Africa and the so-called Third World, we realise once again that our understanding of the situation has been shaped by knowledge claims that are considerably more than just 'neutral'. We must focus on who exactly is reporting the African 'facts' to us, and their reasons for so doing. Why anybody would purposely be instigating and then orchestrating a tidal wave of depressingly bad news, and all of it false, seems totally incomprehensible to the rational, enquiring mind. But orchestrated and false it is, as we shall discover. No one could argue that in the story of AIDS so far, the truth is stranger than fiction. And the 'AIDS in Africa' story is no different. Establishing the truth and identifying the perpetrators of the lies concerning African AIDS can only help put the bounce back into Africa, as well as the other nations equally ravaged by the myth of HIV and viral AIDS.

* * * *

When people in the West discuss the general perception of the Third World AIDS crisis, a largely unspoken, but not uncommon theme seems to be one of resigned acceptance: *'Yes, it's a real tragedy taking place over there.... but with so many people in the world, could this perhaps be Nature's way of evening out the populations of these vastly inhabited and under-resourced regions? And, besides, they will carry on with those rather deviant practices...!'*

In their book *AIDS, Africa and Racism*, Rosalind Harrison and Richard Chirimuuta examine what 'in-built' social and psychological factors there might be that help make it easier for us 'over here' to believe and accept what is going on 'over there'. Quite uncomfortably, one of the key factors examined is 'inherent' racism. Ms Harrison goes on to define the West's general perception of Africa and its inhabitants:

➢ Africans are primitive peoples living in isolated tribes cut off from civilisation, so they could have harboured diseases for centuries before they spread to the rest of the world.
➢ They are evolutionarily closer to monkeys, thus could more readily acquire monkey diseases, perhaps by having sexual relations with monkeys or at least involving them in their sexual practices.
➢ They are sexually unrestrained, and a sexually transmitted disease would therefore spread more rapidly amongst them than any other people.

> Their intelligence is limited and they cannot understand the complexity of a syndrome such as AIDS.

Pliny the Elder was one of the first historians to describe Africa and its inhabitants. His 1st Century *Summary of the Antiquities and Wonders of the World* brought some extraordinary ideas to the attention of a wide audience:

"Of the Ethiopians there are some that have neither nose nor nostrils, but the face all full. There are some called the Syrbote that are eight foot high and live with the chase of elephants. In a part of Affrike be people called Ptoemphane, for their king they have a dog, at whose fancy they are governed. Towards the west, the Arimaspi, a people that hath one eye in their foreheads. The Cinamolgie, their heads are like the heads of dogs... Grammantes make no marriage, but all their women are common.... Gamphasantes go all naked. Blemmy is a people who have no head at all. And others that walk more by training of their hands than with their feet."[251]

Pliny's fanciful imaginings serve only to confirm the fact that in his life he had never really ventured any further than Germany. More accurate world history documents Africa as a culturally sophisticated and thriving continent, rich in mineral deposits and other precious commodities.[252] Between 1509 and 1513, a certain Leo Africanus kept an account of his journeys in Africa. Here he describes one of the regions widely believed to be populated by Pliny's monsters.

"...I myself saw fifteen kingdoms of the Negroes.... In Tombuto (Timbuktu) there are many shops and merchants and especially of such as weave linen and cotton cloth. And hither do the Barbarie (Barbary) merchants bring cloth of Europe... Corn, cattle, milk and butter this region yieldeth in great abundance.... Here are great store of doctors, judges, priests and other learned men that are bountifully maintained at the King's court and charges..."[253]

---

[251] **Reader, John** *Africa – A Biography of a Continent*, Hamish Hamilton, 1997

[252] **Brown, Michael** *Africa's Choices*, Penguin, 1995. Brown notes that Francis Bacon, the founder of modern European science, went to Morocco to learn mathematics.

[253] **Africanus, Leo** *A Geographical Historie of Africa*, 1600

Interspersed with warring of course, Africa enjoyed many centuries of successful trading with other continents. But then, Africa was 'discovered' by the white man and the slave trade began. In 1748, British philosopher David Hume, a leading figure and influential shaper of public attitude, wrote:

"I am apt to suspect the Negroes, and in general all the other species of men (for there are four or five different kinds), to be naturally inferior to the whites. There never was a civilised nation of any other complexion than white.... No ingenious manufacture amongst them, no arts, no sciences... Such a uniform and constant difference could not happen, in so many countries and ages, if nature had not made an original distinction betwixt these breeds of men." [254]

Thomas Atwood, chief British judge of Dominica and later of the Bahamas, stated:

"Negroes are in general much addicted to drunkenness, thievery, promiscuity, and idleness... Idleness is so very predominant in Negroes, and their dislike of labour is so great, that it is very difficult to make them work; sometimes it is necessary to have recourse to measures that appear cruel, in order to oblige them to labour." [255]

With the Victorian era came many bloodthirsty battles contesting African soil. In his book, the self-explanatory *Marching over Africa*, Frank Emery has collated numerous letters written by British servicemen serving in Africa between 1868 and 1898. Included is the following:

"My darling Mother, we had a great fight yesterday, and you will be glad to know I am all right.... The Egyptian dead and wounded looked ghastly as we passed them in our advance, their dusky faces upturned in the blazing sun.... One fellow ran right along in front of the whole line. I should think he ran 600 yards, and it certainly took 30 or 40 shots before he was hit. I felt quite sorry for the poor beggar. It was really quite like rabbit shooting.... I think the big fight to take Tel-el-

---

[254] **Fryer P** *Staying Power: The History of Black People in Britain*, Pluto Press, London and Sydney: 1987
[255] Ibid.

Kebir will be the day after tomorrow. Goodbye now, dearest Mumseh. With best love to all at home and the Park - Marling." [256]

Equatorial explorer Joseph Conrad spent many years working and travelling throughout inner Africa. Conrad's most famous, literary work, a 1901 novel entitled *Heart of Darkness*, tells of a steamer voyage into the unexplored heart of Congo Land, and follows Able Seaman Charles Marlow on his quest to track down a Mr Kurtz, an ivory dealer, living somewhere in the jungle and reported to be dangerously insane. Conrad's book was later to become the chief inspiration for Francis Ford Coppola's Vietnam War epic, *Apocalypse Now*, where, in a similar river expedition, a Captain Willard is assigned to track down and eliminate the bloodthirsty, insane Colonel Kurtz. And as our journey into the AIDS jungle continues, we will be hearing from Conrad and Willard from time to time, the parallels between their perilous journey and ours becoming ever more apparent the further up-river we travel. Conrad's *Heart of Darkness* was widely read and served as an early 'Africa tourist guide' for the Western masses. In the following text Conrad brings a bulletin from the front:

"We penetrated deeper and deeper into the heart of darkness.... We were wanderers on prehistoric earth, on an earth that wore the aspect of an unknown planet.... Suddenly, as we struggled round a bend, there would be a glimpse of rush walls, of peaked grass-roofs, a burst of yells, a whirl of black limbs, a mass of hands clapping, of feet stamping, of bodies swaying, of eyes rolling, under the droop of heavy and motionless foliage. The steamer toiled along slowly on the edge of a black and incomprehensible frenzy. The prehistoric man was cursing us, praying to us, welcoming us - who could tell? We were cut off from the comprehension of our surroundings; we glided past as phantoms, wondering and secretly appalled, as sane men would be before an enthusiastic outbreak in a madhouse.... No, they were not inhuman. Well, you know, that was the worst of it - this suspicion of their not being inhuman. It would come slowly to one. They howled and leaped, and spun, and made horrid faces; but what thrilled you was just the thought of their wild

---

[256] **Emery, Frank** *Marching over Africa*, Hodder and Stoughton, 1986

humanity - like yours - the thought of your remote kinship with this wild and passionate uproar."[257]

One can quite confidently predict that with reports such as these being brought back to English shores, a 'sophisticated Africa' did not immediately spring into the minds of the spellbound readers. And like some sort of intangible heirloom, the perceptions of a *dark, threatening* continent have been passed down through the generations and are with us today.[258]

All local authorities now have a 'racism in schools' policy. The highlighted sentence in the leaflets is always 'Racism has no place in our schools'. But the policy exists because unfortunately racism does have its place in our schools. And in the workplace. A racial harassment trial, one of many in the UK, heard evidence of racist taunts directed towards a competent £50,000 p.a. black employee. Among the many taunts was: *"You lot don't bother getting married, you just have kids all over the place."*[259]

At the 10th International AIDS Conference in Yokohama in August 1994, Dr Yuichi Shiokawa said the African AIDS epidemic could be brought under control only if Africans restrained their sexual cravings. Professor Nathan Clumeck of the Universite Libre in Brussels is skeptical that Africans will ever do so. In an interview with French newspaper *Le Monde*, Clumeck quite nonchalantly claimed:

"Sex, love and disease do not mean the same thing to Africans as they do to West Europeans, because the notion of guilt doesn't exist in the same way as it does in the Judeo-Christian culture of the West."[260]

The notion that AIDS originated from monkeys was proposed chiefly by Max Essex, a colleague of Robert Gallo. Declaring to the world that he had isolated a Zairian strain of HIV dating back to 1959, Essex sent his samples to three different laboratories for verification. The three labs, one at the CDC, the second Gallo's, and the third Abbott

---

[257] **Conrad, Joseph** *Heart of Darkness*, Penguin, 1994
[258] See also **Said, Edward,** *Orientalism. A Historical Perspective of Cultural Imperialism in the West*, Vintage Books, 1979
[259] *Daily Mail*, 7th January 2000
[260] *Sacremento Bee*, 30th October 1994

Laboratories (the multi-million-dollar manufacturer of the ELISA blood test), quite unsurprisingly confirmed the Essex findings. Equally unsurprising is that when sent for *impartial* and *independent* assessment, a virus could not be found. [261] This did not stop Gallo from using the Essex findings to make the completely false assertion that 60% of Ugandan children had been infected with HIV by the early 1970s.[262] Gallo's monkey proposals, coupled with the West's rampant promiscuity, prompted Dr David Benoni of Gabon to ask: *"Why do they not look for a monkey in the US? AIDS started there and could equally well have been brought to Zaire by wealthy homosexuals."* [263]

Harrison and Chirimuuta again:

"Discussion quickly moved on to the question of how the virus crossed the species barrier, and two AIDS 'experts' from St Mary's Hospital in London even offered this explanation: "Monkeys are often hunted for food in Africa. It may be that a hunting accident of some sort, or an accident in preparation for cooking, brought people in contact with infected blood. Once caught, monkeys are often kept in huts for some time before they are eaten. Dead monkeys are sometimes used as toys by African children."[264] Are we seriously to believe that African parents are so desperate for toys for their children that they give them putrefying carcasses of dead animals?"[265]

Separately, Rosalind Harrison details a Dr Serge Voronoff who, in the 1920s, declared he had discovered the cure for ageing. Thousands of European men underwent an operation involving the surgical pairing of 'live' chimpanzee testicles with their own. Having no effect either on longevity or the birth of AIDS, it does however speak volumes of limited intelligence in exalted positions, a common trait to observe as we continue. [266]

---

[261] *The Lancet*, "Evidence for HTLVIII in Central Africa in 1959," 31st May 1986

[262] **Gallo, RC** *Science*, "Evidence for Exposure to HTLVIII in Uganda Before 1973," #227, 1995

[263] *New Scientist*, "Scientists Attack AIDS Slur on Africa," 28th November 1985

[264] **Moss AR** 'Epidemiology of AIDS in Developed Countries', in *AIDS and HIV infection: The Wider Perspective*. Br. Med. Bull. 44(1): 68-88, Churchill Livingstone, Edinburgh, 1988

[265] **Harrison, Rosalind** *"Racism versus Science"* at http://www.sumeria.net/aids/aidsafcar.html

[266] **Harrison, Rosalind** *"Western Medicine as Contested Knowledge,"* Rethinking AIDS Homepage, 1999

Responding to the great swathe of unscientific and prejudiced statements surrounding AIDS and Africa, science and health correspondent Yinka Adeyemi, stated:

"To the average European researcher in virus cancers, the notion that the Acquired Immune Deficiency Syndrome (AIDS) had its origin in Africa is now a scientific fact... Yet, arguments by such scientists, whose minds are made up about the African connection, are replete with fundamental loopholes and illogicalities that render them not plausible...."[267]

And there is little evidence to support Shiokawa's earlier accusations of uncontrollable sexual cravings, a favourite perception shared in the West. In countering the 'African as Frenzied Sexual Being', the *Sacramento Bee* tells us:

"Widespread modesty codes for women, whose sexuality is considered a gift to be used for procreation, make many African societies seem chaste compared to the West. The Somalis, Afars, Oromos and Amharas of North-East Africa think that public displays of sexual feelings demean a woman's 'gift', so that sexual contacts are restricted to ceremonial touching or dancing. Initial sexual relationships are geared to the beginnings of making a family. The notion of 'boyfriends' and 'girlfriends', virtually universal in the West, has no parallel in most traditional African cultures."[268]

This is not to say that there is nothing untoward to report with regard to African sexual customs. There are indeed some highly questionable sexual practices taking place in Africa, Asia and other continents. But however extreme or culturally 'exotic' these practices might be, they are no more bizarre than those practices embraced by their Western counterparts. One need spend only the briefest time on any Internet search engine to realise the interest in the most extreme sexual practices in the West. And in the light of what we have learned concerning the twisted sexual and recreational habits abounding in the Western 'story' of AIDS, what world-wide lurid commentaries might we be reading on the sexual habits of westerners, were the power of the 'global pen' to rest in African hands? Commenting on the power

---

[267] *Nigerian Concord*, July 1985
[268] *Sacramento Bee*, 30th October 1994

wielded by Western interests in Africa, African journalist Hameed Agbareeni noted in the Abuja *Daily Trust*, 18th December 2003:

"It is often argued that we Africans are so terribly poor because we have our corrupt elites and tyrannical regimes that funnel the resources of our countries worth billions and billions of dollars away into private accounts (it should be noted, in Western banks). Superficially, this is true, and is one major cause of poverty, and it is of course significant and needs concerted and continuous engagement. Pointedly however, little is said of the fundamental reasons why impoverished countries are so often governed by dictatorial regimes and often for so long. Western media and academia, with their global power over the creation of knowledge and ideas, largely ignore the fundamental causes of structural poverty and the underlying institutional order that allows such regimes to come to power and to keep power. It is abundantly clear that this global economic and political 'order' survives only because it benefits the wealthier countries, which ironically are democracies, democracies that preserve human rights and democracy at home but so often support tyrannies abroad whenever it happens to suit their economic interests to do so."

Western reporting blames much of African AIDS on promiscuity. Richard Chirimuuta wryly comments that, for there to be such a high number of supposedly infected adults in central Africa, *"life must be one, non-stop orgy."* In contrast, a Western sexual activity survey carried out in 2004 by Durex (who else?) stated that on average, the sexually active Briton will have sex 119 times a year and will have had 9 partners by the age of 21, compared with the global average of 4.1. France tops the bill for annual performance at 133 times per year. Youthful exaggeration allowed for across the study group, when it comes to errant sexual behaviour, we in the West appear to be in no position to cast the first stone.[269] How much one can trust the statistics of a www.durex.com survey on sexual activity anyway is a pertinent

---

[269] The 2003 Durex survey reveals that the 'unprotected sex' championship title goes to the Czech Republic at 65% of the nation admitting to such behaviour, followed closely by Bulgaria at 62% and China at 59%. Interestingly, South Africa comes in at 22nd with 30% of the nation engaging in 'non-condom' behaviour. Quite surprisingly, the amorous Italians 'limp' in last with 19% admitting they had practised unsafe sex.

question. Be that as it may, if AIDS is a sexually transmitted, viral disease, and durex.com is urging more people to sport its products, then a Western AIDS 'epidemic' should be considerably more advanced than in South Africa. *Where is our Western AIDS epidemic?*

So what is everyday life like for the vast majority of Africans? Jeremy Harding has spent many years travelling the troubled regions of Africa. In his book, *Small Wars, Small Mercies*, he documents some of the hardships facing Africa today. Harding reminds us that beyond the often misplaced negative perceptions, Africans do have a number of distressing issues with which they contend on a daily basis.

"I am alert to the negative images of Africa, and the generalities that go with them; that every African country is in chaos, that every African statesman is corrupt or incompetent, that every cubic centimetre of African blood, whether stored, shed or still in circulation, is [HIV] sero-positive, and that the staple diet of 640 million Africans is dust.

Yet it is disingenuous to accuse the media of crying wolf on a continent where so many wolves are at the door. Populous states like South Africa, Zaire, Nigeria and Egypt are in dangerous disarray, whilst large numbers of Africans in Sudan, Liberia, the Horn and parts of Southern Africa are among the most jeopardised people in the world. It is largely from them that we derive our sense of Africa as a vast Laocoon,[270] *caught in the coils of debt, hunger, war, disease and ethnic rivalry."*[271]

Misconceptions of HIV aside, there are indeed many wolves at Africa's door, which are all too real in nature. As Harding's introduction states: *"Across the lives of the African people lie the shadows of larger forces – global rivalries, massive arms flows into underdeveloped states and the glib experiments of the IMF."* [272]

'Glib experiments' and 'shadows of larger forces' are central to the 'AIDS in Africa' story, and will be examined in more detail shortly.

---

[270] The Laocoon is one of the most well-known works of Roman art. It presents Laocoon, the priest of Apollo, and his two sons being overcome by two large snakes.

[271] **Harding, Jeremy** *Small Wars, Small Mercies*, Viking Press, 1993

[272] Harding, Jeremy, op. cit. IMF: The International Monetary Fund

138

With regard to general living conditions in Africa, the following testimonies will convey to the reader the struggles the great majority of Africans face on a daily basis.

"My name is Catherine Nyirenda. I come from Zambia. I live in Lusaka, the capital, a city of about one million people. Within the city, I live in Mutendere, a crowded residential area. My country is very poor. The annual income per person in Zambia is the equivalent of $300 a year. 70% of people live below the poverty line. This means that they spend most of their total income on basic food alone. I am a typical urban person. I earn about 50,000 kwacha a month, which is worth US$50.

This is how I spend my monthly earnings. My rent is $25 per month. If I don't pay for two months, I will be thrown out. I spend the next $11 on maize meal, our staple food. I have about $14 left for everything else. There's charcoal to cook on, cooking oil and vegetables each costing $12 in a month. This leaves $2 for the month to buy sugar, soap, baby requirements, my own clothes, transport, health needs and medical services. We have seen a steady increase in child malnutrition since 1992. Chronic malnutrition now affects 44% of urban children, and 60% of rural children. My impression is that the Western world is sick of poverty and death in Africa – this is all that gets attention in your news. Many may think that suffering is normal for us - but it isn't. We hurt and grieve and hunger as much as you would, and we hate disease, poverty, poor medical services and poor schooling."[273]

Joan Shenton recounts the following story:

"....We stopped off at the town of Rakai. We went to inspect the local water supply, a foul smelling pool next to the effluent from the town drain. When it rained, the water became even more contaminated. Many people did not have the energy or the fuel to boil the water before drinking it. We watched children dipping their plastic containers into the water and carrying them off, gracefully balanced on their

---

[273] Personal testimony given at a plenary session of the Lusaka AIDS Conference.

heads. *But these waters were more dangerous than any supposed virus. These waters carried infections and parasites that could gradually destroy even the strongest man's immune system. Before leaving Rakai village, we drove up to its small rural hospital on the hill. It was completely deserted – no patients, no staff and a large empty ward with dismantled beds leaning against the walls."*[274]

And Jeremy Harding on life in everyday Mozambique:

"Mateus and his wife Catarina were urban Mozambicans. Mateus was a private in the Mozambique army, earning 11,900 meticais a month (700 meticais = 1 US dollar). Catarina had four children to feed and she calculated the family's basic maize consumption at 30kgs per month. Catarina was not from Maputo and, upon arriving in the capital, had qualified for a number of benefits, many of which had since lapsed. Two of the children were suffering from worms, but the cost of a remedy was prohibitive. Yet like most of the people, Mateus and Catarina had a system. Mateus handed over his salary to Catarina, who then bought subsidised food and resold it for a profit... Her way of life simply kept the family ticking over. She would get up at 5am and then hustle for flour or rice or sugar. She would get back by 7:30am to cook for the children, leaving them in the care of her sister as she set off again to trade until dusk. For many people in Maputo, life was even harder.... Like tens of thousands in Maputo, [275] *Catarina cherished the thought of going home."*[276]

Charles Geshekter teaches African History at California State University, Chico. He has spent much of his time studying African health issues. He notes that the many hardships facing Africans render it inevitable that millions will be suffering from weight loss, chronic diarrhoea, fever and the persistent cough of tuberculosis. Says Geshekter:

---

[274] Shenton, Joan, op. cit.

[275] Those hardships have now been dramatically increased by severe flooding, rendering thousands homeless in Mozambique, especially around Maputo. BBC News, 7th February 2000

[276] Harding, Jeremy, op. cit.

"The real threats to African lives are famine, rural poverty, migratory labour systems, urban crowding, the collapse of state structure and the sadistic violence of civil wars. When essential services for water, power or transport break down, public sanitation deteriorates and tuberculosis, dysentery and respiratory infections increase."[277]

Philippe Krynen is director of 'Partage', an organisation dedicated to supporting sick and displaced families (and especially children) in Tanzania. Krynen was the author of *Voyage des Krynen en Tanzanie*, an account of his experiences in a country he dramatically described as 'AIDS-devastated northern Tanzania'. His story was picked up by the media globally and used to shape Western impressions of a viral AIDS epidemic in Africa that was out of control.

Originally believing HIV to be the cause of AIDS, Krynen then began noting certain anomalies in the AIDS patients he was treating. Over half of them tested negative for the virus (whatever that meant). Prostitutes were surviving while their clients were dying. And all those empty houses and huts where the UN said the Tanzanian AIDS victims had once lived? These turned out to be additional homes Tanzanians had owned who had moved to the city. This and other evidence caused Krynen to rethink his beliefs about AIDS:

"There is no [viral] AIDS," Krynen now states unequivocally. *"It is something that has been invented. There are no epidemiological grounds for it. It doesn't exist for us."*[278]

The real problem, Krynen states, has nothing to do with a doomsday virus and everything to do with the standard ills from which Africa has always suffered. In an article on his work featured in *Continuum* magazine, he highlights the gradual decline of Tanzanian lifestyle through poverty, malnutrition, inaccessibility to basic medicines and a growing use amongst the younger generation of marijuana and amphetamines:

---

[277] **Geshekter, Charles** "The Epidemic of African AIDS Hysteria": www.thememoryhole.com
[278] **Hodgkinson, N** *Sunday Times of London*, "African AIDS Plague a Myth," 3rd October 1993; also **Hodgkinson, N** *Sunday Times of London*, "The Plague That Never Was," 3rd October 1993

"For the Africa of tomorrow, the most successful triple therapy we can give the children is food, water and education. Give them these and you can forget about AZT." [279]

Part of Krynen's work is building shattered confidence:

"How can you ask people who believe they are going to die tomorrow, how can you ask them to look to the future which are the children. They give up. They don't invest." [280]

Lucy was one such shattered individual. She had been orphaned, and now at 23 years of age, she was regularly ill with repeated infections. She had lost over 20lbs in weight. Most people believed she was HIV positive, and Philippe Krynen duly discovered that Lucy had been diagnosed as such during one unconfirmed screening. Krynen and his wife decided to support Lucy and help her try to regain her position in the community. They moved her out of her hut and built a small house for her. Within a few months, Lucy began to get better. With regular nutritious food, supplemented with vitamins, Lucy began to put on weight and her skin diseases disappeared. *"Because we didn't support the AIDS tag on her,"* said Krynen, *"she recovered and was proof to the community that you recover from such episodes."*

Says Lucy: *"I am strong and I am back to my old weight. I can do any work I'm faced with. I hope to have children."* [281]

Lucy has since gone on to give birth to a perfectly healthy boy named George. With Philippe Krynen's care and simple 'triple therapy' of food, water and education, Lucy, Julia, Deus, Seledina, Bernadetta and countless others have arisen from the 'death curse' of AIDS. How many more Lucys and Julias are there across 'AIDS-ravaged' Africa who need to hear such good news?

Lucy had been orphaned, and she was a genuine orphan. There is actually a certain relevance to the term 'genuine orphan', as Joan Shenton intriguingly discovered. On her travels through Africa, she gained valuable insight into the true nature of the WHO's much reported 'AIDS orphan crisis':

---

[279] *Continuum*, Vol 5, No 2, Winter 1998
[280] Ibid.
[281] *AIDS and Africa*, Meditel transcript. Dispatches. Channel 4, 1993, op. cit.

"We heard that whenever [Western] visitors arrived in this area, a carefully orchestrated show was put on. All the children were brought together and encouraged to put their hands up when they were asked if they were orphans. In Uganda a child is called an orphan if one parent has died. Many would put up their hands who were real orphans, part-orphans and not orphans at all, for instance if parents had migrated to find work, leaving them with grandparents."[282]

Dr Christian Fiala, author of *Do We Live Dangerously? A Doctor in Search of the Facts and Background to AIDS*, has called the AIDS orphan story *"...one of the most cynical since the 'discovery' of HIV"*, stating:

"It sheds a characteristic light on the nature about the reporting of AIDS: obviously everything is allowed, without reservation, that makes people feel threatened... even European countries would have a large number of 'orphans' if one applied the Ugandan definition."[283]

Local town official Badru Ssemanda is unhappy about the way in which some local entrepreneurs are juggling the statistics and adding to the problem:

"People are trying to make a living out of this AIDS. They think that if they publicise it and exaggerate it, they might win sympathy from the international community and get assistance. We need assistance, but not through bluffing people and saying that people are dying at a rate which is not true."[284]

Krynen has been outspoken at the cynical manipulation of such a serious issue. Quoted in the UK *Sunday Times*, 3rd October 1993, he states:

"...if you ask how the parents died they will say AIDS. It is fashionable nowadays to say that, because it brings money and support. If you say your father has died in a car accident it is bad luck, but if he has died from AIDS there is an agency to help you. The local people have seen so many agencies

---

[282] Shenton, Joan, op. cit.

[283] **Fiala, Christian** "The Ugandan Example", Rethinking AIDS 1999

[284] *AIDS and Africa*, op. cit.

coming, called AIDS support programs, that they want to join this group of victims. Everybody claims to be a victim of AIDS nowadays. And local people working for AIDS agencies have become rich. They have built homes in Dar es Salaam, they have their motorbikes; they have benefited a lot....

We have everybody coming here now, the World Bank, the churches, the Red Cross, the UN Development Program, the African Medical Research Foundation, about 17 organisations reportedly doing something for AIDS in Kagera. It brings jobs, cars; the day there is no more AIDS, a lot of development is going to go away...."

There is good evidence to show that some African doctors have taken part in propagating the 'AIDS in Africa' myth for similarly unscrupulous reasons, as *Spin* reporter Celia Farber discovered for herself whilst in Africa:

"Many believe that the statistics have been inflated because AIDS generates far more money in the Third World from Western organizations than any other infectious disease. This was clear to us when we were there: Where there was 'AIDS' there was money – a brand new clinic, a new Mercedes parked outside, modern testing facilities, high-paying jobs, international conferences. A leading African physician... warned us not to get our hopes up about this trip. 'You have no idea what you have taken on,' he said on the eve of our departure. 'You will never get these doctors to tell you the truth. When they get sent to those AIDS conferences around the world, the money they receive is equal to what they earn in a whole year at home.'

In Uganda, for example, the World Health Organization allotted $6 million for a single year, 1992-3, whereas all other infectious diseases combined – barring TB and AIDS – received a mere $57,000." [285]

* * * * *

[285] **Farber, C** *Spin*, "Out of Africa, Part 1", March 1993, pp.61-63, pp.86-7

Back to 1999 and five thousand miles away. At 1818 H St, Washington DC, World Bank Headquarters, one of many official 'AIDS philanthropy' letters begins circulating to all bank staff and its supporters (UN, USAID, UNFPA and other closely-linked affiliates). This one is dated 2nd June 1999. Condensed, it reads as follows:

Friends and Colleagues,

A wildfire is raging across Africa. HIV/AIDS has spread with ferocious speed. By any measure, its impact is simply staggering. The arithmetic of risk is horrific. A child born in Zambia or Zimbabwe tonight is more likely than not to die of AIDS. In many other African countries, the lifetime risk of dying of AIDS is greater than one in three. This fire is spreading. The global death toll will soon surpass the worst epidemics of recorded history. Combustion is fearfully fast.

To date, two forces have helped feed the flames: ignorance and inaction. Ignorance is rapidly vanishing, largely extinguished by the pandemic itself. AIDS is everywhere evident in Africa. Inaction, unfortunately, remains common. And we must be honest with ourselves: We in the Bank have not done our full part. True, many country and task teams have done excellent work on AIDS. The Bank has published some of the leading analytical work on the subject. The Human Development family in particular has built strong projects and partnerships, and helped bring the scope of the crisis to light. But as an institution, we have failed to bring to bear the full weight of our collective instruments, intellect and influence. As Africa is the hardest hit, we in this Region bear the primary responsibility to lead. It is time we met that responsibility. We announce today ACTafrica. By its terms, we will now put HIV/AIDS at the center of our development agenda. ACTafrica's work will provide several specific services, including:

- *Equipping and supporting country teams to mobilize African leaders, civil society and the private sector to intensify action against AIDS.*
- *Supporting country teams, sector families and task teams in integrating AIDS into their portfolios and country programs.*

145

- *Collecting and disseminating information on the progress of the epidemic, country by country statistics, and best practices.*
- *Strengthening and expanding our partnership with UNAIDS and its co-sponsors, as well as with key agencies, NGOs* [non-Governmental Organisations] *and interested bilaterals.*

ACTafrica begins its work immediately. Those who look back on this era will judge our institution in large measure by whether we recognized this threat for what it was and did our utmost to put out the fire. They will be right to do so. Let's get to work.
Callisto Gadavo. [286]

Can we even begin to comprehend the true enormity of power wielded by this institute and its affiliates? *"Equipping and supporting country teams to mobilize African leaders"* is not the language of the hired hand. The World Bank, The International Monetary Fund, The United Nations, USAID, UNAIDS and other institutions have formally taken up residence in Africa. Invited or not, these agencies are bringing to bear the full weight of their collective instruments to commence the task of mobilising African leaders to put AIDS at the centre of their development plans. And the mission is no different today.

In reality, what we are witnessing are the world's most powerful organisations preparing for an all-out, multi-billion-dollar assault on a virus that has never even been proven to exist. Country after country is being instructed to integrate the HIV=AIDS myth into their development programs. *Why?* These global corporations are far from obtuse. They are quite well aware of the glaring inconsistencies in the AIDS debate. Yet decisions have been made wilfully for those inconsistencies to be ignored. *Why?*

And what about the ideas put forward by Philippe Krynen, Charles Geshekter, or the many other health professionals who have identified what is really needed at ground level for the betterment of Africa and her people? Their suggestions are sensible. They target root causes of

---

[286] World Bank memo. *The New AIDS in Africa Initiative.* 2nd June 1999. Full text can be found at www.IAEN.com

poverty and disease. Their goals are simple, and with the right level of support, they are achievable. Indeed, it was a UN official who declared:

"African farmers are among the best farmers in the world, you know.... I'm a farmer myself and I'll tell you, under the conditions they work in, they are tremendous farmers. All they need is a little support and they'll be able to feed themselves. Africa can feed itself - it used to do so." [287]

In *The Resourceful Earth*, agricultural economist Roger Revelle estimates that, with the right management, the continent of Africa alone is capable of feeding 10 billion people.[288] And in his book *The Greening of Africa*, Paul Harrison tells us of the two million tonnes of maize harvested in Zimbabwe in 1985, more than twice their need, the result of farmers working together with simple tools, and avoiding the debt-burdening mechanisation programs funded by the banks of the West. Says Harrison:

"If small-holders can be helped, the problems of insufficient food production, malnutrition, and widespread poverty are attacked simultaneously." [289]

Common sense tells us that adequate nutrition is a key factor in the battle against the widespread immuno-deficiency illnesses currently ravaging Africa. An article penned by long-standing HIV critic Celia Farber reads as follows:

"I asked Dr Sam Mhlongo [the South African government's chief pediatrician] *what I would see if I went to a local hospital. "If you don't see poverty and malnutrition as the number-one cause of death in South Africa, I am prepared to close my bank account and give you all my money." I asked him how could there be all these media reports about the millions dying of AIDS in Africa? It can't be a wholesale fabrication, can it? Don't they say that AIDS affects the middle and upper classes, not just the poor?*

"There are no death certificates whatsoever. We have no references for anything. All you have is the media, with

[287] **Brown, Michael** *Africa's Choices After 30 Years of the World Bank*, Penguin 1995. A penetrating look at the calamitous results of Western capitalistic interference in Africa.
[288] **Revelle, Roger** *The World Supply of Agricultural Land*, Blackwell, 1984
[289] **Harrison, Paul**, *The Greening of Africa*, Paladin Grafton Books, 1990

television, radio and newspapers, agreeing on this. That stuff about the upper classes being affected by AIDS is really rubbish. I am one of the so-called bourgeois, and I don't see any of this among the middle classes. It's the poverty-stricken, unemployed, black South Africans who are dying, because of diseases related to poverty." [290]

Summarising a meeting of South African and other AIDS health officials in Brussels in December 2003, Dr Mhlongo stated the following:

"The aims and objectives of my presentation at the European Parliament were to remind and educate on South African history - in particular a focus on the history of health disabilities and disadvantages suffered by the African people under apartheid. It was also my aim to compare and contrast apartheid South Africa with present South Africa - in other words, we now have political freedoms but we are still far away from economic freedoms and self-reliance.

In the introduction, I also nailed the international lie that President Mbeki has stated that HIV is not the cause of AIDS - there is no such record. His two questions, however, remain unanswered: Why is AIDS in Africa so vastly different from AIDS in Europe and North America? Why does AIDS in Europe and North America remain largely confined to the same groups it was initially described - i.e., intravenous drug-users and the gay community? Nutritional AIDS dominates the scene in South Africa today as indeed it did during apartheid. In the middle 1950s and 1960s, 50% of black children were dead before the age of 5. The causes of death were recorded as: pneumonia, high fever, dehydration and intractable diarrhoea due to protein deficiency. Today, these clinical features are called AIDS. Today in South Africa, TB is the leading cause of death and morbidity amongst Africans, but this is called AIDS. In conclusion, nutritional AIDS is a direct result of apartheid in association with capitalist iatrogenesis - hence the shacks (favelas), lack of sanitation,

---

[290] **Farber, Celia** *A Contrary Conference,* New York Press, 24-30th May 2000

lack of clean drinking water, unemployment and destitution."[291]

But the major banks and affiliated AIDS agencies still largely refrain from including these necessary and common sense malnutrition-combating suggestions into their plans.[292] Their focus is Infectious AIDS, Infectious AIDS and Infectious AIDS:

"Since AIDS was first described in 1981, well over 20 million lives have been lost, and tens of millions more people - increasingly women and young people - are now living with HIV. Most face the prospect of sickness, destitution and premature death. In the developing world, where 95% of people with HIV live, only 7% of those who needed life-saving treatment could obtain it in 2003 - a stark contrast to the developed world, where such treatment has become standard health practice."[293] [emphasis ours]

What nonsense! Instead of establishing the supply of highly poisonous AIDS treatments, how about establishing a widespread network of support for the reintroduction of localised farming, supplying simple tools and tried and trusted irrigation programs? The outlay would be miniscule and the benefits incalculable. Charles Geshekter again:

"Yes, there is a measurable decline in African health and increases in African mortality. What is in dispute is whether the symptoms of such illnesses are caused by extraordinary patterns of sexual behaviour or whether the signs reflect the deterioration of life on the continent over the past 20 years. The breakdown and decline of public health and medical treatment across Africa is due largely, if not entirely to domestic civil war, impossible levels of indebtedness and sharp declines in the prices paid for commodities produced by

---

[291] **Mhlongo, Sam,** *Public Health Issues and the Role of Medicine in South Africa.* Posting to the AIDS Society Group at AIDSsoc@yahoogroups.com, dated 18th December 2003

[292] *"Outsiders,"* writes Michael Brown, *"should stop offering answers to our perceptions of Africa's problems, and just listen to Africans for a change."* So begins *Africa's Choices, After Thirty Years of the World Bank.*

[293] www.unaids.org, October 2004

Africans. This is standard World Bank and IMF micro- and macro-analysis. Where's the mystery?" [294]

And again, yet more AIDS-focused aid from the World Bank:

"HIV/AIDS poses an unprecedented threat to global health, development and security. About 40 million people are currently living with HIV/AIDS and 5 million contracted HIV in 2003 alone....The pandemic has killed 25 million Africans so far and orphaned more than 12 million others." [295]

The lies surrounding the orphan count we already know about. What about the World Bank's twenty five million dead? In 1999, the World Bank announced that since AIDS records had began, thirteen million had died in Africa. Yet its sister partner, the World Health Organization's own *Weekly Epidemiological Record,* dated 26th November 1999, stated that a cumulative total of only 794,444 cases of AIDS in Africa had been reported to Geneva since 1982. Thirteen million dead versus just under eight hundred thousand? *And now the World Bank adding another twelve million deaths?* Are these super-powers actually talking to each other? An article in the *Sacramento Bee* discusses the part played by officialdom and the press in the reporting of AIDS, suggesting the figures may well be a hoax. One Ghanaian doctor interviewed stated *"If tens of thousands are dying of AIDS in these countries, and Africans don't cremate their dead, where are the graves?"* [296]

On July 10th 2000, the UK *Daily Telegraph* ran an AIDS in Zimbabwe 'disaster' story by David Blair, beginning: *'Children cast adrift with nothing but a begging bowl.... Mortuaries working overtime to cope with the 1,200 deaths every week."* Credence wrote to David Blair three times requesting he please supply the names and addresses of the mortuaries referred to in his article. A reply was never forthcoming. Similarly, South African journalist and AIDS critic Rian Malan went in search of the coffin manufacturers - the industry, that, according to the Western press, is enjoying a boom, 'what with all these African AIDS fatalities to bury'.

294 Farber, Celia, *A Contrary Conference,* op. cit.
295 http://www.worldbank.org/afr/aids/, 27th October 2004
296 *Sacramento Bee,* "The Myth of AIDS and Sex," 30th October 1994

"One newspaper account I found told of a company called *Affordable Coffins*, purveyor of cheap cardboard caskets, which had more orders than it could fill. But the firm was barely two months old when the story ran, and two rival entrepreneurs who launched similar products a few years back had gone under. "People weren't interested," said a dejected Mr Rob Whyte. "They wanted coffins made of real wood."

So I called the real-wood firms, three industrialists who manufactured coffins on an assembly line for the national market. "It's quiet," said Kurt Lammerding of GNG Pine Products. His competitors concurred - business was dead, so to speak. "It's a fact," said Mr A B Schwegman of B&A Coffins. "If you go on what you read in the papers, we should be overwhelmed, but there's nothing. So what's going on? You tell me.*"[297]

This newspaper headline, one of so many wild exaggerations, is comprehensively deconstructed in Christine Maggiore's book *What if Everything you Thought you Knew About AIDS was Wrong?*:

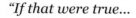

Wednesday November 25, 1998

Kenya Slow to Face Up to AIDS Scourge

by Rosalind Russell

NAIROBI, KENYA (Reuters) - According to U.N. estimates, a Kenyan dies of AIDS every three minutes...

"If that were true...

- *480 Kenyans would die of AIDS each day;*
- *175,000 Kenyans would die of AIDS each year;*
- *Three million Kenyans would have died of AIDS since 1981.*

The fact is that in Kenya...

- *There have been 78,600 diagnosed AIDS cases since 1981 and many of these are people who remain alive and well.*"[298]

---

[297] **Malan, Rian**, "Africa in Perspective", *Rolling Stone*, 22nd November 2001
[298] Maggiore, Christine, op. cit.

But do we hear any of this on World AIDS Day? What about interviewing Philippe Krynen, Lucy and her child for the regular ten-minute slot given over to African AIDS in the annual BBC *Children in Need* appeal? Will Bob Geldof or Bono consider any of this information the next time they take their media teams over to these countries? Joan Shenton:

"We've all seen them, the compassionate celebrities who, with sad expression, don the mantle of corporate grief for AIDS victims and sufferers and feel they are doing good. Granted they are doing this with the best of intentions, but far from good, they are actually doing damage, using their celebrity status to raise funds for AIDS research that is totally misdirected and orchestrated by a profit-oriented and commercially blinkered pharmaceutical industry." [299]

As well as with the maximum of *precision*, one can just as easily follow an incorrect course with the maximum of *compassion*. Neville Hodgkinson again:

"...Religious and medical charities have been promoting the HIV message in Africa in the belief that the continent is in the grip of a deadly new, sexually transmitted disease. They are genuine in this belief. To the extent that these agencies give productive help, such as with nutritional support, funding for new enterprises or farming equipment, drugs for known epidemic conditions such as TB, and empowering education, etc, they really do help. But to the extent that they have concentrated on the HIV message, escalating the figures and terrorising the continent on the basis of a mistaken paradigm involving an unvalidated diagnostic kit purporting to show antibodies to a virus that has not been isolated, they are unwittingly causing great psychological, social and physiological damage." [300]

Writing in the UK *Spectator* magazine recently, South African journalist Rian Malan notes similar anomalies in other so-called AIDS-ravaged African countries:

[299] *Continuum*, Vol 4, No 6, July 1997
[300] Hodgkinson, Neville, personal correspondence, 25th August 2000

"It was the eve of AIDS Day 2003 here. Rock stars like Bono and Bob Geldof were jetting in for a fund-raising concert with Nelson Mandela, and the airwaves were full of dark talk about mega-death and the armies of feral orphans who would surely ransack South Africa's cities in 2017 unless funds were made available to take care of them. My neighbour came up the garden path with a press cutting. 'Read this,' said Capt. David Price, ex-Royal Air Force flyboy. 'Bloody awful.' Doom merchants predict that Botswana may soon become the first nation in modern times literally to die out. This is AIDS in Africa.' Really? Botswana has just concluded a census that shows population growing at about 2.7 per cent a year, in spite of what is usually described as the worst AIDS problem on the planet. Total population has risen to 1.7 million in just a decade. If anything, Botswana is experiencing a minor population explosion...

There are breeds of AIDS activists and AIDS journalists who sound hysterical to me. On AIDS Day, they came forth like loonies drawn by a full moon, chanting that AIDS was getting worse and worse, 'spinning out of control', crippling economies, causing famines, killing millions, contributing to the oppression of women, and 'undermining democracy' by sapping the will of the poor to resist dictators. To hear them talk, AIDS is the only problem in Africa, and the only solution is to continue the agitprop until free access to AIDS drugs is defined as a 'basic human right' for everyone." [301]

Malan's article goes on to note that about 350 million Africans - nearly half the population - get malaria every year, but malaria medication is not a basic human right. Two million get TB, but spending on AIDS research exceeded spending on TB by a crushing factor of 90 to one. Malan concludes:

"I think it is time to start questioning some of the claims made by the AIDS lobby. Their certainties are so fanatical, the powers they claim so far-reaching. Their authority is ultimately derived from computer-generated estimates, which

---

[301] **Malan, Rian**, "Good News! Africa Isn't Dying", *Spectator* magazine, 13th December 2003

they wield like weapons, overwhelming any resistance with dumbfounding atom bombs of hypothetical human misery."

Why does the World Bank seem so caring about Africa's AIDS 'crisis'? And why is it that certain, powerful organisations seem intent on flooding Africa and Asia with poisonous AIDS drugs? Such questions open up a whole, new area for malevolent possibilities. A similar scenario befell Able Seaman Conrad and his crew when, at a certain point during their journey up-river, they suddenly found themselves cut off from the comprehension of their surroundings, with unchartered and threatening scenery closing in on them. Likewise, it is at this point in our journey into the African AIDS story, that we suddenly realise we are now in very unfamiliar territory. A marked sense of unease accompanies this mission. For up-river, there are indeed coherent explanations for these eerie statistics and for the enforced medication programs in Africa. The indistinct shadows of 'larger forces' that loom and flit ahead of us soon begin to take definite shape. And like Conrad, we will soon discover, to a much greater degree, the extent of man's inhumanity to fellow man.

LUCAS: "Captain, you heard of Colonel Walter E Kurtz?"
WILLARD: "Yes, sir, I've heard the name."
LUCAS: "He was brilliant and outstanding in every way, and he was a good man too. A humanitarian man, a man of wit, of humour. He joined the Special Forces. After that his ideas... methods have become unsound... unsound. Your mission is to proceed up-river. Pick up Colonel Kurtz's path, follow it, learn what you can along the way. When you find the Colonel, infiltrate his team by whatever means available and terminate the Colonel's command."
WILLARD: "Terminate? Colonel Kurtz?"
CORMAN: "He's out there operating without any decent restraint. Totally beyond the pale of any acceptable human conduct. And he is still in the field commanding his troops."

From the film, *Apocalypse Now*

CLOSING IN ON KURTZ

AIDS and population control: convenient bedfellows?

The approaching four-wheel drive creates billowing clouds of dust as it doggedly makes its way across the rough terrain towards the village. This Landcruiser could be flying any one of a number of flags, for it is one of literally hundreds of USAID, UNAIDS, UNFPA, NACP, WHO and associated Non-Governmental Organisation (NGO) all-terrain vehicles which, day and night, trundle back and forth, busily going about their work out in the AIDS mission field. In and around the townships, across the great plains, busy, busy, busy across Africa.

By the time the truck reaches the village, a crowd of inquisitive children has gathered, excitedly awaiting their official visitor. The driver, clipboard in hand, dismounts and takes stock of the scene. Village men and women, leaning or sitting in their doorways, peer at him curiously. He is now surrounded by a sea of little black faces. *"Orphans?"* he asks the assembled throng. A forest of hands. A quick count and an entry is made.

The village has no clean water supply. Food is scarce, and there are a number of thin-looking individuals. One young woman is persistently coughing. It hasn't really registered with her that a visitor has arrived, she's too weak to notice. She has propped herself up against a wall and just sits there listlessly in the shade. She's been ill for some time. No-one really goes near her. The village thinks she might have AIDS. Our man from the 'AIDS ministry' approaches her. He has no ELISA blood test kits in the back of his truck to confirm the villagers' suspicions – the ELISA tests are too expensive. He could carry out a urine test if he wanted to.[302] The AIDS experts have shown that a urine test for HIV is as 'accurate' as the blood test, but he doesn't opt for this measure either.[303] Instead, with shortage of time always a real problem, the

---

[302] *Sexually Transmitted Diseases*, "Uganda Studies in Urine and HIV," November 1999

[303] A 1994 study in *The Journal of Infectious Diseases* entitled "HIV Tests are Notoriously Unreliable in Central Africa" concluded that HIV tests were useless in that region since the microbes responsible for tuberculosis, malaria and leprosy were so prevalent that they registered over 70% false positive results. Geshekter, op. cit.

visiting official conducts the now widely employed World Health Organisation standard, Bangui 'visual only' diagnosis.[304]

According to WHO guidelines, an AIDS diagnosis can now be confirmed by the simple observation of clinical symptoms such as persistent coughing, high fever, 10% weight loss and generalised itching.[305] Health reporter Richard Rath:

"The criteria for AIDS diagnosis in Africa overlap considerably with the symptoms of endemic diseases such as dysentery, tuberculosis, cholera and malaria. This is why a growing number of African scientists and researchers have criticized the WHO premise and insist that addressing structural poverty and unhealthy living conditions – not behaviour modification programs – constitutes an appropriate patient-centred approach to achieving better healthcare". [306]

This sentiment is echoed by AIDS dissident journalist Liam Scheff. He has interviewed many health professionals who have worked in Africa. He notes:

"In light of this nonspecific, cross-reacting test, how does the World Health Organization (WHO) diagnose AIDS in Africa? Simple: they don't require any test at all. In 1985, the WHO created a new definition of AIDS for African nations and Third World countries. The WHO's 'Bangui Definition' allows Africans with common physical symptoms, including diarrhea, fever, weight loss, itching and coughing, to be automatically designated as AIDS patients, with no HIV test. But these very symptoms define life for the majority of Africans who lack essentials like sufficient food, safe drinking water, proper sanitation and basic medical care. These symptoms are also synonymous with the biggest killers on the continent: malaria, infectious diarrhea and tuberculosis."[307]

---

[304] WHO Global Program on AIDS; Provisional WHO clinical case definition for AIDS, *Wkly Epidemiol Rec*, 1986; 7th March; No.10: pp.72-3

[305] Shenton, Joan, op. cit. Maggiore, Christine, op. cit. See also **Tamarit Tamarit, Brauli** *Health and Life Magazine*, freenews.dragonfire.net

[306] DISS/cuss, News Flash, 8th December 1997

[307] Liam Scheff, op. cit.

The medicines and water purification treatments, which might help prevent and treat these diseases, are not in the back of the truck parked in the village. But these interventions could be made available, subject to political will. Nurse Namuburu Maxensia gave Joan Shenton a guided tour of her medicine cabinet:

> *"....she unlocked a large wooden cupboard and showed us a stock of drugs supplied free by the WHO's Essential Drugs Programme. These medicines used to be supplied free to the villagers but, under a new plan, a reduced fixed rate was being charged - as if anyone in the village could afford it.... Nurse Maxensia told us that before the new plan, the hospital was full and there were sometimes 50 outpatients. "But now we get so few," she said ruefully, "because they can't afford to pay."*[308]

The global reverence for the Western medical model has blinded us to the fact that most of these so-called 'medicines' are entirely useless. The recent admission by a very senior executive at GlaxoSmithKline as to the ineffectiveness of conventional 'nostrums' was a refreshing corporate gaffe. *"The vast majority of drugs - more than 90 per cent - only work in 30 or 50 per cent of the people."*[309] Dr Allan Rose's days as a senior executive at GSK are surely numbered, yet he serves us to consider the salient question: *Is Nurse Maxensia's empty medicine cupboard really such a terrible thing?* African historian David Lamb:

> *"Foreign drug companies have discovered a bonanza in black Africa, which they have turned into a dumping ground for their pills, by capitalising on the absence of consumer protection laws and advertising standards. Everywhere, there are billboards which, in the main, are advertising downright lies. Aminopyrine and Ipyrine were virtually withdrawn from US and UK markets after discovering these drugs halted the production of white blood cells in bone marrow. A study of African MIMS revealed no less than 31 preparations containing these drugs were being prescribed for minor conditions. And in the same publication, anabolic steroids, which can lead to stunted growth, changes in external*

---

[308] Shenton, Joan, op. cit.

[309] Connor, Steve, Independent Newspapers, 8th December 2003 at http://millennium-debate.org/ind9dec033.htm

genitalia and liver tumours, were being promoted as treatment for malnutrition, weight loss and excessive fatigue in school children. And methadone is included as a cough repressant."[310]

According to Philippe Krynen, it costs little more than £5 per week to support a child and meet all his/her nutritional and sensible medical needs. Readers wishing to support Philippe Krynen's work can find further details at the back of this book.

Meanwhile, back at the village, our visiting official has conducted his visual diagnosis of the sick woman. And for the pathetic figure sprawled out on the floor before him, there's only the one disease that makes sense. It isn't malnutrition, it isn't tuberculosis, it isn't cholera or dysentery. Philippe Krynen's triple therapy of water, food and education is not the priority here. The victim's weight loss and persistent cough fulfil the WHO criteria. The villagers' suspicions have been confirmed. She has 'the dreadful and incurable' HIV/AIDS. Another entry is made.

The official learns that someone else in the village is suffering from a persistent cough, and also that others in the village are quite ill but insist they're feeling OK. They lead him to the home of an elderly man. He became ill two months ago, but has refused to visit a doctor. While in Uganda, Joan Shenton met with journalist Sam Mulondo to discuss the very real fears Africans now have of going to the doctor and being diagnosed as an AIDS victim. Mulondo told her that when people developed diarrhoea, they would be so terrified it could be AIDS that they got worse and often died.

"People are dying psychologically.... Somebody gets simple malaria, they fear to go to the doctor because they will be branded as a clinical case of AIDS. People are just left at home. They don't go for any treatment whatsoever." [311]

The visual diagnosis carried out on the elderly man 'confirms' another case of AIDS. Another entry is made and another village, it seems, is teetering on the edge of an AIDS epidemic. Winifred Mwebe

---

[310] **Lamb, David** *Africans*, Methuen, 1985
[311] Shenton, Joan, op. cit.

lived in Uganda for thirty years, and worked as a volunteer for several Ugandan organisations. Winifred says:

"I have never seen or heard of any Ugandan, young or old, dying of any illness other than so-called HIV-related illnesses. Whenever you ask what happened if someone died, the answer is "What else?" I think that shows how ignorant our community is about these controversial issues. Ignorance kills. It will not stop unless we educate our people. And education is never widespread when there is big money and politics involved. Many Africans still think the white man is superior and that they do not make mistakes." [312]

Another ominous twist in WHO diagnostic techniques is the announcement of a new medical theory, which can be found in their 'Global Program on AIDS'.

"More than 12 million people are thought to have latent TB infections. If they become infected with HIV, TB can quickly develop." [313]

According to the World Health Organization's convoluted wisdom, TB is no longer just TB. It appears that WHO are suggesting that the main agent behind a patient's quickly developing tuberculosis is HIV infection. Therefore, at future HIV 'planning' meetings, can it now be intimated that TB = HIV?

Our AIDS official has now finished his village visit. He tabulates his 'horrifying' AIDS statistics and departs. Within a few hours the World Bank in Washington and UNAIDS in Geneva will have been informed another Ugandan village can now be included in the growing pandemic. In turn, the World Bank and UNAIDS will relay to Reuters, the *New York Times*, Associated Press and other world news agencies that *"the fire is spreading."* This from News24.com in London, dated 6th August 2004:

"AIDS remains untamed in Africa, states a bi-annual UN report. The continent is still seeing increasing rates of infection in the poorest

---

[312] **Mwebe, Winifred** *Continuum*, "London's Timid Africans," Vol 5, No 2, 1998

[313] *Facing Up To AIDS: The Socio-Economic Impact in Southern Africa*, Sholto Cross, Alan Whiteside (Editor) Hardcover 1993, Macmillan Press, 1996

countries, but the disease is spreading fastest in Eastern Europe and Asia, which is home to 60% of the world's population."

In fact, it is not the fire of AIDS spreading across the continents of Africa, Asia and now Eastern Europe, but an inferno of data-stretching, misdiagnosis, disinformation and deceit. Sadly, the misinformation distributed by these shameful agencies is not limited just to the African AIDS issue. One example of how much Africa has been affected by Western media meddling is provided by Kenyan writer, Ngugi wa Thiongo, who notes the consternation among some European power-brokers, writing in his native language, Gikuyu. In his book *Decolonising the Mind*, Thiongo says:

"It was almost as if, in choosing to write in Gikuyu, I was doing something abnormal. The very fact that what common sense dictates in the literary practice of other cultures is questioned in an African writer is a measure of how far imperialism has distorted the view of African realities. It has turned reality upside down: the abnormal is viewed as normal and the normal as abnormal. Africa actually enriches Europe: but Africa is made to believe that it needs Europe to rescue it from poverty. Africa's natural and human resources continue to develop Europe and America: but Africa is made to feel grateful for aid from the same quarters that still sit on the back of the continent. Africa even produces intellectuals who now rationalise this upside-down way of looking at Africa." [314]

Ironically, the World Bank has a link on its web page entitled 'Reporting Fraud'. Credence Publications used this facility to report the 'orphan count', the visual diagnoses and the World Bank's refusal to look at the overwhelming evidence against the HIV hypothesis. To date no reply has been received. In all, fourteen requests for information and clarification on certain issues have been posted to The World Bank and UNAIDS by The Campaign for Truth in Medicine. All of these requests have remained unanswered.

* * * * *

[314] **Thiongo, wa Ngugi** *Decolonising the Mind*, Heinemann Press, 1986

A little while later, more clouds of dust appear on the horizon. Another vehicle is approaching the village, this time driven by a UNFPA official (United Nations Fund for Population Activities). It's distribution time for the villagers. The driver unpins the tailgate and begins unloading an assortment of supplies to be distributed throughout the village free of charge. But the locals aren't exactly rushing forward for these handouts. They know what's on offer. It's not medicine. No simple malarial treatments,[315] nothing for diarrhoea, nothing for cholera, no water purification tablets. The UNFPA truck is carrying condoms and safe-sex pamphlets. The locals can also try on the safe-sex T-shirts. There are also sterilisation and abortion pamphlets, foil strips of the Yuzpe 'morning after' pill[316] and instructions on inserting IUDs. And sometimes, even, safe sex videos. Charles Geshekter again:

"While health officials fixate on condom distribution or make evangelistic demands for behaviour modification, approximately 55% of Sub-Saharan Africans lack access to safe water, 60% have no proper sanitation and over 50 million pre-school children are malnourished." [317]

In essence, the UNFPA truck contains everything to do with stopping life, but nothing to do with preserving it. And that is because UNFPA exists to enforce one ideology, and one ideology alone - that of population control. And they are very busy doing so, not just in Africa, but the world over, delivering birth control items to people who really only need food, clean water, medicine and shelter. Wherever disaster is unfolding and there is real human need, there you will invariably find UNFPA agents handing out their condoms, safe-sex leaflets and other related paraphernalia. In the conflicts in East Timor, Afghanistan and Rwanda, in the hurricane disaster regions of Honduras, Mozambique, Venezuela and the Philippines, and in the tsunami-ravaged lands of Indonesia and Thailand, UNFPA has responded to the populations' needs with the entirely inappropriate supply of reproductive health and human sterilisation equipment.

---

[315] *"Malaria accounts for 32% of deaths in Tanzania and 36% of hospital admissions."* Personal correspondence. Philippe Krynen, Partage, Tanzania.

[316] Emergency oral contraceptive, to be taken within 72 hours of sexual intercourse to terminate any pregnancy.

[317] Geshekter, Charles, op. cit.

What do these desperately needy people really gain from any of the above? Similarly, in 1998, after Hurricane Mitch, and again in 2001 after the earthquakes that shook Nicaragua, international aid organizations refused to give Nicaragua financial help unless the government adopted population control quotas and reproductive health' programs. On the Nicaraguan 'relief effort', Human Life International had this to say:

"Furthermore, the road system is wretched and very little of it has been repaired since the time of Somoza. But international funds are not dedicated to providing basic medical care for the people: 'reproductive health' care is what derails all the foreign assistance. International organizations have shown no significant commitment to repairing roads, building hospitals, schools and infrastructure, etc., the very things that Nicaragua really needs for the benefit of its people. Sadly however after several decades of 'contraceptive imperialism' the international abortion promoters have gained major territory over the hearts and minds of the Nicaraguan people and convinced them that their main social disgrace is that they have too many little Nicaraguans."[318]

It was former World Bank director, Robert Macnamara, who stated:

"More children means more expenditure on food, on shelter, on clothing, on health, on education, on every essential social service. And it means correspondingly less expenditure on investment to achieve the very economic growth required to finance these services.... Nurturing children drains away resources that could otherwise be invested into industrial projects."[319]

The governmental concern is for global over-population. But is there really an over-population crisis across the planet? Once again, we must remind ourselves that *"...science and research must be studied in the context of all the interested parties involved.... one should always*

---

[318] Human Life International Nicaragua and El Salvador Report 2003 at
http://www.hli.org/sr_8_2003.html
[319] Kasun, J, op. cit.

162

ask what social, institutional, political and philosophical interests lie behind often apparently 'neutral' knowledge claims." This is especially important when dealing with the science of over-population. Because the 'science' supporting this theory is bunkum.

Despite the claim that the world's population is spiralling out of control, it is interesting to note that the Earth's entire population could fit quite comfortably into an area the size of Texas. By converting the land mass of Texas (approximately 262,000 square miles) into square feet and dividing this area by the latest estimate of six billion, a family of five could thus occupy approximately 6,300 square feet of living space - a mansion by any means - leaving the rest of the planet completely empty and available for all mankind's agricultural, manufacturing, educational and recreational activities! Idealism aside, no one in the near future is likely to fall off the edge.[320] [321]

In her book *War Against Population*, a critique of 'population control' policy, Jacqueline Kasun notes those World Bank policymakers who consistently use the term 'assume' in their reports the perceived threat of population growth. Says Kasun:

"The astonishing fact is that these assumptions have neither been verified nor questioned by official policymakers: they have simply been taken on faith, with no resort to the means for testing them, which have been and are readily available. One would suppose that a major policy of the US and the international lending agencies such as the World Bank – a policy extending over many years, costing billions of dollars and involving significant risks in terms of economic welfare and international goodwill – would be based on thorough investigation of the relevant facts. Population policy however has not." [322]

But UNFPA and related agencies ignore the evidence that there is no real population crisis and press on with their agendas regardless.

---

[320] Chapman, Howard, op. cit.

[321] Population growth is not the concern, natural resource-stripping is. The West is by far the leading polluter through fossil fuel combustion, garbage and toxic waste production, as well as water contamination.

[322] Kasun, Jacqueline, op. cit.

An article alerting people to the more extreme family-planning measures linked to UNFPA aid appeared in the *Washington Times:*

DON'T FUND UNFPA POPULATION CONTROL: For at least 30 years the UNFPA has been a complicit partner in some of the most unspeakably brutal population control programs around the globe. Last year the US Senate Committee on Human Rights heard from witnesses of the China population program, how rural women are forcibly strapped to steel tables in 'hospitals' and their babies aborted, in some cases in the 7th, 8th and 9th month of pregnancy. UNFPA still spends millions each year on population-control programs in China. There are many Third World hospitals that lack bandages and basic medicines, but are filled to the brim with boxes of condoms stamped UNFPA or USAID. The cause of world hunger and environmental disasters in the world today is not too many people. It is too much statism."[323]

Professor H Miller of The Stanford University Institute of International Studies writes:

"Say hello to the bio-cops. Backed by bloated and inefficient bureaucracies, and undeterred by their own meagre scientific expertise, UN officials are now jostling to become international environmental super-regulators."[324]

Steve Mosher is head of the Population Research Institute. Its mission is to stop human rights abuses committed in the name of family planning, and through research and education, dispel the myth of overpopulation. Interviewed in 2004, Mosher stated:

"We should be dealing with the health problems of poor women in the Third World, but not by preventing them from having children. The United Nations Population Fund and other UN agencies argue that when they sterilize a woman, they are actually preventing her from dying in childbirth. Well, it is true that a woman who has had her fallopian tubes ligated is not going to get pregnant again, and therefore is not going to be at risk of dying in childbirth.

---

[323] Washington Times, 9th October 1999

[324] *Wall Street Journal*, 24th October 1995. For a list of UN and affiliated organisations relevant to this subject, please refer to the section entitled *Acronyms* .

But let's be honest about what the real purpose of the organization is. The real purpose of the UNFPA's sterilization emphasis is to prevent children from being born, not to save mothers from dying in childbirth. That's just a secondary, indirect consequence of what they are really about. It is equivalent to my saying let's reduce the number of traffic fatalities in this country by forbidding everyone to drive a car. Well, if we did that, we would reduce the number of automobile accidents to zero. But most people would agree that the cure is worse than the problem.

In the same way, the UNFPA says they'll reduce maternal mortality by preventing women from having babies. Even when they want children, even when they and their husbands decide they would like children, the UNFPA would like to put them out of the business of childbearing. It is the wrong solution to the wrong problem."[325]

In his essay entitled 'The Myth of Over-Population', Mark Leonard makes the humanitarian point that:

"...we have to recognise that in an inter-dependent world, it is in all our interests to give the six billionth member of the human race a world worth living in."[326]

But UNFPA has little interest in giving us such a world. *Why?* Because UNFPA, The World Bank, IMF, UNDP, USAID and other key players in the AIDS program, adhere fundamentally to the philosophy of population control. And in the current 'manufactured' AIDS crisis, the more powerful movers and shakers have found a remarkably convenient vehicle to deliver various ethnic-cleansing services across Africa and now the Asian continent.

Sound extreme?

---

[325] Interview with Steve Mosher, *Abolish The United Nations Population Fund programme,* October 5th 2004 at
http://www.pop.org/main.cfm?id=232&r1=2.00&r2=1.40&r3=0&r4=0&level=2&eid=678
[326] **Leonard, Mark** *New Statesman,* "The Myth of Over-Population," 11th October 1999

CORMAN: *"Well, you see Willard, in this war, things get confused out there, power, ideals, the old morality, and practical military necessity. Out there with these natives it must be a temptation to be god, because there's a conflict in every human heart between the rational and the irrational, between good and evil. The good does not always triumph. Sometimes the dark side overcomes what Lincoln called the better angels of our nature. Every man has a breaking point. You have, and I have. Colonel Kurtz has reached his. And very obviously, he has gone insane."*

WILLARD: *"Yes, sir. Very much so, sir. Obviously insane."*

Philippe **Krynen**, with some of his precious charges. Readers wishing to contribute to the valuable work at Partage Tanzanie will find details at the back of this book

A TALE OF TWO LUCYS

Lucy from Africa (left), diagnosed and left for dead in 1992, was cared for by Krynen who refused to interpret her condition as 'terminal'. Pictured here in March 2000, the healthy mother of son **Joseph**. **Luci** (above) had just celebrated her 16th birthday. She was receiving conventional AIDS medications from her loving and dedicated carers. A copy of this book was been sent to Luci's home in the hope that she will celebrate many more birthdays

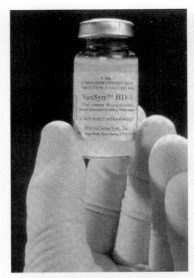

One of many AIDS vaccines now making its way towards Africa. These products are largely a mystery in their chemical make-up. What are the long-term effects of these mostly untested vaccines? How exactly are they supposed to combat a virus that has never been isolated?

The terminator
Life expectancy at birth
Years

Propagandising the HIV psycho-product: The notion that Africa is being 'devastated by AIDS' is a complete falsehood. Yet Third World nations that declare their countries 'AIDS Disaster Zones' are delighted to receive huge United Nations and foreign aid hand-outs. They are, however, largely unaware of the population control agenda simultaneously at work

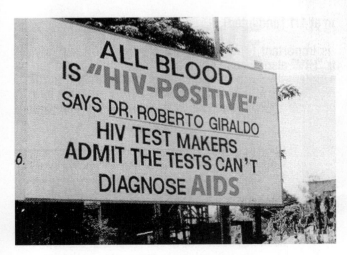

ALL BLOOD IS "HIV-POSITIVE" SAYS DR. ROBERTO GIRALDO HIV TEST MAKERS ADMIT THE TESTS CAN'T DIAGNOSE AIDS

Taking the Message on the Road: One wonders what the locals make of this unusual road-sign in Nagpur, India

'AIDS-infested Africa' represents a commercial bonanza for First World drug companies to pioneer yet another vaccine. But what will the vaccine be based on? Protestors who recognise the track record of these companies are fearing the worst.

Spin reporter **Celia Farber** discovered one truth about AIDS during a visit to Africa: *"Where there was 'AIDS' there was money – a brand new clinic, a new Mercedes parked outside, modern testing facilities, high-paying jobs and international conferences."*

Children such as **Deus** and **Jovina**, diagnosed HIV positive from a very young age, thrive under the Krynen triple therapy regime of food, water and education. Millions of children just like these could survive and benefit from inexpensive help and care. Instead, African towns and villages are beset with UN aid meddling, corrupt national officials siphoning money from the agricultural development and health budgets and UNFPA's unsinkable truck convoys of condoms, 'reproductive aids' and safe-sex tee-shirts and videos.

Positively False author **Joan Shenton** found the fear of AIDS endemic in African villages because of western propaganda: *"People are dying psychologically.... Somebody gets simple malaria, they fear to go to the doctor because they will be branded as a clinical case of AIDS. People are just left at home. They don't go for any treatment whatsoever."*

What is devastating Africa? The same things that have always devastated Africa? Western meddling, malaria, tuberculosis, and contaminated water. 2 billion people around the world (a third of the world's population) do not have access to basic sanitation. Over 1 billion do not have a safe supply of water close to their homes. Every six seconds, one person dies from a water-contamination illness, and yet these basic problems are largely overlooked by the global health agencies in their headlong rush to promote 'a killer AIDS epidemic'.

Hungry... Disturbing questions remain unanswered in the matter of Third World food aid. Is the phantom HIV really killing Africa, or is the real answer simpler and more unpalatable?

Western populations were told that millions were starving in Somalia because grain shipments sent by the West to feed the people were being pillaged by local warlord, Mohammed Farah Aidid.

The US Marine Corps was duly sent to Somalia to stop Aidid but later reported that 'they couldn't find him'.

With a multi-billion-dollar satellite system that can read the words off a cigarette packet from 120 miles up, how was it that the US National Security Agency and the Marine Corps couldn't find one balding tin-horn rebel in Mogadishu to end the hold-up of grain shipments to the starving refugees? The press found him. They even gave him interviews. But Farah Aidid remained officially undiscovered. The grain shipments continued to get pillaged. Lots of black people died.

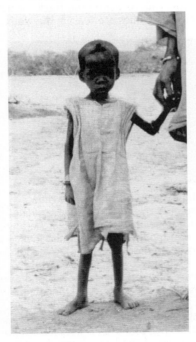

INSIDE THE MIND OF KURTZ

'Free cheese can be found only on the mouse-trap.' - Russian proverb

The false belief that a growing world population might soon become a serious issue owes its origins chiefly to the work of statesman Henry Kissinger. On 10th December 1974, a classified memorandum was completed by the American National Security Council under National Security Advisor Kissinger. Its official title read: *'Implications of Worldwide Population Growth for US Security and Overseas Interests.'* This National Security Study Memorandum 200 (NSSM 200) asserted that population growth in the so-named Lesser Developed Countries (LDCs) posed a threat to American national security. Kissinger had drawn on the findings of the Royal Commission on Population, initiated by Britain's King George VI in 1944, *"...to consider what measures should be taken to influence the future trend of population."*[327] The Royal Commission reported that Britain was gravely threatened by continued population growth in its colonies and that *"...a populous country has decided advantages over a sparsely-populated one for industrial production."* It was British eugenicist[328] Sir Julian Huxley who was famed for declaring that *"...overpopulation is, in my opinion, the most serious threat to the future of our species."*[329]

---

[327] The Royal Commission on Population, London 1944, involved studies that attempted to forecast the future population impact of millions of servicemen returning home after World War 2 to lonely females.

[328] Eugenics is the study of how to improve a race by judicious mating and/or destroying the undesirable genetic stock of the subject race. This racist philosophy was to reach a tragic climax with SS leader Heinrich Himmler's sanctioned eugenics program under Dr Josef Mengele in Auschwitz concentration camp during World War 2. Eugenic philosophies were not the sole prerogative of the Nazis however. Many British and American politicians, steeped in Darwinian evolution espousing 'survival of the fittest' sentiments, were active during the late 19th and early 20th centuries in supporting the idea of racially purifying human stock and doing away with the 'useless eaters'. See also: **Day, Phillip** *The Mind Game*, Credence Publications, 2002

[329] Sir Julian Huxley, the devout eugenicist and social Darwinist, served as the founding Director-General of the United Nations Education, Scientific, and Cultural Organisation. In 1947 Huxley wrote that one of UNESCO's most urgent tasks was *"...to see that the eugenic problem is examined with the greatest care, and that the public mind is informed of the issues at stake so that much that now is unthinkable may at least become thinkable."* Accordingly, it was unsurprising that the International Union for the Conservation of Nature, which Huxley co-founded, produced the United Nation's Global Biodiversity Assessment, which suggests that the

The language of NSSM 200 was dressed in the philanthropic clothing of 'concern for the planet'. Kissinger requested that special attention be paid to the following questions:

➢ What new initiatives by the United States are needed to focus international attention on the global population problem?
➢ Can technological innovations or development reduce population growth?
➢ Could the United States improve its assistance in the population field and if so, in what form and through which agencies?

The NSSM 200 recommendations that followed were to limit population growth in the target nations through birth control, and covertly through war and contrived famine.[330] These measures were adopted as official foreign policy under the Ford presidency in November 1975. Brent Scowcroft, who had replaced Kissinger as National Security Advisor, was put in charge of the initiative and CIA Director George Bush (Sr) was ordered to assist Scowcroft, along with the secretaries of State, Treasury, Defense and Agriculture.[331] The emerging problems of famine, genocidal war and economic failure were to be addressed through strategically placed Western-led government agencies, with the promise of food and economic aid to be used as a bargaining tool, in order to persuade the target nations to adopt the population control strategies presented to them.

Especially earmarked for attention were the countries of India, Bangladesh, Pakistan, Indonesia, Thailand, the Philippines, Turkey, Nigeria, Egypt, Ethiopia, Mexico, Brazil and Columbia. Population growth in these nations was regarded as 'worrisome', since these larger

---

human population be reduced to one billion and huge areas rendered devoid of human presence. (*The New American*, www.newamerican.com)

[330] Population Research Institute, PO Box 1559, Front Royal, VA 22630. Text for NSSM 200 is displayed at www.pop.org and www.Africa2000.com.

[331] **Cooper, William** *Behold a Pale Horse*, Lite Technology Publishing, 1991. Author Cooper worked for many years within America's covert Office of Naval Intelligence as an encryptions technician. In this capacity, he was privy to a great many sensitive documents. His controversial and at times unlikely book reportedly blows the whistle on the covert activities of the military and political infrastructures that formerly employed him. Cooper's book on its own has been discounted by sceptics, yet other works written on the subject of population control essentially agree with Cooper's information on main details.

populations would supposedly increase relative political, economic and military threats to the US.[332]

The public, of course, looks on at the under-developed world and wonders why, in spite of the billions it receives in 'aid', it is still under-developed. Why doesn't the West supply the target nation with fresh, clean water to alleviate cholera, parasitic infections and dysentery? Three billion people on this planet do not have access to safe water and proper sewerage.[333] Why haven't proper sanitation facilities been purchased with the West's cash and plumbed into every village in Africa to prevent cholera, typhoid and other diseases? Why haven't proper agricultural programs been installed to help the poor of these nations provide themselves with a sustainable food chain to avoid the malnutrition chronically afflicting the Third World today? In short, why hasn't the money been used to help train these nations to develop themselves economically, *so they could henceforth provide for themselves?*

These are the questions most people ask themselves whenever the issue of Third World poverty hits the headlines. Most citizens are baffled at the apparent complexity governments bring to bear on these issues when the simple answer seems to be staring them in the face: 'Give a man a fish and you feed him for a day. Teach a man to fish and you feed him for a lifetime.' What's the complication?

Helping developing nations with food and water and then educating them to become self-sufficient by assisting them with the development of their economy makes common sense. These are very achievable goals and in fact form the central agendas for many a well-intentioned Third World relief organisation. These organisations however become more than a little baffled by the strange lack of support they receive from national government or the UN in pursuing these matters. Why?[334]

---

[332] Cooper, William, op. cit.

[333] WaterAid, Prince Consort House, 27-29 Albert Embankment, LONDON SE1 7YY UK, tel no: 020 7793 4526

[334] **Mullins, E,** *Murder by Injection,* Iconoclast Books, Ketchum, ID, USA

The confusion facing the average citizen and aid organisation contemplating these matters arises because both are unaware that the UN and First World governments are desperately implementing an altogether different agenda, namely NSSM 200's systematic reduction (eradication) of burgeoning populations viewed as a strategic threat to the First World. Put simply, Western society and its associated power structures have ruled the world for five hundred years, and naturally wish to continue doing so, either through the Western-dominated UN or an eventual Western-influenced global government. A Central Intelligence Agency document puts the perceived problem this way:

"World population growth is likely to contribute, directly or indirectly, to domestic upheavals and international conflicts that could adversely affect US interests. Population growth will also reinforce the politicisation of international economic relations and intensify the drive [of less developed countries] for a redistribution of wealth and of authority in international affairs." [335]

Interestingly, it was primarily not the *growth* of Third World populations that began to destabilise the world demographic picture, *but a marked decline in Western birth-rates*, which raised in the minds of strategists the spectre of the West's eventual marginalisation by new, Third World economic and military superpowers. The need for the West to act to secure its continued survival as the world's dominant cultural and political power was succinctly if brutally put by commentator Bertrand Russell:

"It cannot be expected that the most powerful military nations will sit still while other nations reverse the balance of power by the mere process of breeding." [336]

Pierre Lellouche, aide to French premier Jacques Chirac, reports the disparity of birth-rates between the First and Third Worlds thus:

"The African population is projected to triple within the next 30 years, reaching an estimated level of 1.6 billion. Moreover, the Middle East, Central Asia and the Indian sub-continent all have volatile admixtures of acute poverty,

---

[335] **Central Intelligence Agency** *Political Perspectives on Key Global Issues*, March 1977 (declassified in part, January 1995). p.4
[336] **Russell, Bertrand** *Marriage and Morals*, London: 1985, p.161

demographic explosion and political instability. Together these regions will have some 4 billion people within 30 years, while due north sit 500 million ageing Europeans already in a squall of demographic depression." [337]

Ben Wattenberg, an analyst with the influential American Enterprise Institute, is one of many scholars who believes the First/Third World growth trends are probably now irreversible:

"Western culture was dominant forty-odd years ago after the end of World War 2, when the West made up 22% of the Earth's population. Today the West comprises 15% - and we are still dominant. [But] it is just about a sure thing that it will decline to under 9% by 2025 and probably down to about 5% by 2100 if present trends continue.

Even if Western fertility should climb back to the replacement level in the decades to come, the population of the Third World will be a much greater proportion of the world's population than it is now. Those Third World nations will also likely be richer and more powerful than they are now.... Do we know enough about the Chinese, the Indians, the Indonesians, the Nigerians and the Brazilians? Do we know their languages? Do we know their cultures? We ought to. These are the demographic superpowers of the next century. " [338]

The evidence shows the existence of Western-sponsored measures designed to curtail population in those developing nations. We also see agendas underway to keep these burgeoning peoples in a state of perpetual emergency, either through the introduction of real or perceived threats to their national security, such as AIDS, famine and local conflicts, making the developing nation dependent on the West for relief and assistance. When Africa cries out for simple agricultural tools and fresh water, the UN hands out condoms. When Africans ask for food for their children, the UNFPA gives the kids safe-sex tee-shirts. When Rwandan women cry out to the UN to help bring an end to the deliberate mass-murder perpetrated by rival tribes with

---

[337] **Lellouche, Pierre** "France in Search of Security", *Foreign Affairs*, 72, no.2 (Spring 1993): pp.123-124

[338] **Wattenberg, Ben** *The Birth Dearth*, New York: 1987: pp.97-98

machetes,[339] the UN responds by pulling out its peacekeepers and instructing the AID organisations to send in the condoms, bodybags and IUDs.[340]

Susan George, author of *How the Other Half Dies,* is one of many socio-political commentators who reminds us that it is the exploitative actions of key élite agencies which are largely to blame for world hunger and poverty. She comments: *"We all have the physical and technical resources to feed the world. World hunger and poverty is a scandal, not a scourge."*[341]

Largely as a result of NSSM 200, and by a process of gradualism, over-population is now perceived as a very serious issue. Following the Cairo 'population summit meeting' in 1994, global headlines such as *'time-bomb', 'crisis'* and *'spaceship running out of oxygen'* began appearing regularly.[342] Chief in attendance at the UN-inspired Cairo conference were all the familiar names in the AIDS debate, including The World Bank, IMF, UNFPA and UNDP. To the trained eye, even a cursory glance at the literature and web pages of these institutions reveals an unwavering commitment to NSSM 200 and consequently, an all-consuming interest in reducing the number of people on this planet.

When the guts of the UNFPA machine are exposed, its population control philosophy can be seen for what it is: an attempt by Western powers to maintain and even increase control over the global agendas, as we shall see. The public's nodding support over the years for this Malthusian evil [343] is almost entirely due to the skill of silver-tongued,

---

[339] Disturbing CNN documentary footage shows besieged Rwandan Tutsi women and children, protected in UN-guarded compounds, begging the soldiers not to pull out and leave them, all the while machete-wielding Hutu circle the compounds and neighbourhoods in pick-up trucks waiting for the kill. The UN eventually pulls out and the expected massacres subsequently ensue. One million Tutsis are hacked to death by Hutus in just 100 days in 1994.

[340] Inter-uterine devices, a form of birth control.

[341] **George, Susan** *How The Other Half Dies,* Rowman & Littlefield, 1984. See also Kasun, J, op. cit.

[342] **Chapman, Howard** *Too Many Stars in the Sky,* Image National Conference manual, 1994

[343] **Wood, John** *Thomas Robert Malthus. A Critical Assessment,* Croon Helm, 1986. Thomas Malthus (1766-1834) - a political economist who was concerned about what he saw as the decline of living conditions in 19th century England. He blamed this decline on three elements: The overproduction of young; the inability of resources to keep up with the rising human population; and the irresponsibility of the lower classes. To combat this, Malthus suggested the family size of

172

compromised politicians and associated strategists until the unpopularity of their programs manifests itself in public outrage over an unpopular war, such as Iraq. At a conference held in Strasbourg in October 2004, European and world leaders mixed with assorted UNFPA affiliates to discuss the population 'crisis'. Their rhetoric, it goes without saying, was syrupy-smooth. Fortunately, a brief translation can be provided:

"For many women, pregnancy in developing countries is still a death sentence," said Agnes van Ardenne, Minister for Development Cooperation, the Netherlands." Translated: if giving birth is so dangerous in Africa (which it is not), then sterilisation is the most sensible option for African women today.

"At the closing, participants endorsed a strong set of commitments to advance the Cairo goals. They recognized that "the decision to defend these principles is the difference between a life with hope and opportunity and a life of despair and desperation." Translated: We, the uninvited visitors to your countries, decide on the morals and values best suited for you and on how best to run your family life. You obviously cannot cope without us. You should be grateful for our intervention.

"Examples of the commitments agreed upon today include calls to: Strive to devote at least 10 per cent of national development budgets and development assistance budgets for population and reproductive health programmes; Mobilize an additional $150 million a year for commodities needed by programmes supported by UNFPA, the United Nations Population Fund, and the International Planned Parenthood Federation. Translated: By commodities, we mean more condoms, more sterilisation equipment and more

---

the lower class be regulated so that poor families did not produce more children than they could support. Malthus' view that poverty and famine were natural outcomes of population growth and food supply was not popular among social reformers, who believed that, with proper social structures, all ills of man could be eradicated. *"Here then at last, I had a theory by which to work."* Charles Darwin on Malthus' *'Essay on the Principle of Population'* **Milner, Richard** *Encyclopedia of Evolution*, King Holt and Co. 1990

173

sterilisation programs, but no commodities of any actual benefit to the communities at large.[344]

Whether we care to accept it or not, population control programs have been, and are being routinely 'integrated into country portfolios' by AIDS governments on a scale that is breathtaking. In November 1990, the World Bank launched a US$27 million population project for Ghana with the goal of cutting the size of the next generation of Ghanaians in half, from approximately 45 million to only 25 million by the year 2020. The fact that Ghanaians do not wish the size of their country to be manipulated by outsiders prompted the bank to commission Opia Mensah Kumah, senior program officer for the US government's population communication campaign in Africa, to produce a 'procedural' report. This document stated that deeply-held traditional beliefs and values would hinder population-control efforts, making persuasion more difficult. Indeed, in many parts of the continent, cultural prohibitions exist against even counting one's children, believing them to be a blessing, not a curse.[345]

Based on Kumah's research, both the World Bank and USAID implemented programs designed to overcome resistance to population reduction and bring about drastic changes in public attitudes and personal conduct. Involving coercion and deception, their tactics conformed exactly to the tactics outlined by Colonel Michael Dewar in his book *The Art of Deception in Warfare*, a study on psychological warfare and covert actions. Colonel Dewar, with whom Phillip Day briefly worked in a commercial capacity, is a former army intelligence officer who runs his own public relations agency in London. He outlines these six, basic principles:

➢ The operation must be well planned and centrally co-ordinated, so as to be consistent and sustained.

---

[344] Activities headed by the controversial group, Planned Parenthood, should be carefully watched. This organisation has proven quite happy to fund schemes to remove those ten, tiny fingers and toes from their mother's womb well beyond the first trimester.

[345] Sensible family planning is, of course, the responsibility of both partners. *"There's a lot of gender education saying "Set girls free, set women free." But what is the role of men? If men are seen as the ones who incapacitate women, then the men need to be educated alongside the women."* Gladys Mwiti from the Oasis Counselling Centre, Nairobi. Taken from *People Count* Tear Fund information brochure, 1995.

- Preparation is essential. Those conducting the campaign must be thoroughly familiar with their audience, and able to gauge its probable reaction to the campaign.
- False information must be made to appear absolutely logical, seeming neither out of harmony with current events nor in any way suspicious.
- The greater the variety of sources that can be used to plant false information, the more believable it becomes.
- Timing is critical; people generally notice marked events, but are very poor at perceiving gradual change.
- The operation and its purpose must be concealed from the enemy.[346]

With almost military precision, the WHO population control strategy for Ghana incorporates each of these six principles:

- The activities of the World Bank, USAID and other donors are carefully co-ordinated, and strict monitoring procedures are in place to enforce the terms of the agreement at every stage.
- Extensive background research was carried out in Ghana. Surveys were conducted to determine how best to sell the idea of family planning, gradually exposing the populace to subtle messages, allowing new contraceptive ideology to take root slowly, without arousing suspicion.
- In all campaigns such as these, messages are discreet and shy away from the controversial. They are kept at a muted, persuasive level, repeated exposure to the message influencing the people to accept birth control to such an extent that they eventually identify with the message.
- WHO and relevant associates held approximately 80 special conferences and presentations during the first three years of operations in Ghana. These included presentations to traditional chiefs, private meetings with top government officials, dozens of seminars for journalists and government ministers, special briefings for private sector leaders, and a variety of special events. More than 100 pre-packaged radio broadcasts, numerous television productions and hundreds of propaganda packets were carefully prepared and distributed.

---

[346] **Dewar, Michael** *The Art of Deception in Warfare*, David and Charles, 1989

> Foreign policy had now been successfully incorporated into indigenous broadcasting systems. As such, the campaign progressed from a general raising of the level of awareness to actually influencing attitudes, opinions, and beliefs favourable towards WHO ideas on birth control, those ideas now being promoted within and by the targeted populace.

> The existence of this Western orchestrated, Western-led Ghanaian population control program remains largely unknown to the public. [347]

Where the World Health Organization, USAID and UNFPA do not have the time to carry out the above 'softening' procedures, they implement much swifter and blunter programs. James Miller, a correspondent for Human Life International, brings us the following report on population control measures covertly carried out in Tanzania, Nigeria, Nicaragua, Mexico and the Philippines - all executed in the name of humanitarian aid.

During the early 1990s, the World Health Organization conducted an extensive vaccination campaign against tetanus in a number of countries. In October 1994, Human Life International became suspicious of the campaign protocols. They obtained several vials of the vaccine and had them analysed by chemists. Some of the vials were found to contain human chorionic gonadotrophin (hCG), a naturally occurring hormone essential for maintaining a pregnancy.

When introduced into the body coupled with a tetanus toxoid carrier, antibodies will be formed not only against tetanus but also against hCG. In this case the body fails to recognize hCG as a friend and will produce anti-hCG antibodies. The antibodies will attack subsequent pregnancies by killing the hCG which naturally sustains a pregnancy. When a woman has sufficient anti-hCG antibodies in her system, she is rendered incapable of maintaining a pregnancy.

---

[347] www.africa2000.com A comprehensive resource for information on population and demographic issues; race, class, and competitive fertility; international 'aid' & economic development; reproductive freedom v. control; covert activities & military strategy. This site presents research and analysis by journalists from all over the world, as well as information from hundreds of formerly classified documents that are available from no other source.

HLI reported the sketchy facts regarding the Mexican tetanus vaccines to its affiliates in more than 60 countries. Soon additional reports of vaccines laced with hCG hormone were received from the Philippines, where more than 3.4 million women were vaccinated. Similar reports came from Nicaragua, which had conducted its own vaccination campaign in 1993.

The Known Facts concerning the WHO tetanus vaccination campaigns in Tanzania, Nigeria, Mexico and the Philippines.

Only women were vaccinated, and only women between the ages of 15 and 45. Why? Aren't men at least as likely as young women to come into contact with tetanus? And what of the children? Why were they excluded?

Human chorionic gonadotrophin (hCG) hormone was found in the vaccines. WHO has been actively involved for more than 20 years in the development of an anti-fertility vaccine utilizing hCG tied to tetanus toxoid as a carrier - the exact same coupling as has been found in these vaccines.[348]

Allied with the WHO in the development of this particular anti-fertility vaccine have been UNFPA, the UN Development Program (UNDP), the World Bank, the Population Council, and the Rockefeller Foundation. The US National Institute of Child Health and Human Development was the supplier of the hCG hormone in some of the vaccine experiments. [349]

These incidents are by no means isolated. Covert population control measures have been carried out by these agencies for many years. Kasun details many disturbing cases of coercion being used to implement mass sterilisation. In a 20,000 persons per annum sterilisation program carried out in El Salvador, financed by USAID,

---

[348] More than twenty articles, many written by WHO researchers, document WHO's attempts to create an anti-fertility vaccine utilising tetanus toxoid a carrier. Some leading articles include: "Vaccines for Fertility Regulation," Chapter 11, pp.177-198, Research in Human Reproduction, Biennial Report (1986-1987), WHO Special Programme of Research, Development and Research Training in Human Reproduction (WHO, Geneva 1988). "Observations on the antigenicity and clinical effects of a candidate anti-pregnancy vaccine: B-sub unit of human chorionic gonadotrophin linked to tetanus toxoid," *Fertility and Sterility*, October 1980, pp.328-335

[349] Human Life International, www.hli.org, January 2000

there was little or no provision for informed consent. Similarly in Bangladesh, financial incentives were offered to individuals to go out and recruit candidates for sterilisation. Money was also offered to those being sterilised, but with a great many of those people not really understanding the nature of the operation. In that same country, sterilisation programs were also linked to oral re-hydration programs for children with diarrhoea. Since treatment usually meant life or death for the child, the mother was placed in a position of very little choice. [350]

In the UK, in the year leading up to 2000, there was the Jubilee Campaign, in itself a thoroughly worthwhile global initiative to urge the financial institutions to cancel much third world debt. Many thousands of signatures had been collected from the general public, petitioning the World Bank, IMF and other financial institutions to write off the debts owed by HIPCs (Heavily Indebted Poor Countries[351]) and to examine sensible ways in which future monies could be spent wisely and above all, transparently. The goals of the Jubilee Campaign seemed, at least on the outside, to be quite heartening. The banks appeared to be listening and as a result, various debt cancellation speeches were being made by these institutions.

Sadly, though not unsurprisingly, and despite the good work of Jubilee, at a much higher level, another agenda was at work behind the outward display of institutional goodwill. HIPCs were having their debts cancelled only on condition that they divert substantial funds into 'poverty reduction programs', a thinly veiled euphemism for 'child reduction' programs and other forms of population control.[352] The 'less children the better' policy is perfectly in keeping with Kissinger's NSSM 200, and mirrors UNDP's callous insights

---

350 Kasun, J, op. cit.

351 Debts which have arisen largely as a result of Western financial aid policies. See **Rich, Bruce** *Mortgaging the Earth*, Beacon Press, 1995. A critique of the policies the World Bank has imposed, bringing misery to the very people it was originally founded to help – the poor. *"For those who have long had their suspicions of the World Bank, 'Mortgaging the Earth' proves they were right."* - New Statesman

352 *"At the Annual Meeting of the World Bank and the IMF in September 1999, a new approach to poverty reduction was agreed. The strategies will set out how poverty will be tackled, and specify how resources, including savings from debt relief, will be spent."* DFID Background Briefing, October 1999

into the Hurricane Mitch disaster, i.e. less children in existence would have resulted in less people being affected by the disaster, therefore leading to less, all-round poverty. Once again, World Bank director, Robert Macnamara:

"More children means more expenditure on food, on shelter, on clothing, on health, on education, on every essential social service. And it means correspondingly less expenditure on investment to achieve the very economic growth required to finance these services.... Nurturing children drains away resources that could otherwise be invested into industrial projects."[353]

Naturally the many signatories to the Jubilee petitions had no idea these chicaneries were taking place. And while Jubilee 2000 in no way aligned itself with the philosophy of population control (in fact its website reported on some of the less upright aspects of these global, finance-house tactics[354]), the fact remains that the single A4 Jubilee leaflets distributed to the masses made no mention of these matters, despite the fact that senior executives at Jubilee 2000 knew these inhumane policies were in place. A full report on this topic can be found at *"Drop the debt? A drop in population more like..."* [355] Contact details of these financial institutions are included at the end of this book, so readers may themselves directly campaign for a halt to these inhumane, debt-relief conditions.[356]

Away from the public eye, the UK government has been playing a substantial role in 'poverty reduction', not least via the UK Department for International Development (DFID). While DFID is involved in a number of worthwhile, overseas-aid initiatives, it is also a generous sponsor of both UNDP and UNFPA. DFID released a campaign

---

[353] Kasun, J, op. cit.

[354] www.jubilee2000uk.org

[355] www.credence.org/features/jubilee.htm

[356] BBC News, dated 26th November 2003, reported on some 800 of Africa's leading churchmen and -women who had been tested for HIV at a meeting in Cameroon. At the eighth assembly of the All Africa Conference of Churches, these leaders lined up to take the tests to encourage others to know their HIV status. The AACC Secretary General told the BBC that anyone who tested positive would be supported by other church leaders. Bishop Mvume Dandala also urged those who tested HIV positive to reveal their status to fight the stigma of HIV/AIDS: *"I think it is important for people like that to come out into the open and for us all as a church to learn how to handle one another in a responsible way."* African Church Leaders Take HIV Test at http://news.bbc.co.uk/1/hi/world/africa/3239926.stm

brochure entitled *'Beyond ICPD + 5'*, a Third World sexual and reproductive health paper, which details governmental measures to tackle Third World 'poverty' issues. Included in the brochure, which now features prominently on the UNFPA web-site, are statements such as *"We believe WHO, UNFPA and UNAIDS have important roles as global champions.... WHO's 'Make Pregnancy Safer' initiative is an example of the leadership needed.... AIDS has now affected 50 million.... DFID is supporting the social marketing of female condoms in Zimbabwe.... DFID working intensively in more than 20 countries.... Working in partnership with the World Bank..."* etc. etc.

As with many DFID health documents, population-control measures have become increasingly clothed in emotive rhetoric championing women's rights. A deceptive outward appearance, pleasing to both the eye and the ear, but hiding the more distasteful inner workings, is a fairly typical industrial manoeuvre, again not dissimilar to the Windscale/Sellafield name-change. Formally known as Western meddling, cultural interference and mass sterilisation, population control is now been disarmingly described as 'choices and freedom for women'.[357]

The translation of 'ICPD+5' is 'five years on from the International Conference on Population and Development' - the infamous population conference held in Cairo in 1994. Many so-called Third World or 'developing' country representatives at that gathering were disappointed by the lack of discussion on development, finding instead that they were attending countless seminars focused almost entirely on overpopulation, and *"what are we all going to do about it?"* Objectives were agreed at these meetings and targets were set on population reduction. Those targets are being worked on to this day. A spokesperson for DFID agreed that 'Beyond ICPD+5' does indeed detail policies for reducing the global populace. She believed also though, that whilst it would not have been straying from the truth to

---

[357] While there are indeed many cultures oppressive towards females, it is interesting to note that out of the £140 million given by DFID to the UN's global activity fund in 1999, £45 million went to UNDP and UNFPA, whilst UNIFEM, the UN organisation supposedly fighting for a fairer world for women, received just £1 million. In many instances, it seems, women's rights are simply the Trojan Horse to gain access to reticent countries when it comes to implementing population reduction measures.

name their brochure *'DIFD's Population Control Measures'*, this title would not have been entirely appropriate.[358]

UNFPA has since revised ICPD+5 and has renamed it 'ICPD at 10': "Keeping the promise. 1994-2004." The web page includes the following glowing statement:

> *"Many countries have translated the commitments they made in Cairo into policies and programmes designed to transform the lives of women, men and children. But much more remains to be done. Most member states, UNFPA, and other partners believe that the best way to commemorate the ICPD is through an in-depth, country-by-country analysis of achievements, constraints, lessons learned and way forward to full implementation of the ICPD program of action."*[359]

Much remains to be done, eh? The recklessness with which WHO, USAID, UNFPA, UNDP and associates are applying population control across the globe, and especially Africa, is causing many African observers much consternation. Charles Geshekter again.

> *"The nebulous linkage of HIV to a complex of widespread symptoms has been greeted with justifiable skepticism by many Africans for another reason: they fear the WHO claims of a pandemic will become an excuse for using Africa as a laboratory for unwarranted and unregulated vaccine trials or for testing powerful cytotoxic drugs, using Africans as guinea pigs."*[360]

As seen with their sterilisation programs, WHO and associates have also been conducting covert, unregulated vaccine trials all too frequently across Africa, the Sub-Sahara and other Third World countries.[361] WHO itself confirms that more than twelve billion injections are performed every year, throughout the world, and at least one third are not being carried out in a safe manner. Says Philippe Krynen:

---

[358] Steven Ransom telephone conversation with DFID spokesperson, 2nd February 2000

[359] 10th Anniversary of the International Conference on Population and Development at http://www.unfpa.org/icpd/10/index.htm

[360] DISS/cuss, News Flash, 8th December 1997

[361] **Douglas-Hulme, Ethel** *Pasteur Exposed. The False Foundation of Medicine*, Ennisfield Press, 1989

"Since the IMF became responsible for the Health Budget, only vaccinations are free. Not only free, but hammered in... There are no roads, no disinfectant or sterilisation at the dispensary, no refrigerators for the vaccines on the way, but the magic EPI (Extended Program of Immunisation) like Superman is always on time. No matter how skinny, how feverish the buttocks – immunisation will not be missed."[362]

Leaving aside the general dangers of mass vaccination programs[363], there is surely no point at all in an AIDS vaccine. If vaccination theory is based on giving your immune system a taste of the foreign invader and there is no HIV to begin with, what then is the nature of the chemical solutions being injected into African people? An injection of common sense into Africa's Western-dominated bureaucratic regime would seem a more appropriate approach. The uncomplicated issues of poverty, malnutrition, contaminated water and poor sanitation would then perhaps have a chance of being addressed. But will they ever be?

At the United Nations General Assembly summit in 2000, a number of Millennium Development goals (MDGs) were discussed and promises were made, including the cutting by half the number of people in the world's poorest countries suffering poverty, hunger and ill-health and a pledge to implement sanitation and clean water programs to achieve these goals. Not surprisingly, the World Bank and International Monetary Fund issued a report in April 2004 that accepted the goals would not be met.

A recent 'scorecard' report was jointly issued by the World Wildlife Fund, Water Aid, Care, Tearfund, Green Cross and Oxfam on the state of funding to water and sanitation projects. The press release was headed, 'World governments fail to act on aid as water crisis worsens.' Oxfam International issued an independent press release in April 2004, stating:

"The World Bank and IMF celebrate their 60th birthdays in Washington DC. Meanwhile, millions in poor countries around the world wait to know whether their countries must continue to pay crippling debt and receive minimal aid, or whether

---

362 *Continuum*, Vol 5, No 2, December 1998

363 For a full treatment on the dangers of vaccination, please see **Ransom, Steven,** *Wake up to Health in the 21st Century*, Credence Publications, 2003

182

their children can go to school.... On one hand, donors claim to be totally focused on poverty reduction and reaching the millennium development goals. At the same time, the new framework on how much debt a country can afford to repay is not linked to the poverty levels of that country and what is needed to reach the Millennium Goals."[364]

Furthermore, the April 2004 World Bank report concluded that it could not offer any solutions to the crisis.

Naturally, the Bank is perfectly capable of financing simple solutions, as already discussed. Instead, however, Western vaccine magic is performed in Africa and across other poverty-ridden continents, and on a breathtaking scale. At the turn of the new century, Uganda agreed to an AIDS vaccination campaign 'fully integrated into its country program'.[365] And now, the plan is to accelerate the vaccination schedule. A recent study conducted amongst the Ugandan population, funded almost entirely by the World Bank, found that, doubtless due to progressive 'educational programs', almost all those interviewed would be willing to pay for an AIDS vaccine if one became available, despite the average daily wage in Uganda amounting to a paltry US$1.97. Other convincing rhetoric abounds:

83 New Medicines in Development for HIV/AIDS -
The pharmaceutical research industry is continuing its effort to develop more effective ways to prevent and treat HIV/AIDS, with 83 new medicines in development, a new survey by the Pharmaceutical Research and Manufacturers of America (PhRMA) shows.

"In addition to the 80 medicines already approved, these new medicines in the pipeline demonstrate the pharmaceutical research industry's commitment to combat this terrible scourge that afflicts patients all over the world," said PhRMA President Alan F. Holmer. "We'll continue until we've conquered the disease."

---

[364] *World Bank Chief Admits United Nations Development Goals Cannot be Met*, at http://www.wsws.org/articles/2004/may2004/bank-m18.shtml
[365] "AIDS Vaccine Being Tested in Africa for First Time," Associated Press, 9th February 1999 *"The National Institutes of Health says the first test of a human AIDS vaccine in Africa has begun in Uganda.... AIDS has devastated Africa. In Uganda alone, it has killed nearly a half-million people and left 1 million children orphaned...."* etc., etc.

The medicines in development, all of which are either in human clinical trials or are awaiting approval by the FDA, include 15 vaccines. Vaccine research is considered crucial to control the AIDS pandemic. [366]

Over the years, AIDS and associated vaccine research has been funded through various 'philanthropic' channels, not least from the coffers of Microsoft giant Bill Gates, this 'donation' reported in the *Wall Street Journal*, dated 14th October 2003:

"The Bill and Melinda Gates Foundation said it is doubling its commitment to fighting AIDS in India to $200 million, and disbursed the first $65 million in grants to groups working with truckers, sex workers and drug-users at high risk. Last year Mr. Gates, the Microsoft founder-turned-philanthropist, visited India and pledged $100 million to fight AIDS in the subcontinent, where the next wave of the disease is expected to explode."

José Esparza, William L Heyward and Saladin Osmanov are the authors of a WHO report on large-scale human testing of vaccines in Africa. Disarmingly entitled 'Phase III' trials, the authors note:

"Phase III trials will require extensive international collaboration and co-ordination, and it is likely that developing countries will play a major role in these trials. This is appropriate since some of the highest HIV incidence rates are found in developing countries..." [367]

And 'the major role' these developing countries will play? The inhabitants will innocently bare their upper arm, trusting that what is being locally tested and injected into their bloodstream is being done for their own well-being and best interests. The large number of pharmaceutical corporations wishing to conduct and monitor the effects of unproven vaccines will find in Africa and other 'far-away' regions ideal laboratory conditions. [368] Who really cares?

---

366 NewsOnLine, Monday 24th November 2003 at
http://biz.yahoo.com/prnews/031124/dcm018_1.html
367 www.who.ch/lowband/document/vaccines/aids/8
368 *Associated Press*; Thursday, 27th February, 1997. Three South African researchers said they intend to continue their work despite criticism for violating accepted procedures in testing their experimental AIDS drug Virodene. The panel, the Medicines Control Council, accused the

Dangerous vaccine programs are just the tip of the iceberg. AZT and its derivatives are also set for African shores. Since its inception in 1948, the World Health Organisation has been responsible for setting the standards in development, manufacture, distribution and administration of essentially all pharmaceuticals used throughout the world. WHO has also been responsible for setting all the major research agendas, and is intimately involved in determining which drugs should be made or remain illegal.[369] And from that date too, WHO has enjoyed absolute freedom to roam the globe with its programs. WHO is now planning its 'Three by Five' whereby 3 million people are set to be handed out AIDS drugs by 2005. With full knowledge of the enormous destruction these drugs and vaccines are capable of visiting upon their recipients, all treatment programs are nevertheless being fully implemented.[370]

The Durban AIDS conference, held on 9-14th July 2000, received the funding of fifteen sponsors, eleven of whom were pharmaceutical companies and/or organisations who had a direct interest in population control. The 2004 AIDS conference in Bangkok, Thailand was sponsored by GlaxoSmithKline, Abbott Laboratories, Roche, Boehringer Ingelheim, Microsoft, Pfizer, UN, CDC, US Health and Human Services, The Bill and Melinda Gates Foundation, The World bank, USAID, The Rockefeller Foundation, Nike, UNDP, UNAIDS and Nestlé and others.

That the Ford Foundation has been one of the sponsors will come as little surprise to readers au fait with the population control 'league of friends'. This organisation is billed on its web-site as *providing grants and loans to projects that strengthen democratic values, reduce poverty and injustice, promote international co-operation, and*

---

researchers of exposing AIDS patients to a toxic industrial solvent. It also said the researchers failed to obtain required permission from medical authorities to conduct experiments on humans. According to the report, the amount of toxic solvent in the drug used in the human trials was well above environmental exposure limits. It said also that the researchers bypassed all conventional funding and controlling bodies that normally scrutinise such applications.

[369] DOD Appropriations. Part 5. *R&D Test & Evaluation. US Army Printing Office*, Washington DC, 1969

[370] Project AIDS International's Fraud Investigation Team submitted a dossier to the United Nations Human Rights Commission in March 1993, detailing the deadly effects of AZT, the fraudulence of the HIV=AIDS hypothesis and the bogus nature of the 'AIDS test'. It sought especially to draw the Commission's attention to the routine practice of treating 'HIV positive' infants with known deadly poisons. Their brief was ignored.

advance human achievement.' Whilst The Ford Foundation funds a number of worthwhile projects across the globe, it also funds various 'reproductive health' programs that do not best serve the interests of the recipient.[371] Also, the Ford Foundation's long-standing links with the Rockefeller Institute, coupled with its own history of CIA collaboration in Africa in the early 1970s, makes the purpose of the corporation's attendance at any supposedly philanthropic convention highly questionable.[372]

Given the source of sponsorship monies, what opportunities were there at Bangkok 2004 to discuss the ethics of widespread, untested vaccinations on men, women and children? Who was there to inform the shareholders that Lucy, Deus, Julia, Seledina, Bernadetta and many others have all responded excellently to Philippe Krynen's 'food/water/education' triple-therapy in Tanzania, and that Lucy, once written off for dead, is now alive and well and the proud mother of a healthy, four-year-old son?

Who drew attention to the clinical evidence that conventional AIDS pharmaceuticals are highly carcinogenic, and that had Lucy been treated with these drugs, both she and her child might not be with us today? Who catalogued the internal damage and deformities that AIDS drugs mete out to the recipient and especially to the unborn child? Who reminded those in attendance that back in the US, the children at the Incarnation Childrens' Centre *'...walk around in various states of deformation and retardation because of life-long exposure to AZT and protease inhibitors'*? Who openly denounced Bangkok 2004's all-consuming profit-driven mentality? Who, in fact, stood up to declare this whole gathering despicable?

WILLARD: I was going to the worst place in the world, and I didn't even know it yet. Kurtz was close. Real close. So close you could feel him.

---

[371] Kasun, J, op. cit. Includes further detail on Ford Foundation population-control spending.

[372] **Williams, M J** US Department of State Bulletin, November 1973. Covert action in Sub-Saharan Africa. Operation PUSH. *People to Save Humanity*, comprising WHO, World Bank, Rockefeller Foundation, Ford Foundation, CDC, USAID and AFRICARE. Aims: Under the guise of humanitarian aid, covertly to install US intelligence agents in certain African countries, destabilise anti-US leaderships, and install US policy sympathisers.

CHIEF: My orders are, I'm not supposed to know where I'm taking this boat, so I don't.

WILLARD: We're going up-river about 75 klicks above the Do Lung bridge.

CHIEF: That's Cambodia, Captain.

WILLARD: That's classified.

THE POLITICS OF AIDS

How come all this isn't in the papers?

And just as Captain Willard nears his mission's end, his only co-ordinates 'somewhere up river', we are now deep into enemy territory - the highly restricted zone - looking for an exit, any exit, the whole mind focused on an escape from the enormity of what is being discussed in these pages. The lies about AIDS and AIDS 'medicines'; the lies about AIDS in Africa and the Third World; and the lies about the supposed 'hopelessness' of the African situation.

And then...an exit appears. A huge sigh of relief...

"OF COURSE! If thousands upon thousands of people in countries the world over were being routinely exposed to callous, pharmaceutical experiments, and if hundreds of thousands were dying as a direct result of these highly toxic chemicals, or as an indirect result of basic human needs purposely not being met.... if anything as monstrous as this were going on in our world, surely it would be in the newspapers!"

Unfortunately that exit does not provide the necessary means of escape. Several decades ago now, before a packed New York Press Club, John Swinton, the former chief of staff at The *New York Times* approached the podium to address his colleagues. Known as 'The Dean of His Profession', the legendary newspaperman proceeded to deliver a monumentally important statement on the notion of an independent press.

"There is no such thing, at this date in the world's history, in America, as an independent press. You know it and I know it. There is not one of you who dares to write your honest opinions, and if you did, you know beforehand that it would never appear in print. I am paid weekly for keeping my honest opinion out of the paper I am connected with. Others of you are paid similar salaries for similar things, and any of you who would be so foolish as to write honest opinions would be out on the street looking for another job. If I allowed my honest opinion to appear in one issue of my paper, before

twenty-four hours my occupation would be gone. You know it and I know it, and what folly is this - toasting an independent press? We are the tools and vassals of rich men behind the scenes. We are the jumping jacks, they pull the strings and we dance. Our talents, our possibilities and our lives are all the property of other men. We are intellectual prostitutes."[373]

The recent multi-billion-dollar merger between Time Inc. and AOL makes this conglomerate now the most powerful information disseminator in the world. Independently fostering enormous influence before the merger, the two groups combined now exert even more authority in the global arena of film, TV, Internet, advertising and public information services. In her article on the AOL/Time merger entitled "Dangerous Liaisons", Wendy Grossman, writing for *Intellectual Capital*, stated:

"What disturbs me about these scenarios is the concentration of media into too few, extremely powerful hands. The danger is not so much that all media will express the same opinions; people are quite capable of reading an opinion and disagreeing with it. The danger is that certain kinds of stories simply will not get covered - and despite the Internet's capacity for lengthy, detailed exposes of all types, most people derive their sense of what today's important issues are from the major media." [374]

Health writer Martin Walker has this to say on the influential medium of television news:

"Like almost everything else on television, news programmes leave us feeling bereft of control over our own lives. They report with certainty what has happened through the eyes and mouths of the most powerful groups in society. Except for some inevitable exceptions, the news is rarely news, but a presentation of the virtual consensus decreed by the most powerful. The news is brought to us like a meal in a restaurant; we question the way it is served only when we find the content distasteful.... We the public, in all our diversity, have struck a contract with our governors: realising that life is

---

[373] Campaign Against Fraudulent Medical Research, "Vaccinations", winter newsletter, 1995, www.pnc.com
[374] **Grossman, Wendy** "Dangerous Liaisons", *Intellectual Capital*, 20th January 2000

short, we refrain from criticising or disturbing consensus as long as it does not disturb us, and that we are left alone to be ourselves."375

On the subject of our news being organised for us by powerful groups, Richard M Cohen, senior producer of CBS Political News, stated:

"We are going to impose our agenda on the coverage, by dealing with the issues and subjects that we choose to deal with." 376

And Richard Salent, former president of CBS, had this to say:

*"Our job is to give not what they want, but what we decide."*377

So who are the rich men, the decision-makers behind the scenes at Time Warner/AOL?

'Time-Warner Inc' is a corporate member of the Council on Foreign Relations or CFR. Time's president Richard D Parsons and its editor-in-chief Norman Pearlstine are longstanding CFR members. Formed in 1921, CFR membership requires wealth, influence and a desire to shape international policy. In his biography of CFR member Henry Kissinger, Walter Isaacson describes this élitist group as:

*"...a private organisation that serves as a discussion club for close to three thousand well-connected aficionados of foreign affairs. Beneath chandeliers and stately portraits in its Park Avenue mansion, members attend lectures, dinners and round-table seminars featuring top officials and visiting world leaders."*378

Wining and dining at these CFR round-table discussions are the people at the top of every influential organisation on our planet, *including the media.* It is an open secret that when it comes to the stories that matter, our 'news' is invariably given to us in accordance with the directives of Swinton's 'rich men behind the scenes'.

---

375 **Walker, Martin** "Totalitarian Science and Media Politics," *Continuum*, Vol 5, No 5, January 1999
376 Campaign Against Fraudulent Medical Research, op. cit.
377 Ibid.
378 **Isaacson, Walter** *Kissinger, A Biography*, Simon & Schuster, 1992

In keeping with NSSM 200, a CFR policy objective is substantial world-wide depopulation.[379] This policy, which naturally has received no public airtime whatsoever, is largely funded by the Rockefeller Foundation and the Merck Fund, both financially linked to Merck Pharmaceuticals, the world's largest vaccine manufacturer.[380] *Parenting Magazine*, a subsidiary of Time Inc., contained a feature on vaccines and vaccination in its March 1999 issue, which included glowing passages such as *"...saving countless children from death and permanent disability..."* The article did not, however, include the French government's moratorium on childhood hepatitis B vaccinations as a result of links to neurological disorders including multiple sclerosis; neither did it include the current civil actions facing Merck and other manufacturers with regard to tainted oral polio vaccines, now being linked to certain forms of human cancer.[381]

What, then, must be made of the following Norman Pearlstine announcement, reassuring the planet of the TIME/TIME WARNER/TIME Inc./AOL/CNN/TNT/TURNER Inc. global commitment to maintaining editorial values?

> *"...We should be honest in our judgments and truthful in our reporting. We've had a lot of practice applying this principle over the past 10 years.... A respect for journalistic independence has been part of our company's values for so long that it's encoded in our DNA.... As we cover the corporate complexities that swirl around us, let us assure you that we - as individual journalists and critics with pride in what we do - will continue to be loyal to, and represent the interests of our most important constituency, our readers."* [382]

The above statement is, of course, devoid of anything meaningful. In reality, Time Inc. and its massive network of media subsidiaries print and screen only what Time Inc. and its subsidiaries want us to

---

379 Horowitz, Leonard, *Emerging Viruses...* op. cit.

380 Merck is over 400 years old, achieving $10.96 billion per year in sales today. It has numerous links with IG Farben and was instrumental in producing chemicals and pharmaceuticals in Germany during the power of the Third Reich. (Leading Edge Research Org. www.trufax.org)

381 **Horowitz, Leonard** *Parenting with Deadly Timely Propaganda*, Atlantean Press, summer 1999

382 *Time*, 24th January 2000

know. Billionaire media mogul Ted Turner of CNN, TNT and other cable networks fame, now vice-chairman at Time Warner, stated:

"We are the ones who determine what people's attitudes are. It's in our hands." [383]

And here is a glimpse into the mind and philosophy of Turner, the man who dictates so much of the globe's media content - who describes his management style as *"lead, follow or get out of the way."* [384]

CNN'S TURNER CALLS FOR ONE CHILD PER FAMILY, June Preston. Reuters. 11th September 1998 - ATLANTA: *Ted Turner called for a world-wide, one-baby-per-family policy and said of his five children, "If I was doing it over again I wouldn't have done it, but I can't shoot them now that they're here." Turner said he considers it his personal responsibility to worry about overpopulation. "I've got to worry about the totality of the planet.... They think we can just let Africa and Central and South America and parts of Asia stew in their own juices. I don't agree," he said. "A lot of people will stay in India and Bangladesh and Africa and El Salvador and starve. But a lot of them won't. They're going to come where the prosperity is, and they know where the prosperity is, baby! We should work to try to convince everybody that they should have one child like China has. People who abhor the China, one-child policy are dumb-dumbs."*

And Turner's worry about overpopulation and care for the planet is further reflected in his generous donation to UNFPA:

TED TURNER'S UN FOUNDATION GIVES UNFPA $4.3 MILLION TO ADOLESCENT SEXUAL HEALTH - *Executive Director Dr Nafis Sadik today welcomed the announcement by the United Nations Foundation, directed by Ted Turner: "The Foundation's funding of our programs demonstrates an extraordinary commitment. We appreciate the speed and determination with which the United Nations Foundation has acted...."* [385]

---

[383] Taken from a speech given to broadcasters and presenters. www.holysmoke.org/turner
[384] www.cyber-nation.com, "Quotes to Inspire", January 2000
[385] *Independent Daily News*, 28th September, 1998

On Turner's desire to reduce the planet's population to no more than 350 million, the following question was posed by one member of the population, less favourably disposed to Turner's viewpoint: *"How will this be achieved? Will Turner and [now ex-]wife lead the way?"*[386]

There are a number of very logical reasons why Western powers would want to 'thin out' Africa in particular, reasons succinctly expressed in the African publication, *The Baobab Press*.

"The West has a great deal at stake in Africa - both because the continent is a source of minerals critical to military-industrial uses, and because of its strategic location. The emergence of populous, powerful African nations, capable of developing their own trade systems and able effectively to bargain for fair trade, would threaten the economic interests of Western powers. Thus the presence of strong, nationalist leadership in any African nation - even a relatively small one - would give rise to heightened aspirations on the part of others on the continent. The ultimate result, of course, would be a monumental increase in Third-World liberation movements that would place grave limits on US imperialism and perhaps even cause the permanent decline of the Western hegemony."[387]

And the following text details Africa's incredible wealth of natural resources:

"In terms of resources, Africa has 90% of the world's cobalt, 80% of the world's chrome, 50% of the world's gold, the same in platinum and the majority of the world's industrial diamonds: the bulk of the world's gems, including diamonds, sapphires, topaz, malachite, opal, rubies, tanzanite, substantial amounts of manganese, iron ore, copper, vanadium, bauxite, lead and zinc. The biggest beneficiary of all this mineral wealth is the West and its industries. And the West is the main manager of this wealth."[388]

And a study written after the 1974 world population conference in Bucharest (not declassified until 1990) is considered the primary

---

[386] **Muelhenbury, Bill** www.thewinds.org
[387] *Baobab Press,* Vol 2, No 6, 1992
[388] **Mazrui, Aia** *The Africans,* BBC publications, 1986

theoretical document on US demographic intervention overseas. It advises that population control is in the political and economic interests of the United States because large populations in developing countries could jeopardise American foreign investments, provoke rebellions, and threaten access to important raw minerals and other resources. It recommends that several strategically important countries be targeted for massive efforts to reduce birth-rates. [389]

Western agitators who have probably had the most influence in shaping not only Africa's population control policies, but also the gross inequality of Western/African business opportunities, are the Rockefellers.

"In all of world history, it would be difficult to link as much mischief to any one name as can be traced to the Rockefeller family over the past century." [390]

So begins one account of the Rockefellers, one of many detailing a dynasty of absolute power sliding rapidly towards absolute corruption. It was John Davison Rockefeller who built the family fortune with the Standard Oil Company he founded in 1870 at the age of 31. By the mid 1880s, John D Rockefeller had become a millionaire many times over. He also became one of the most hated men in America, if not the world. Several state attorneys tried in vain to have him jailed for his corrupt business dealings. The Rockefeller fortune was amassed by extortion tactics, by implementing totally ruthless business practices to eliminate competition, and employing some of the most oppressive labour practices imaginable.[391] Rockefeller labourers worked scandalously long hours under extraordinarily risky conditions, receiving only substandard family housing and food and no expendable wages. Rockefeller, a staunch 'survival of the fittest' evolutionist, said of his business practices:

"This is not an evil tendency in business. It is merely the workings out of a law of nature and a law of God." [392]

The Rockefellers knew well the science of creating a need and then manufacturing its fulfilment to massive profit. New substances began

---

[389] www.africa2000.com
[390] *Baobab Press,* Vol 4, No 13, 1994
[391] **Kutz, Myer** *Rockefeller Power*, Pinnacle Books, 1974
[392] **Ghent, William** *Our Benevolent Feudalism*, MacMillan Press, 1902

to be licensed as 'drugs' and approved by the Rockefeller-sponsored American Medical Association and Food & Drug Administration with doctors and specialists trained in their dispensation and use through Rockefeller-financed institutions. Author G Edward Griffin reports:

"Abraham Flexner, author of the famous Flexner Report of 1910, led the crusade for upgrading the medical schools of America, all the while he was in the employ of Andrew Carnegie and John D Rockefeller, who had set up gigantic tax-exempt foundations for that purpose. The end result was that all medical schools became heavily oriented towards drugs and drug research, for it was through the increased sale of drugs that the donors realized a profit on their donations.

A brief backward glance at the total landscape will help us appreciate more fully the present extent of [pharmaceutical] cartel influence, not only in the FDA [United States Food & Drug Administration] but at all levels of the federal government. The list of men who are or were in key positions within the Rockefeller group reads like a 'Who's Who' in government."[393]

Rockefeller money almost single-handedly transformed medicine from the old-fashioned barber's shop practices into the modern, well-organised allopathic[394] industry we recognise today. JD's organisational abilities were legendary in the projects to which he turned his hand and impressive fortune. Ironically JD's father William had peddled quack remedies off the back of his wagon in the mid-1800s, the family firm making outrageous profits palming off bottled petroleum called 'Nujol' as a supposed cure for cancer and, later, constipation.[395] But William's son JD was to have altogether more grandiose designs. Largely through JD's efforts, doctors underwent the metamorphosis from poorly paid wagon-quacks to sophisticated, well-educated and highly-paid luminaries, trained in the new centres funded and built by Rockefeller and billionaire Andrew Carnegie. Foundations were formed; chemical research financed. The 20th century began with obvious medical promise of great deeds to come.

---

[393] **Griffin, G Edward** *World Without Cancer*, American Media, 1996
[394] **allopathy** – orthodox medical practice, treatment of diseases by drugs.
[395] Kutz, Myer, op. cit.

In 1913, the Rockefeller Foundation was launched, describing its goal as the advancement of *"...the civilization of the peoples of the United States and its territories and possessions and of foreign lands..."* In 1928 the Drug Trust was formed by an alliance of the Rockefeller Empire and the German chemical company, IG Farbenindustrie or IG Farben. Drug profits from that time onwards rose exponentially and by 1948, drugs had become a $10 billion a year industry.[396]

Rockefeller influence and money accrued from partnerships such as these were to become the foundation for virtually every medical college in the US from 1945 onwards. Morris Bealle writes:

> *"The Rockefeller Foundation 1948 Annual Report itemizes the gifts it has made to colleges and public agencies in the past 44 years, and they total somewhat over half a billion dollars. These colleges, of course, teach their students all the drug lore the Rockefeller pharmaceutical houses want to be taught. Otherwise there would be no more gifts, just as there are no gifts to any of the 30-odd drugless colleges in the United States."*[397]

By the early 1950s, the Rockefeller multi-billion dollar financial empire extended over much of the world, and had been a major funder of such influential associations as the Council on Foreign Relations, the Center for Strategic and International Studies and the Overseas Development Council. In 1952, John D Rockefeller III, Nelson's older brother, established the New York-based Population Council and a pattern of influence soon emerged. Two years after the Population Council was inaugurated, the China Family Planning Association was formed.

By the mid 1960s, such 'planned parenthood' societies had been set up in almost every developing country, leading later to organisations such as the International Planned Parenthood Federation, now a powerful voice in the US for all methods of birth control.[398] In 1968, a

396 Ghent, William, *Our Benevolent Feudalism*, op. cit.

397 Bealle, Morris, op. cit.

398 Not unsurprisingly, in a slick marketing move by UNFPA and IPPF, Geri Halliwell of Spice Girls fame was inaugurated into the fold as the 'acceptable face' of population control. Ignorant or otherwise of the end result of her PR, Ginger Spice helped promote UNFPA's sex education,

Presidential Committee on Population and Family Planning was organised. Under the leadership of John D Rockefeller III, the panel recommended that foreign population control programs be expanded *"...as rapidly as funds can be properly allocated by the US."* [399]

It was Rockefeller money that aided the meteoric rise of Henry Kissinger, the man responsible not only for NSSM 200, but also for the 1970 Department of Defense Appropriations request: HB 15090. In 1969, Kissinger demanded a report on US biological weapons capabilities. This in turn prompted a DOD request to Congress for ten million dollars to update the US bio-weapons arsenal. This huge sum of money was apparently to be used for the express purpose of developing artificial viruses with the capacity to attack the human immune system. The precise terminology of 'HB 15090 pt. 5' memorandum was that the funds be used to develop *"...an agent refractory to the immunological and therapeutic processes upon which we depend to maintain our relative freedom from infectious disease."* [400]

The money was granted, and contracts were awarded to major defence contractors across the US, particularly Litton Bionetics, a subsidiary of Litton Systems and Litton Industries, one of the most frequently contracted biological warfare companies in the US at that time. [401] Litton Bionetics was Robert Gallo's employer throughout his virus research years in Maryland. Alongside research into viruses that might catastrophically disrupt the human immune system, there is ample evidence that Gallo was one of a number of virologists, including Peter Duesberg, working specifically on cancer viruses. Duesberg's work in particular was to study *"...the mechanism by which tumour viruses might bring about malignant changes in humans."* [402]

Rockefeller money continues to be a major force in public and private 'security' operations in the US, and despite government

abortion and sterilisation programs across the globe (www.altavista.com image search on UNFPA).

[399] "The Pharmaceutical Drugs Racket," www.trufax.org 2000

[400] DOD Appropriations for 1970. US Government Printing Office, Washington DC

[401] Special Virus Cancer Program. Progress report 8 and 9, Viral Oncology, US Govt. Printing Office, p 233, 1971

[402] Special Virus Cancer Program, op. cit.

assurance to the contrary, Western biological weapons research continues to this day, and on a huge scale. Millions of Rockefeller dollars are also spent each year for research and policy studies related to US political and economic interests abroad. In recent years, Rockefeller grants have significantly funded African enterprises, including thousands of dollars for population 'education' in Benin, Nigeria, Tanzania and the Sahel. A UN directory of population activities lists still more operations, the same type attributed to the Population Council.[403]

If confirmation was needed that JD Rockefeller was the founding father of 20th century population control policy, that confirmation is surely represented in this single sentence, delivered by Rockefeller himself to a group of Sunday school children, his country's flowering youth:

"The 'American Beauty' Rose can be produced only by sacrificing the buds that grow up around it." [404]

It was the general malevolence of Rockefeller influence that prompted one critic to comment:

"Those who fornicated with the devil and deceived all the kings and the wealthiest men of all the nations are the Rockefellers." [405]

In her paper "AIDS in Africa?" Dr Eleni Papadopulos-Eleopulos includes the following observation:

"The uppermost question in the minds of intelligent Africans and Europeans is this: Why do the world's media appear to have conspired with some scientists to become so gratuitously extravagant with the truth?" [406]

Which prompts the further question: *Is the promotion of conventional AIDS beliefs some sort of mass, medical conspiracy?* ABC news journalist Nicholas Regush, a long time critic of the

---

[403] US National Archives, the Library of Congress, published resources of the United Nations Population Fund and the US Agency for International Development.

[404] Kutz, Myer, op. cit. *"Rockefeller power is real, far-reaching and much of it hidden from view. A provocative probe into the origins, extent and misuse of Rockefeller power."*

[405] *Bio Warfare, Who or What is the Threat?* www.thewinds.org

[406] **Papadopulos-Eleopulos, Eleni** *AIDS in Africa?* Rethinking AIDS, 2000

conventional AIDS hypothesis, was asked, *"But these are massive numbers of people, in the community, the medical establishment, the media, government – have they all hoodwinked themselves into this belief?"* Regush replied:

"Not hoodwinked. It's a process of information assimilation over time. Quite often, in science, you have a small group of opinion leaders who spread the message. The secondary and tertiary groups [doctors and related care providers at ground level] do not do the reading and thinking. That has a lot to do with time, and peer pressure, and the kind of networking that's built up among scientists. This is not a mass conspiracy. This is not a colossal derangement of mind. This is normal medical business, exacerbated by the huge money that's pumped into the AIDS bureaucracy."[407]

These writers would certainly agree. At the lower levels within the HIV/AIDS and associated humanitarian organisations, it is ignorance of the bigger picture which allows these population control activities to continue. Nicholas Murray Butler, chief spokesman for the hugely influential J P Morgan & Company, once stated: *"The world is divided into three classes of people: a very small group that makes things happen, a somewhat larger group that watches things happen, and the great multitude which never knows what really happens."*[408]

Within all governmental corporations and organisations, there is an established hierarchy. It would be quite true to say that most people at the lower levels have little idea what is actually going on at the upper level. At the same time, there are those mid-rankers who *do* know what is going on, who are told what to do and who are afraid to speak out. Then, of course, there are those in the top-level positions, whose consciences have been seared, who are responsible for making the top-level decisions.

Today, at the start of the new millennium, under the finest crystal chandeliers, population control is just one of a number of élitist ideologies being planned for world-wide implementation. To safeguard the power and influence of Western political supremacy, officials from

---

[407] **Strausbaugh, John** *The AIDS Heretics*, New York Press, 13th December 2000
[408] 'An Introduction to President Clinton's Political Mentor' at http://radiobergen.org/powergame/tragedy.html

the World Bank, IMF, Trilateral Commission, CFR, WHO, USAID, UNAIDS, UNICEF[409], CNN, Time Inc., Rothschilds, Bilderberg Group,[410] Rockefeller/Ford/Gates Foundation, and related media consortia are meeting to decide on their exact approach to 'solving' certain presentation problems pertaining to the 'Third World and Sub-Saharan AIDS' campaign.

As per the Dewar protocols, the entire operation will be well planned and centrally co-ordinated, so as to be consistent and sustained. Officials will be thoroughly familiar with their audience, and able to gauge its probable reaction to the campaign. They will have prepared a great deal of false information which will appear absolutely logical, seeming neither out of harmony with current events nor in any way suspicious. They will fully utilise the wide variety of media resources at their disposal to disseminate this false information. They will pay particular attention to the timing which is critical, people generally noticing marked events, but not gradual change. And they will endeavour to keep this whole operation and its purpose concealed from the enemy. Consequently, any AIDS item from CNN, Time, SKY, Reuters etc., regarding the latest developments in the African AIDS 'crisis', will tell us only what 'the rich men behind the scenes' want us to know. There has been a slow and steady build-up in stories telling us that AIDS is now a security threat to the West. This from Ted Turner's CNN:

---

409 *"Public records reveal United Nation's Children's Fund works closely with WHO, UNDP, UNFPA and other organisations promoting population control programs world-wide, including China, Angola, Philippines, Vietnam, Guinea Bissau, Nigeria and Tanzania. UNICEF director James Grant called for the US government to give more money to UNFPA '...as a means of giving an important boost to family planning.'"* CRI Information pack, *Behind the Mask of UNICEF.* www.pop.org, Special Publications

410 The Bilderberg meetings were founded by HRH Prince Bernhard of the Netherlands, a former SS officer and employee of IG Farben. The group was named after the Bilderberg Hotel in Oosterbeck, Holland, where the first meeting took place in 1954. Comprising international financiers, politicians, media and other key global leaders, and by invitation only, the Bilderberg meetings are conducted in the strictest secrecy, at varying world venues, the agendas unpublicised, and the group's existence almost entirely unreported. All attempts by Credence to gain further information on the May 1998 Bilderberg meeting held at the Turnberry Hotel, Scotland, were met with *"No comment."* 1998 Turnberry attendees included Conrad Black, now disgraced ex-chairman UK *Telegraph Newspapers*, Anatole Kaletsky, associate editor UK *Times*, Christopher Hogg, chairman *Reuters*, Jim Hoagland, associate editor *Washington Post*, David Rockefeller, chairman of *Chase Manhattan Bank*, Henry Kissinger, *Kissinger Associates*, James Wolfensohn, president *World Bank*, Jan Leschly, CEO *SmithKline Beecham Pharmaceuticals*. For an insight into Bilderberg influence over the current British, European and US governments, visit www.watch.pair.com/discernment.html and related links.

200

US STEPS UP GLOBAL FIGHT AGAINST AIDS.
CNN, 10ᵗʰ JANUARY 2000 – *"US military to be used in anti-AIDS effort. The administration is seeking another $50 million for research, purchase and distribution of life-saving vaccines in developing nations," said Gore. The administration's budget request for next year would contain specific funding for the US military to work with the armed forces of other nations to combat AIDS. Gore urged other nations to consider the AIDS epidemic a true threat to peace in Africa and make it a priority on the world's security agenda."*

And most certainly, these articles are having the expected influence. Take a look at the following article penned by Nigel Marsh from World Vision International, entitled *Potential Security Implications of HIV and AIDS in Africa*:

"This is the season for security scares, so let's imagine a crazed dictator unleashes a new disease, with a long time-lag between infection and death to ensure further spread, yet killing most who contract it in their prime. After 20 years, 40 million people are dead, with six million more infected each year. It ruins economies, devastates societies, and even threatens governments. What wouldn't we do, what wouldn't we spend, to confront that evil?

Unfortunately, we don't need to imagine the disease, and we don't need some twisted malefactor to unleash it – Human Immuno-deficiency Virus came to us two decades ago, apparently quite naturally. All those effects we've imagined, and more, are our reality today.

Why should a disease threaten security? Let's take a look at Africa, where most people living with HIV and AIDS will be found (until, perhaps, 2010, when Asia takes over the mantle). The answer is two-fold: AIDS exacerbates the factors associated with crime and civil disorder, and reduces the capacity of police forces and armies to counteract such lawlessness. What sort of adults will these children become?

Tens of millions will watch loved ones around them pass away painfully, share in the generalised clinical depression in their communities, suffer increased hunger as care-givers fall too sick to farm, stay home to work in gardens, see teachers die and miss their childhood. They will pine for love and protection, and never soak up the socialising lore of their cultural history.

They may hear about a rich world where AIDS has been controlled, they will wonder if it is true that drugs exist that could have helped their parents, and they will continue to see the lifestyles of their richer peers flaunted in their faces. If they do decide that social structures, governments and laws have not helped them, and set out to help themselves, through crime and prostitution, or by joining the burgeoning ranks of rebel militias largely composed of children, who will stop them?"[411]

World Vision International is the preferred voice on AIDS/HIV for the Anglican Church worldwide. In complete accord with Colonel Dewar's essentials for the covert approach, public opinion has been expertly influenced in the required direction. We will 'stay tuned' to the heroic entreaties of the UN and will no doubt identify positively with the *"fierce public sentiment."* [412] This combination will then gradually 'convince' the pharmaceutical industry to do the humanitarian thing and let Africa have AZT and other AIDS drugs at 'below cost'. We will then applaud the generosity of these benevolent corporations, seen to be bowing to the pressure. And now, according to Ted Turner, this 'humanitarian aid' operation will be 'reassuringly' overseen by WHO and the full might of the US military.

With NSSM 200 a live agenda, and HB 15090 immune-crashing programs being worked on to this day, along with the enormous amounts of money now being invested in gene and vaccine research, the implications for Africa are potentially catastrophic. Who will be able to tell what is being injected into the bloodstream of the African people? How long before we hear CNN telling us *"...despite the best*

---

[411] **Marsh, Nigel** *Potential Security Implications of HIV and AIDS in Africa* at http://www.talesfromthemarshes.co.uk/security_hiv.htm

[412] Carthage, TN NEWS 16th June 1999 *AIDS ACTIVISTS DISRUPT GORE'S PRESIDENTIAL CANDIDACY ANNOUNCEMENT. 15 protestors blew air horns and chanted "Gore is killing Africans. AIDS drugs now!" calling attention to the pivotal role the Vice President has played in preventing HIV positive South Africans from obtaining the drugs they need to survive. "Al Gore's devout loyalty to the drug industry is literally costing millions of lives," said Emily Winkelstein from AIDS Drugs for Africa, the grass-roots activist group that organized today's event.*

efforts of the US army vaccination program, we are witnessing unprecedented numbers succumbing to the deadly HIV"? What statutory agencies will be in place to assure the public these widespread deaths are not the by-product of indiscriminate vaccine research? Will the global viewer be able to differentiate between slow death by pharmaceuticals and those suffering from perfectly treatable malnutrition? Who will carry out the post-mortems? Will there even be any post-mortems?

Concerns over drug efficacy and the HIV=AIDS hypothesis led to requests by President Thabo Mbeki of South Africa to include AIDS dissident scientists in the Durban 2000 conference. This request upset the AIDS establishment, some members even boycotting the event.[413] Meanwhile, in a cynical move to counter growing world attention to Mbeki's concerns over Western policy towards AIDS, the US media announced on 30th April 2000 that President Clinton had formally determined AIDS was now a national security threat.[414] In an unprecedented move, Task Force meetings involving various government-affiliated health agencies took place in the National Security Agency situation room. Those opposing the consensus view on AIDS - the AIDS dissidents - have now been deemed a threat to US national security. The US National Security Agency, acting on a 'report' from the National Intelligence Council, has moved to put the control of AIDS 'health' under military intelligence command (CIA/NSA). As a result we can expect that CIA action against dissidents will intensify and become a priority, since dissidents, by direct implication, are now a threat to US national security.

James Wolfensohn

Negative propaganda campaigns against sources of true information about AIDS/HIV have been ongoing for some time. In its regular 'winners and losers' column, *Time* magazine has described Thabo Mbeki as a loser - *"ignoring the weight of science by insisting HIV may not cause AIDS."* The winning column opposite features

---

[413] *Newsweek*, "Flirting with Strange Ideas", 17th April 2000
[414] *Washington Post*, 29th April 2000

World Bank chief James Wolfensohn, who glowingly *"promises unlimited money to fight AIDS in developing countries."* [415]

The following is just one of several outwardly benevolent announcements delivered by the global power-brokers.

*"**WHO Boss Makes AIDS Pledge** - The new director-general of the World Health Organisation says he will provide three million HIV and AIDS patients in poor countries with key anti-retroviral drugs within two years. On his first day in office, Dr Jong-Wook Lee, a tuberculosis expert from South Korea, stressed that tackling the HIV pandemic must be the WHO's top priority. He said that supplying the latest anti-retroviral drugs for HIV positive people in Africa was a realistic goal."* [416]

And this from UN AIDS spokesman Stephen Lewis:

"It's time for one of the major countries, in particular one of the G7 countries, to announce the manufacture and export of generic drugs to Africa," he said, referring to generic cheap copies of drugs. "I would wish it to be my country, Canada, but it really doesn't matter which." Acknowledging that the approach was "somewhat unorthodox," he added: "If the WHO is going to boost treatment in Africa, they will need a fast, reliable, scientifically sound flow of generic drugs in order to keep the prices low at $250-$300 per person per year." Lewis said there was an urgent need to adopt his proposal because 42 million people are infected with HIV worldwide with 29.4 million of them in Africa. Lewis said because of the high costs, only one percent of four million Africans who need the ARVs to fight AIDS receive them. [417]

With generic AIDS drugs now set to flood Africa, the public has, of course, witnessed the required spectacle of pharmaceutical companies giving way to demands that Africans manufacture their own drugs. The

---

[415] *Time* Magazine, 1st May, 2000. On the same page as the 'Mbeki loser' column, World Trade Organization chief Michael Moore is quoted as saying, *"Blaming the World Bank for poverty is a bit like blaming the Red Cross for starting World Wars 1 and 2."*

[416] BBC News, Monday 23rd July 2003 at http://news.bbc.co.uk/2/hi/health/3084455.stm

[417] Reuters News Desk, *UN Africa AIDS Boss Asks G7 for Special Drugs Deal*, 25th September 2003

following information is included here to underline the vital nature of the information contained in this book.

In the week beginning 13th December 2004, National Institutes of Health AIDS researcher Dr Jonathan Fishbein publicly spilled the beans on the head of the NIH's AIDS division, Dr Edmund Tramont, revealing that Tramont had been concealing evidence of drug toxicity and fatalities in African drug trials.[418]

Documents obtained by the *Associated Press* show that Tramont censored the reporting of thousands of toxic reactions and at least 14 deaths in the ongoing Nevirapine study in Uganda. Nevirapine is the key component of George W Bush's $500 million donation to get AIDS drugs to Africa. And this is why South African President Thabo Mbeki has been accusing Nevirapine manufacturer Boehringer Ingelheim and other drug companies of using Africans as 'guinea pigs' - justifiable accusations which, naturally, drew intense vilification from the mainstream media.

Most shameful of all, perhaps, is that the gruesome facts on Nevirapine have been known since 2000, when the FDA put a label on the outside packaging, warning of the drug's ability to cause fatal liver damage and bloody rupturing of the skin. BI had originally aimed the drug at pregnant and supposedly HIV-positive women in the US, but its toxicities were so great, the company withdrew it from the FDA approval process. Then BI did what all AIDS drug manufacturers do with their 'off-cuts' - it dumped the drug into the foreign market as an AIDS medication.

The hushed-up BI Nevirapine study conducted in Uganda by a Dr Guay has so far resulted in the deaths of thirty-eight babies. Sixteen babies died on Nevirapine and twenty-two on AZT. It is estimated that Dr Fishbein's outing of internal Boehringer-Ingelheim documents have added at least 16 more deaths, mostly in the Nevirapine group. And these are just the deaths we know about so far.

---

[418] **Scheff, Liam**, "The Truth About Nevirapine", 20th December 2004 at
http://www.gnn.tv/articles/article.php?id=1011

On Friday 17th December 2004, the NIH fired Dr Fishbein, the whistleblower who exposed Dr Tramont. Furthermore, the NIH is currently recruiting patients in Africa, India, Brazil, the US and Puerto Rico for further Nevirapine trials.[419]

Does any more need to be said? What began as politicised medical error has now developed into a convenient conduit for delivering highly toxic drugs to nations that do not need them - populations that will most certainly suffer by not having their correct needs met. Many people will needlessly die as they are denied the simple treatments for their environmentally-induced illnesses, taking only the much-promoted, toxic pills to 'combat HIV'.

The World Bank's web-page commitment is to strive towards 'the eradication of poverty'.[420] The facts indicate that what we are witnessing is an ongoing eradication of populations.

WILLARD: *"Part of me was afraid of what I would find and what I would do when I got to Kurtz. I knew the risks, or imagined I knew. But the thing I felt the most, much stronger than fear, was the desire to confront him.... Everything I saw told me that Kurtz has gone insane."*

---

419 Ibid.
420 www.worldbank.org

206

Through a complex series of interlocking companies and devious corporate name changes, the Rockefellers were able to use men like **Walter Teagle**, president of Rockefeller Standard Oil, to hold stock in drug giant IG Farben to mask their involvement with the German drug corporation. Teagle would later tell a Securities and Exchange Commission investigation he had no idea who actually owned a block of 500,000 shares in IG Chemie, a subsidiary of Farben, that had been issued in his name

John D Rockefeller Sr., hated for his ruthless business practices, spared no effort to improve his public image. At public gatherings, he would often give away shiny dimes to young children on the advice of his public relations advisors.

Members of the G8 - possibly the most powerful, visible group in Europe. These are the men who are deciding the finer details of Africa's mass vaccination program. Writing in the 13th January 2005 UK *Times*, health correspondent Helen Rumbelow confirms the plan is coming together as expected. *"In Dar es Salaam, UK Chancellor Gordon Brown unveiled a plan for putting a stop to the 'pandemic' that would form the crowning glory of Britain's presidency of the G8. "These [vaccine] proposals will save six million lives," said Gordon Brown. An 'advance purchase scheme' would make a vaccine accessible to Africa by committing huge sums to buy the first 300 million vaccine courses to be given free to the needy on the continent."*

DEPARTMENT OF DEFENSE APPROPRIATIONS FOR 1970

HEARINGS

BEFORE A

SUBCOMMITTEE OF THE
COMMITTEE ON APPROPRIATIONS
HOUSE OF REPRESENTATIVES

NINETY-FIRST CONGRESS

FIRST SESSION

SUBCOMMITTEE ON DEPARTMENT OF DEFENSE APPROPRIATIONS

GEORGE H. MAHON, Texas, *Chairman*

ROBERT L. F. SIKES, Florida
JAMIE L. WHITTEN, Mississippi
GEORGE W. ANDREWS, Alabama
DANIEL J. FLOOD, Pennsylvania
JOHN M. SLACK, West Virginia
JOSEPH P. ADDABBO, New York
FRANK E. EVANS, Colorado [1]

GLENARD P. LIPSCOMB, California
WILLIAM E. MINSHALL, Ohio
JOHN J. RHODES, Arizona
GLENN R. DAVIS, Wisconsin

R. L. MICHAELS, RALPH PRESTON, JOHN GARRITY, PETER MURPHY, ROBERT NICHOLAS, AND ROBERT FOSTER, *Staff Assistants*

[1] Temporarily assigned.

PART 6

Budget and Financial Management
Budget for Secretarial Activities
Chemical and Biological Warfare
Defense Installations and Procurement
Defense Intelligence Agency
Safeguard Ballistic Missile Defense System
Testimony of Adm. Hyman G. Rickover
Testimony of Members of Congress and Other
Individuals and Organizations_____

Printed for the use of the Committee on Appropriations

The infamous **HB 15090** sparked many rumours that this was
the document that unleashed AIDS. In spite of the provocative
wording though, known immuno-suppressant drugs pre-dated
this committee meeting by some years

agents that we have ever considered. So, we have to believe they are probably working in the same areas.

SYNTHETIC BIOLOGICAL AGENTS

There are two things about the biological agent field I would like to mention. One is the possibility of technological surprise. Molecular biology is a field that is advancing very rapidly, and eminent biologists believe that within a period of 5 to 10 years it would be possible to produce a synthetic biological agent, an agent that does not naturally exist and for which no natural immunity could have been acquired.

Mr. SIKES. Are we doing any work in that field?

Dr. MACARTHUR. We are not.

Mr. SIKES. Why not? Lack of money or lack of interest?

Dr. MACARTHUR. Certainly not lack of interest.

Mr. SIKES. Would you provide for our records information on what would be required, what the advantages of such a program would be, the time and the cost involved?

Dr. MACARTHUR. We will be very happy to.

(The information follows:)

The dramatic progress being made in the field of molecular biology led us to investigate the relevance of this field of science to biological warfare. A small group of experts considered this matter and provided the following observations:

1. All biological agents up to the present time are representatives of naturally occurring disease, and are thus known by scientists throughout the world. They are easily available to qualified scientists for research, either for offensive or defensive purposes.

2. Within the next 5 to 10 years, it would probably be possible to make a new infective microorganism which could differ in certain important aspects from any known disease-causing organisms. Most important of these is that it might be refractory to the immunological and therapeutic processes upon which we depend to maintain our relative freedom from infectious disease.

3. A research program to explore the feasibility of this could be completed in approximately 5 years at a total cost of $10 million.

4. It would be very difficult to establish such a program. Molecular biology is a relatively new science. There are not many highly competent scientists in the field, almost all are in university laboratories, and they are generally adequately supported from sources other than DOD. However, it was considered possible to initiate an adequate program through the National Academy of Sciences-National Research Council (NAS-NRC).

The matter was discussed with the NAS-NRC, and tentative plans were made to initiate the program. However, decreasing funds in CB, growing criticism of the CB program, and our reluctance to involve the NAS-NRC in such a controversial endeavor have led us to postpone it for the past 2 years.

It is a highly controversial issue, and there are many who believe such research should not be undertaken lest it lead to yet another method of massive killing of large populations. On the other hand, without the sure scientific knowledge that such a weapon is possible, and an understanding of the ways it could be done, there is little that can be done to devise defensive measures. Should an enemy develop it there is little doubt that this is an important area of potential military technological inferiority in which there is no adequate research program.

CROSS-COUNTRY SHIPMENT OF LETHAL AGENTS

Mr. SIKES. Now, let's talk about shipments. There has been a great deal of discussion—most of it hostile—about the proposal to ship certain stocks of nerve gas across country for transporting to a deep

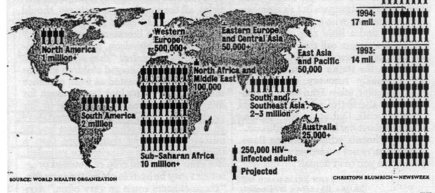

The Demographics of Death

Since the mid-1970s, HIV has infected more than 17 million people, most of them in Africa. With the epidemic now exploding in Asia, experts say the number of infections worldwide will exceed 40 million by the year 2000.

Western Europe 500,000+

Eastern Europe and Central Asia 50,000+

North America 1 million+

North Africa and Middle East 100,000

East Asia and Pacific 50,000

South America 2 million

South and Southeast Asia 2-3 million

Australia 25,000+

Sub-Saharan Africa 10 million+

250,000 HIV-infected adults

Projected

1994: 17 mill.

1993: 14 mill.

SOURCE: WORLD HEALTH ORGANIZATION

CHRISTOPH BLUMRICH—NEWSWEEK

AUGUST 22, 1994   NEWSWEEK **37**

Promoting the HIV Product – Articles and write-ups such as this *Newsweek* feature serve to reinforce in the public's mind the concept of an unstoppable global AIDS plague. This in turn compels populations and their governments to allow huge resources (and even extra funds raised through tax increases) to be allocated to global UN agencies in order to combat this supposed threat to world health.

CNN media giant **Ted Turner** is an outspoken advocate of population control, having donated millions of dollars towards élitist aims.

Henry Kissinger – Architect of peace or a man espousing a more sinister agenda?

WHO THEN IS KURTZ?

In her book *Positively False*, Joan Shenton recounts the battle she fought to get acceptable media and TV coverage for her work on exposing the fraudulence of the AIDS industry. After the screening of *The AIDS Catch*, an exposé on AIDS, the production team soon found itself having to sit before the Broadcasting Complaints Commission for 'misleading' the viewers on a number of accounts, not least the hazards of AZT. Despite Joan Shenton's team having in its hands the Wellcome AZT trial results - trials funded and supervised entirely by Wellcome - the Shenton team was judged to have been unfair to Wellcome on three of four counts, the predominant count being the misrepresentation of established views.[421]

Joan Shenton's team was pressing in on the 'restricted area'. It had ventured into Kurtz's territory.

Jeremy Paxman, influential writer and bulldog interviewer of the BBC, has written one book in particular that demonstrates his understanding of this 'restricted' area. Entitled *A Higher Form of Killing*, this book was co-written by Robert Harris and contains a detailed account of the history of biological warfare. It is regarded by many as the definitive 'behind the scenes' guide to the many covert operations carried out by various governments world-wide, and includes details of what is probably the first US biowarfare operation, namely the US government's winter distribution of deliberately infected smallpox blankets across various Indian reservations.[422] Paxman's undoubted intellectual ability, and his track record of tough questioning (winning him 'Interviewer of the Year'), made him the ideal candidate in the public's eyes to grill the richest man on the planet, Microsoft multi-billionaire William Gates III.

---

[421] Shenton, Joan, op. cit.

[422] **Paxman, Jeremy & Robert Harris** *A Higher Form of Killing*, Hill and Wang, 1982. Documents numerous accounts of bio-warfare operations. *"This definitive bio-warfare study stands as a testimony of man's inhumanity to man. Required reading for everyone interested in protecting our planet from this biologic 'higher form of killing.'* **Cantwell, Alan** *Queer Blood*, Aries Rising Press, 1994

At the time of writing, Gates does not walk the corridors of 'perceived' power, he roams the 'restricted' zone of CFR, World Bank, IMF, Rockefeller, Ford, Chase, Time, Turner's CNN and Bilderberg - *real* power. These areas are not unfamiliar to Paxman. So, it was with much anticipation that cognisant viewers waited for the much-billed 'Paxman-Gates' showdown.[423]

Viewers were treated to nothing further than a pleasant discussion on electrical hobbies, early life, family memories and other non-event questions. Not even the superficially important questions such as software market-share wheeling and dealing were approached with any vigour. Exactly the same thing happened when earlier in the year, Paxman's 'Start the Week' was guested by none other than Henry Kissinger. Admittedly his time on air was short, but yet again we were treated to a meandering discussion about inconsequential matters. Kissinger also roams freely in the 'restricted' areas. The receiver of several peace awards, Kissinger co-ordinated not only NSSM 200, but also HB 15090 and numerous other population-control directives.[424]

Little of this information would have been outside the realm of Paxman's knowledge or understanding. Whilst Paxman is to be congratulated for documenting high level corruption in the biowarfare arms race, Credence Publications attempted to contact Mr Paxman several times, specifically to discuss the possibility of him having been directed by 'rich men behind the scenes', with regard to the Gates and Kissinger interviews. To date there has been no satisfactory reply from Mr Paxman on these matters.[425]

---

423 BBC2 8:00pm, Sunday, 17th October 1999

424 Paxman, Jeremy, op. cit. See also **Preston, W** *The Real Treason*, Covert Action Information Bulletin #25 1986. William Preston, Professor of History at John Jay College, New York, and Ellen Ray were chief administrators for the Fund for Open Information and Accountability Inc., and were frequent contributors to the Covert Action Information Bulletin. Kissinger played an important recruitment role in Project 63 – to secure the employment in the US of certain German and Austrian WW2 scientists, specialising in rocketry and biological warfare. By altering, hiding and/or destroying evidence of human atrocities, US officials were able to subvert judicial proceedings and bring the specialists out of Nazi Germany, (via the 'Rat Line'), men including V1 & V2 rocket scientist Wernher von Braun, Traubb, Klaus Barbie, Josef Mengele, Blome and Schreiber. Chief among the many inhumane experiments carried out were direct injections into the eyes for eye-colour experimentation, removal of limbs with and without anaesthetic, and Mengele's infamous 'twins' experiments. Stangl, chief of Treblinka camp, escaped down the 'Rat Line', and later worked in Latin America for Volkswagen, as did Adolf Eichmann for Mercedes Benz. **Farago, L** *Aftermath*, New York: Avon, 1975

425 After asking Mr Paxman repeatedly if he could please reply to our simple question, Credence

Jeremy Paxman had ample opportunity to confront Kurtz. In this instance, however, why was it that a long way up-river, our less-than-intrepid BBC bulldog committed the cardinal sin, abandoned his public, and clambered out of the boat?

Never leave the boat.

Anatole Kaletsky, associate editor of *Times Newspapers*, is a frequenter of the inner circle of power and has himself attended Bilderberg meetings. Credence wrote to him, asking him why his newspaper never reports on these meetings. After all, in these meetings are gathered the most influential, newsworthy people on the planet. Kaletsky replied:

"There are lots of meetings going on all over the world all the time between all kinds of people. Most of them are of no interest whatsoever to our readers. In any case, what people say to each other in private meetings is up to them." [426]

Until his recent, public disgrace for certain financial irregularities, Conrad Black (now Lord Black) was chairman at *Telegraph* Newspapers and had attended Bilderberg meetings. Upon requesting further information, the following reply was received from *Telegraph* corporate relations department:

"In reply to your query regarding our chairman Conrad Black being a member of the Bilderberg group: The meetings are held in complete privacy with no accompanying staff or media present. The sessions are entirely expressions of opinion and have no executive consequences. It would be totally inappropriate for the Telegraph titles to report on these confidential meetings, and would contradict the purpose of the Bilderberg Group, which is to encourage international relations and problem resolution in a completely 'safe' environment away from public scrutiny and the media. It would also violate the undertaking of those who attend to maintain discretion, thus to encourage the frankness and spontaneity of the discussion." [427]

Publications eventually received an email on 18th February 2000 containing a single word - "No."

[426] Credence correspondence, 31st January 2000

[427] Credence correspondence, 8th February 2000

The information contained in *The Truth About HIV* highlights the paucity of the above statements and especially those two lines *"of no interest whatsoever to our readers"* and *"of no executive consequence."* Of course, the content of these meetings is of interest to the reader, and, of course, decisions made at these meetings have immediate and direct, executive consequences. Rather, it is the utterly unsavoury nature of some of the items up for discussion on the Bilderberg agenda which demands discretion and *"a completely safe environment away from public scrutiny"*. If these meetings are geared towards global problem-solving, why not publicise the outcome of these important discussions? The replies from both Kaletsky and *Telegraph Newspapers* serve only to reveal the double-standards that prevail in the editorial departments of our revered British broadsheet newspapers. Their replies also mirror Swinton's definition of the 'fawning, intellectual prostitute, owned and in the pockets of the rich men behind the scenes'.

We like to think that here in the West, we engage in free debate over the major contentious issues. Unfortunately, this is rarely the case. Limitations to the extent and reach of important debate are almost always controlled, the appearance of the debate however exuding depth and expansive content. To set the limitations to a debate such as the AIDS controversy, certain methods are employed by those who feed us our 'news' to keep us within 'safe' debating boundaries. And judging by the current level of debate, in both the media and amongst leading liberated, 'dissident' AIDS thinkers, the debate often *appears* to be far-reaching, but unwittingly or otherwise, is quite safely limited.

The art of orchestrating and then assisting in the continuance of limited debate in 'free' society is admirably described here by Noam Chomsky, American linguist and US media and foreign policy critic. He states:

> *"The smart way to keep people passive and obedient is strictly to limit the spectrum of acceptable opinion, but allow very lively debate within that spectrum - even encourage the more critical and dissident views. That gives people the sense that there's free-thinking going on, while all the time the presuppositions of the system are being reinforced by the limits put on the range of the debate."*

In the context of the AIDS debate, nowhere is this ploy more apparent than in the *"Did HIV originate from the early administration of the polio vaccine, or through other such covert anti-human experiments?"* discussion. We all gasp at the horror of it all (and yes, the activities discussed are generally horrific). And by focussing 'in a lively way' upon *"that nasty WHO and related agencies, with their grubby Sub-Saharan HIV-spreading vaccine programs"*, the loftier HIV/AIDS debaters really do believe they are getting to grips with the nub of it all. In actual fact, nothing could be further from the truth.

All that is really taking place in this 'free-thinking' arena is the subliminal reinforcement of the notion that HIV does indeed exist. This feat is achieved primarily through the occasional appearance of 'no-holds-barred', centre-spread exposures of activities that in actual fact are not that unknown anyway. Allowing this type of debate is quite safe. It bypasses the need to address the key issues such as 'does HIV exist', the pharmaceutical links to the media, the poisonous drugs, the population control agenda or other such 'unsafe' subjects. The only thing achieved by these shock-horror AIDS exposés is that they play straight into the hands of those same powerful AIDS agencies, in whose direct interests it is to continue the lucrative 'search' for the $multi-billion, HIV antidote.

The final, all-important, central questions remain: With the truth about AIDS now 'out of the bag', will our newspaper editors demonstrate the necessary will to break the mould? Using the vast media resources at their disposal, will these 'shapers of public attitude' now help firmly to establish the truth about AIDS and HIV in the public domain? Will they stand for truth and honest debate?

Who then is Kurtz?

Kurtz is Western apathy. Kurtz is corporate, vested interest and 'rich men behind the scenes'. Kurtz is compromise. Kurtz is *"...you have kids all over the place."* Kurtz is turning a blind eye or *"hiding under a pile of blankets and hoping it all goes away."* Kurtz can masquerade as an angel of light.[428] Kurtz's reign will continue wherever

---

[428] 2 Corinthians 11:14

211

and whenever even the genuinely motivated aid-worker propagates the lie. [429]

WILLARD: I felt I knew one or two things about Kurtz that weren't in the dossier.

And what of Durban 2000? What of the International AIDS conferences 2001, 2002, 2003 and Bangkok 2004?

WILLARD: This was the end of the river alright.... hundreds of miles up a river that snaked through the war like a main circuit cable and plugged straight into Kurtz. At first, I thought they handed me the wrong dossier. I couldn't believe they wanted this man dead. Third generation West Point, top of his class, Korea, Airborne... About a thousand decorations. He was being groomed for one of the top slots of the corporation. General, Chief of Staff, anything...

The gathering so respectable... WHO, UN, USAID, UNFPA, UNDP, IMF, World Bank, Rothschild/Rockefeller/Ford Foundation, Bilderberg, Time Inc., Turner, CNN and other associates...

CONRAD: We glided past, secretly appalled, as sane men before an enthusiastic outbreak in a madhouse... No, they were not inhuman. Well, you know, that was the worst of it - this suspicion of their not being inhuman. It would come slowly to one. They howled and leaped, and spun; but what thrilled you was just the thought of their wild humanity - like yours - the thought of your remote kinship with this wild and passionate uproar.

And Kurtz?

"His covering had fallen off, and his body emerged from it, pitiful and appalling. I could see the cage of his ribs all astir, the bones of his arms waving...an animated image of death carved out of old ivory... I saw him open his mouth wide – it gave him a weirdly voracious

---

[429] This calls for a major reassessment of genuine aid agency work and the supporting corporate literature, particularly those well-intentioned and people-focused NGOs and church programs.

aspect, as though he had wanted to swallow all the air, all the earth and all the men before him.[430] *His was an impenetrable darkness."*[431]

*****

It has been a harrowing journey to Kurtz's compound. There's a Bible verse that says, *"My people die through lack of knowledge."*[432] If ever there was a syndrome that had the capacity to wreak so high a death toll through lack of knowledge, that accolade must go to AIDS. But it is to the infamous HIV that we must award the ultimate prize – the trophy given for the most complete and convincing global pharmaceutical health fraud ever to have been perpetrated on trusting humankind. The killer virus that never was.

But with knowledge comes power; power to reverse mindsets, circumstances and situations. We remind the reader that both Conrad and Willard witnessed the demise of the mighty Kurtz.

Lies are the ally of Kurtz.

Truth is his conquering enemy.

---

[430] Isaiah 14:13-16
[431] Conrad, Joseph, op. cit.
[432] Hosea 4:6, New International Bible

Part 3

ENDING AIDS

SOME CONQUERORS

"The greatest darkness cannot extinguish the radiating
light of even the smallest candle." (anon)

And now for the good news! Let us remind ourselves that lies are conquered by truth. What better way can there be to introduce the beginning of the end of AIDS than by reading the tremendous testimonies of those individuals who are alive and well in spite of their diagnosis. These are the stories of people who have come out or are coming out from under the curse of the myth of HIV.

Details for the following testimonies are on file with Credence Publications and associated organisations. Please contact us at Credence Publications if you have a genuine enquiry, or if you have a testimony too you would like to share.

"I had my positive diagnosis in 1987. In setting up the Long Term Survivors Network, I have been challenged on using the term 'survivor', the argument being that if the HIV test is not an indication of future ill-health then we haven't survived, as we had nothing to survive. I would dispute that, for we have survived an assault on the very basic human spirit; ostracism from society, poisoning of the mind by fear, attempts to control our sexual and reproductive needs as well as pressure to take toxic and experimental drugs. No mean feat! The point is, it's a possibility we may not be survivors of HIV, but we are survivors in life. We should not forget that alongside the questions around HIV and the dilemmas and decisions we make, we are dealing with other things that life throws at any of us." **Claire W**.

"When I tested positive in 1988, I was told I had only three years to live. Twelve years later, I'm doing just fine. I have never taken any AIDS drugs, even though they were suggested and even pushed. In 1996, I got married – five years after I was supposed to be dead. I'm very much alive and healthy and wish people would listen to me and other people like me for a change. Ignorance is the real epidemic." **Michele M.**

"I've known over 200 people who died of so-called AIDS. Every one of them had sufficient drug abuse or medical terrorism to account for their immune suppression. When I was told in 1988 that I was HIV positive and had about two years to live, it came as a complete shock to me because I did not have a history of what was considered high-risk behaviour. By 1992, I had learned enough to convince me that AIDS was the greatest medical error of all time. As I write this, it has been eleven years since I first got tested. I've never developed any AIDS-defining illnesses. In fact I've never had a cold in nineteen years. I ride a bike, I take no medications and no treatments – just good food and ten minutes a day exercise for the immune system. I thank God I was smart enough to 'just say no' to the doctors, so it didn't cost me my health. If anything, as a result of what I've learned, I'm healthier today than I have ever been." **Ed L.**

"I tested positive in 1989 and have been living in wellness without the meds [medications] for ten years - something that still shocks people, even though I've always been just fine. After watching my friends get sick and die on AIDS drug therapies, I decided that HIV drugs are poison and you can't poison yourself back to health. I learned to do nothing for HIV. Instead, I focus on being healthy." **Kim F.**

"In 1989, my husband Philip and I were tested HIV positive. We couldn't believe that two people like us, nice people from nice families, were having to deal first-hand with AIDS. The doctor provided Philip with experimental drugs six months to a year before they were available to the public. At least ten times the doctor told me that Philip would not pull through whatever infection he was going through. Ten times I went through the fear, heartache and panic that I was losing my husband.

Six years after being told he had just months to live, Philip died in my arms. When I was told it was my turn to take the drugs, I realised I had to make the most important decision of my life. In desperation, I called Christine Maggiore. I asked Christine to give me just the scientific information and nothing else. No stories, no emotional hype, only the facts. I had to go to her office several times to read because I became so distraught that I couldn't continue for more than fifteen minutes.

Everything I was reading described and explained what I had been through with my husband. My worst fears were being confirmed - the

218

drugs had made my husband suffer tremendously and had eventually killed him. I started attending 'Alive and Well' events... ultimately deciding that AIDS drugs were not for me. I decided to trust my own life. Believing in health is the first step to creating a healthy life. Holding onto the possibility of health is everything." **Cynthia R.**

"I tested positive in 1990 and nine years later I am healthy and medication-free. When I was first told I was positive, I went through the standard terror with my life flashing before my eyes. I followed my doctor's orders for treatment with AZT. After a year of feeling sick, I listened to my inner voice and quit AZT. Except for a brief foray into ddI, I've been off meds ever since. I have three recommendations for anyone who tests positive - education, education and education about all aspects and points of view on HIV and AIDS." **Erik D.**

"What I find hardest is living with the stigma of HIV. I'm young, healthy, intelligent and very well educated on HIV and AIDS. Yet I am isolated by the fear and ignorance surrounding a condition I don't even believe in. Being a leader rather than a follower can be lonely and difficult. Maintaining a stance against the majority of the human population is a trying task. I don't have the time to educate everyone, even if they were interested. When I do tell others about what I know, they are so convinced that HIV=AIDS=Death, that they think I am doomed and that my optimism is merely fear or hope or both.

I do have hope. I hope that people will look deeper and listen more. That they will demand to be treated as precious beings more important than politics, money and abstract theory. It takes people like us to be the first and the most determined. Life goes on. Choose to be part of it." **Dean W.**

"I was required by law to take an HIV test in June 1995. The test is mandatory in Colorado for pregnant women, and I was expecting my second child. I was shocked when the result came back positive, because I'd been married and monogamous for nine years.

I started taking AZT in my fifth month. After ten months on AZT, I was sick all the time. I had constant diarrhoea, nausea, fever, night sweats and was totally exhausted. I was crawling to the bathroom and vomiting for hours. My doctor told me the HIV was making me ill, and that the virus had mutated into a form that was resistant to AZT. Further drugs turned my skin yellow with jaundice. Since it was clear that the drugs weren't keeping me from getting AIDS and were actually destroying my liver, I let my prescription run out. I figured I'd rather die from AIDS than liver failure.

Almost immediately after I stopped taking my medicines, within a matter of days I started to feel much better.... My daughter is considered a success by medical standards because she tests negative(!), but I don't care about HIV anymore. I am concerned about the effects of the AZT she was poisoned with while I was pregnant. Rachel has an enlarged cranium, seizures and a strange deformity near the base of her spine. At age three she still does not speak. I went to this conference on HIV and pregnancy at The Children's Hospital here in Denver. A lot of mothers there had taken AZT during pregnancy and had their kids with them. Every single one of those kids had enlarged craniums. Their heads looked exactly like Rachel's. They're all AZT babies. I'm working now to repeal Colorado's mandatory [HIV] testing law." **Kris C.**

"In those days, the late eighties, the media pressure was unbearable. I had used heroin for more than two years between 1979 and 1982, so I knew I was at risk. I still remember the dreadful feelings I had, seeing and hearing the TV press campaigns. They pictured tombs, blood and zombie faces, with frightening headlines like "AIDS KILLS... DON'T DIE OF IGNORANCE."

In February 1988, I finally summed up the courage to go and be tested for the AIDS virus. I waited nervously in the infectious diseases clinic. I can still remember the doctors' sad faces as they told me I was HIV positive and that I shouldn't think to get pregnant until more research on the issue brought better news. The world fell in on me. Having successfully fought drug use six years previously, the future looked hopeless. According to the impression I had been given, I had at best another five years....

I had met my husband in 1992 and, after we got married in 1994, we started to think about having a child. The doctors tried hard to discourage me from the idea of conceiving. I was disturbed by their conviction that it would be advisable to take AZT during pregnancy, to have a caesarean section and to refrain from breast-feeding. I took AZT for one month only before stopping.

I gave birth to a wonderful, bouncy, baby girl. My daughter had her first HIV test when still in hospital, and then when she was three and six months old. The tests were all positive. I resisted the intense pressure to administer AZT to her. The last test was done when she was one year old, which was negative. I have decided not to go for any more ritual blood tests. What's the point if I am convinced there is a gross error at the very base of HIV theory? Meanwhile, I hope to remain as healthy as I am, enjoying my life together with Michael and our daughter." **Monica G.**

To Robin Keene, SCHNS,
Communicable Disease Supervisor,
Manatee County Health Department
3ʳᵈ June 1999

Dear Ms Keene,

Please accept my resignation from employment with the Health Department. After months of struggle and extensive research, I regret I can no longer fulfil the Public Health mandate requirements of my position in good conscience.

Upon careful investigation, it is woefully apparent that a grand schism has existed in AIDS since Robert Gallo's politically charged announcement to the world that HIV is the probable cause of AIDS. Unfortunately, only one side of the scientific data has been made readily available to the general public. This side is far more powerful, backed by the financial storehouses of federal government agencies like the CDC and the NIH, who fund most public information campaigns and research programs. This dominant science is promoted and even manipulated by pharmaceutical giants who have an obvious profit motive. Aided by a willing media, the Public Health Service has all but silenced contrary scientific opinions and thus denied the people their fundamental right to informed consent.

I hereby withdraw my participation in what may one day be seen as the greatest violation of the principle of informed consent in the history of Public Health.

Most sincerely,
Mark Pierpoint
HIV/AIDS Prevention Program Co-ordinator.

(Celia Farber writes: *"I tracked Pierpoint down, mainly to ensure that he was for real and not some magical dream I was having. Sure enough, he answered his phone, literally while packing his stuff over at the Manatee Health Department.*

"I'm not the only one in here with serious questions about all this," he said. *"We all talk about it, and I can tell you there are several more who may follow me."*) [433]

On May 1, 1992, at the age of twenty-nine, I was given five to seven years to live by an HIV specialist. I had been solicited for the test when I went to a health clinic for an entirely different reason. At first I was suicidal, but then I sat about preparing myself for an excruciatingly painful early demise and made ALL my decisions based on the fact I was 'HIV-positive' and doomed to die of AIDS.

Over the next ten years, I experienced excellent health and prospered in my business. I married a man who said he did not believe I had HIV or that I would die of AIDS. He said he loved me enough to assist with euthanasia if it came to that, and I felt I owed him my life for his understanding and support.

I supported this man financially and lived my life for him. Feeling I had nothing to live for anyway, I gave him everything he wanted. Unfortunately, all he really wanted was my money. He was incapable of having a loving relationship, and my attempts at creating one with him were met with violence. I endured abuse of every kind, all the while having feelings of guilt for possibly exposing him to HIV. I believed this was the best I could expect and would have sacrificed anything to have this one person in my life who didn't believe I was going to die of AIDS.

Eventually I learned how not to get beaten up, but there was no intimacy in our marriage, only my giving and him taking. After nearly ten years of that, and in light of my continued good health, I decided I could divorce him, even if it meant I would have to face AIDS on my own. Something had always seemed wrong with the diagnosis anyway. I wasn't certain, of course, but there were unanswered questions in the back of my mind: "How did I catch this?" "Why am I always so healthy?" "Why are antibodies bad?"

One month after I filed for divorce, a man entered my home at 1:40 in the morning and crushed my skull with a 5-pound steel rod while I lay sleeping. When I opened my eyes, he said, "Your husband wants

433 **Farber, Celia,** *A Crack in the Wall, Impressions* Magazine, 5th July 1999

you f****ed and killed, and I'm just gonna kill you." He continued to strangle me and eventually damaged most of the bones in my face. But then he stopped and cried: "I can't do this.... I'm not a murderer.... Why does your husband want you dead?" My husband stood to inherit about half a million dollars upon my death.

The man who attacked me went to jail convicted by a jury of premeditated, attempted first-degree murder, but my ex-husband was never charged. I made a full recovery, except for a barely visible scar above my right temple. I even escaped a brain surgery some of the doctors wanted to perform. I was granted an emergency divorce a month after the attack.

It's now nearly thirteen years after my 'diagnosis', and I've had barely a sniffle in the meantime. I've never taken any anti-AIDS medicines. Despite my excellent health, the same HIV specialist still insists I'm infected with a contagious, lethal virus and that I've put myself at risk having unprotected sex.

When I decided to see the specialist one last time just three months ago, asking her to change my 'diagnosis', begging her actually for my life, she refused and wanted to put me on medication; yet she pronounced me in excellent, physical health. I showed her HIV test kit inserts from the tests she gave me that state they are not to be used for diagnosis or confirmation, that positive test results should be 'confirmed', that they should not be used as the sole basis for the diagnosis of HIV. She patronizingly explained the testing procedure to me, knowing full well that I completely understood it already, and then stated, "I've done everything I'm supposed to do." She promised to send me a documented study that proves heterosexual transmission of HIV, but no study ever came in the mail.

That's because as far as I can tell, no such study exists. I've asked everyone for it. I've posted it on the Internet and I've asked doctors and scientists and I've searched everywhere I can think to look. No one seems to have the study. It's just assumed one must have contracted the virus through heterosexual contact in the absence of any other risk factors.

My life has been totally altered because someone doesn't want to admit they were mistaken. Even though I have no fear of AIDS now, I still must live with the stigma of a diagnosis people go to jail for if they have sex. I can't get disability, life or health insurance; and of course, there's absolutely no chance of ever having a normal dating relationship. I'm forty-two years old, single, and childless because I didn't want to have to take AZT or have a C-section. No one wants to hire, train and promote an HIV-positive person. There is a long list of things I used to take for granted as my rights that I no longer have.

So I have filed a court case against the makers of the HIV tests used to 'diagnose' me. The case is barely underway at this time. The disclaimers the manufacturers put in their kit inserts to protect them are no good under the laws of the State of Kansas if they don't make certain the person buying the test actually knows the disclaimers exist. Well, I didn't know about those disclaimers, and it was pretty difficult to get my hands on them after I heard about them. I'm asking the court not to allow this to continue to happen to people.

I urge everyone never to take an HIV test. No one knows what they mean, and even the manufacturers state they don't know how accurate the tests are in 'low-risk' populations. After nearly three years of constant study, I'm convinced that HIV=AIDS=Death will turn out to be the biggest snake-oil-remedy scam to which mankind has ever fallen prey. Just follow the money.

Kim Marie Bannon - www.kimbannon.com

"As a child of the sixties' sexual revolution I participated in the craziness like everyone else. Sex was freely available, and was 'de rigeur' for all sexual persuasions. When the 'great epidemic' arrived from the US in the early eighties we were all told to be terrified, and that many would die.

Well many did, and nearly all of my gay friends of that time are now gone. All of them accepted the HIV=AIDS paradigm as promoted by the American AIDS industry. Fortunately, I was sceptical enough not to believe in this lethal virus. When I finally tested 'positive' after already two negatives, I resolutely kept away from all conventional AIDS doctoring. I observed that my immune system remained intact and I had no health problems at all that I couldn't cope with myself.

I took a job as an 'HIV Educator' with our major government organisation in New South Wales, Australia, generously funded also by drug companies. On my own initiative I discovered the *Reappraising AIDS* team in the US and *Continuum* in the UK, confirming that my intuition was right. Upon informing my 'AIDS education' employer of my suspicions I was quickly relieved of my post.

Seventeen years later in the year 2000, in the wake of hundreds of deaths of my friends, I enjoy exceedingly good health, and remain AIDS drug- and AIDS doctor-free. But I am eternally frustrated by the continued ignorant and misleading reports in all the media about the ongoing expansion and fear of this 'world epidemic'. May this book help to educate." - **Paul B.**

"When I first came across this book, suggesting that AIDS was not the threat that it was supposed to be, I was very sceptical. I had heard nothing but the most serious of warnings and dreadful stories of people suffering from AIDS. However, when I started reading *The Truth About HIV*, I was shocked that I had been so taken in, and for so long, by so many misleading 'facts'. What used to be a confusing issue for me has now become rather too clear. It is vitally important that everyone should hear about the contents of this book, so the truth can be exposed. I will not hesitate to give a copy to anyone who is considering taking an HIV test, or who is suffering from 'AIDS'. As everyone's Dad says: "Don't believe everything you read in the papers." **Simon H.**

"To my shame I have absorbed and relayed facts and figures about the 'AIDS pandemic', and not asked fundamental questions such as, 'does the Human Immunodeficiency Virus exist?' and 'where have they got the African nations' fatality rates from?' I assumed they came from test results. *The Truth About HIV* has stirred me to find out the truth for myself and given me a sharper focus as I work amongst British teenagers in sexual health education. As a response I recognise my need for increased compassion, integrity, righteousness and strength to confront these huge financial and power strongholds. Thank you for your research and provocation." **Rachel M.**

I do not claim to know what really causes AIDS, but I do have knowledge of scientific procedures. I studied under Nobel Laureate A. Butenandt at the school of medicine in Munich and earned a Ph.D in chemistry from SUNY at Stony Brook (recognized as one of the top five research universities in the US). My highest rank in academia was associate professor, and I did my share of publishing. When a scientist believes he/she has found the cause of a major disease like AIDS, the facts are written up in a scientific paper and submitted to a corresponding journal for publication. The editors for the journal review the paper and then send it out to have the work peer-reviewed by fellow scientists. Only when the peer reviews are favourable is the work finally published and the hypothesis is (most likely) accepted as proven.

As a matter of fact, none of these scientific procedures was followed with the hypothesis that HIV is the sole cause of AIDS. The HIV=AIDS hypothesis was never peer-reviewed and never published, merely proclaimed at a Washington press conference in 1984. With $50 billion spent on it, there are zero applicable results, such as treatments or vaccines that return AIDS patients to health. Even more serious are the scientifically well-documented claims by the AIDS dissenters, namely that HIV is a relatively harmless passenger virus [if it exists at all] and that it's the AIDS drugs (AZT and others) given to HIV-positive people that destroy the immune system and thus induce AIDS.

Fact: Healthy HIV-positive people (non drug-users), who are given the AIDS drug AZT, soon get sick and show the AIDS-defining diseases. When those people stop taking AZT, they become healthy again. In the light of these facts, doesn't it suggest that those health authorities, who blacklist these AIDS researchers rather than do research to prove or disprove their claims, ARE HIGHLY IRRESPONSIBLE, ALLOWING WHAT COULD BE THE MEDICAL SCANDAL OF THE MILLENNIUM TO HAPPEN? **Hans Kugler, PhD.**

"When I was tested positive, my doctor told me I was exceptionally healthy, that I was fortunate to have detected the condition early, but that there was nothing I could do to prevent devastating disease and eventual death from AIDS. He warned me against wasting money on vitamins and other foolish attempts to save my immune system, advising me that I simply wait to become sick and then take AZT....

Life came to a grinding halt. I bought a wedding ring to ward off potential suitors. A year or so into my diagnosis, I found a caring doctor who urged me to take another test. Further testing produced a positive followed by a negative and another positive. In my search for more information, I became more and more convinced that AIDS research had jumped on a bandwagon that was headed in the wrong direction. In the seven years since receiving my death sentence, I have gone from frightened victim to AIDS activist to HIV dissident to spokesperson for new views about HIV and AIDS. Although my HIV status has been decidedly positive for the last five years, I enjoy abundant good health and live without pharmaceutical treatments or fear of AIDS. My book 'What if Everything You Thought You Knew About AIDS was Wrong?' is now in its fourth print, with editions in Spanish, Portuguese and Italian, and even a bootleg version in French. In 1996 I met a wonderful man I plan to marry as soon as I take a day off. Robin and I have a beautiful healthy little boy aged two, our miraculous little Charles Dexter. Between them, they fill my days with so much love, joy and laundry! **Christine Maggiore**

Open Letter to the World Health Organization No.14

From: Dr Michael Mulugheta
PO Box 4221
Asmara, Eritrea,
Africa
Tel/Fax 291-1-641-323

After having worked as a tropical doctor in Malawi, I returned to the Netherlands at the end of 1988. I worked in Malawi for 3 years in a mission hospital where I was the only doctor. My duties included, among other things, surgical and gynaecological operations, especially caesarean sections.

AIDS was at that time about 4 years old and the issue was 'hot'. Six months after my return, I developed a urinary tract infection and decided to take antibiotics. To avoid what we call the 'ping-pong' phenomenon, I gave the same regimen also to my wife. Seven days after the start of therapy, I developed partial deafness. Over the next several months, both of us subsequently (but only temporarily) developed an array of illnesses with an astounding similarity to those

227

attributed to HIV. Because of my worries of the possible infection with HIV, I suggested an ELISA test for myself. I turned 'strongly' positive on ELISA. An Amsterdam specialist, Dr Meenhorst, ordered a confirmatory Western Blot test. He told me I had antibodies against HIV. I started asking him questions.

Not satisfied, I went to the Tropical Institute in Antwerp, Belgium. The head of that institute was Professor Peter Piot, the current director of the World Health Organization's (WHO) Global Program on AIDS (GPA). He prescribed AZT and other drugs for me to take immediately. Had I followed his advice, I would have long been in my grave by now. His personal prescriptions are still in my possession.

Next stop was the University of Hamburg, Germany. Professor H G Thiele did the same as the others before. He falsified on the instructions from Netherlands and Germany. I don't want to dwell on my experiences in more than 10 countries - there is a book on this matter being prepared.

For trying to disprove AIDS scientifically, my doctors declared me insane and threw me out of my job. When I insisted to seek the truth through disseminating their conspiracy to the rest of the world, they even resorted to physical harassment. I crossed Europe many times, covering 40,000 kilometres, wrote to more than 40 universities, research centres, medical journals, and in so doing spent over $40,000. I appealed to the European Commission for Human Rights in Strasbourg, France, but they gave me no heed. I staged a hunger strike at the International Court of Justice in The Hague, Netherlands, but they gave me a deaf ear also.

I appealed to the Ministers of Justice of five European countries where the doctors live, but there was no response from any one of them. I sent copies of documentation to many medical journals, such as *Nature, Lancet, New England Journal of Medicine, Journal of the American Medical Association, Scandinavian Journal of Medicine,* etc., and got no positive response. The *Lancet* editors wrote to tell me that I *'write a very good tale'*. Finally, I filed an action against the Dutch doctors at the National Commission of Complaints on Medical Malpractice, but they didn't want to listen to my complaints. Worst of all, they kept me in suspense for two years, and finally discarded my complaints as 'unfounded' without listening to my arguments or reviewing the documentation.

On 22nd February 1991, having tried all possible options, I paid a visit to the WHO offices in Geneva, Switzerland to air my complaints. For trying to present my documentation and arguments to the WHO, Professor Peter Piot advised a Dr Dorothy Blake of the GPA to have Swiss police take me away to jail. I then knew there was no justice in Europe, especially when the offenders are white and high in social status, and the victim a black man.

When all attempts to uncover the truth failed, and my very existence and that of my family was in danger, I fled the country (Netherlands) where I had lived for around 15 years as a political refugee and went to Eritrea. Now that I live in the relative safety of a country I can call my own, I am writing again to unravel the scandalous acts of these European doctors.

Ladies and gentlemen, if my wife and I have never employed the condom or any other mechanisms of the so-called 'protection' and yet are alive and thriving after more than 10 years, where is the HIV? We are still robust and energetic and fit to compile this report.

* * * * *

"Lots of thanks! I have read *The Truth About HIV*, and my comment is this: Your work clearly reveals the depths of man's inhumanity to man. Like William Golding's *'Lord of the Flies'*, we are the children marooned on the Island of Fraud. HIV is the 'Beast' and we are waiting for a sign from 'the grown-ups' (Robert Gallo et al), but all we can see is our loved ones poisoned and dying. As for myself and for those who will listen, I will do all I can to unmask this beast. And despite my limited capacity, I will spend the rest of my life challenging the most unbelievable fraud of our modern times, the fraud of HIV. May God bless you." **Peter Kasule**

"In 1985, I decided to take the test. I tested positive. Since I had heard and read that the virus could be dormant for a long time, I opted to eat well, exercise, take high quality vitamins and limit 'risky sex'. However, my gut feeling was that something wasn't adding up with

AIDS, and I almost immediately chose not to accept the virus as detrimental to my health. To this day I have never been hospitalised, and have not taken any of the drugs that are supposed to control or eradicate HIV." **C.J.**

"My friends started to die in 1982. Ann was the first to go. We used to 'shoot up' together. My room-mate Diane tested positive and moved in with her lover, Julie. I moved into a squat. I was shooting dope or coke every hour and I weighed about 90 pounds. My friends were all dying around me and I knew if I didn't take charge of my life, I'd join them.

I kicked coke, ate well and renovated my self-esteem. Diane's condition worsened. She ate her AZT and gave up the ghost. Had I followed my doctor's advice to take AZT, I wouldn't be writing this - I'd be dead. I know now that my low T-cell count was because of my depression, and my depression was as a result of my diagnosis.

I now no longer believe the prophecy of doom. I consider myself cured, and I haven't had to spend a dime. I'm as healthy as a horse, have lots of energy and look ten years younger than I am. But don't be envious. I've been through hell and back. I'll continue to fight for a reappraisal of the HIV hypothesis as long as I live. I only wish that Ann, Diane and Julie were still here to fight with me." **Frank G.**

"I attribute my wellness to refusing doctor's orders, listening to my body and practising a pretty good diet. Love and support from the family helps too." **J.P.**

"In May 1998, I found out I was pregnant with my first child. I received a frantic phone call from my doctor informing me I had been tested HIV positive. I had no idea I had even been tested. My husband also tested positive. Nothing seemed to add up - we have been together many years, we are completely monogamous and exceptionally healthy.

I was told to take AZT for the remainder of the pregnancy, and my husband was told to take the cocktails. These should have been the darkest days of my life, but as serendipity would have it, there was a copy of *What if Everything You Thought You Knew About AIDS Was*

Wrong? sitting on our bookshelf. I read it, contacted Christine Maggiore and HEAL and with their help, began an immediate plan of action that included leaving my doctor of seven years in order to elude the HIV police.

The result is a healthy, happy, breast-fed baby girl. Our family leads a totally normal life, normal except for the fear that we could have our daughter taken away from us because of the choices we'd made regarding our health. The only sense we have discovered is in the data that shows that most of the ideas we all have about AIDS are wrong." **Stacey A.**

"Dear Sirs, I have just finished reading your book, and I must tell you that I am quite impressed. I would not have thought before that the ideas expressed in your book could be realistic. After 22 years in senior scientific marketing positions of international research pharmaceutical companies, I am now living in South Africa, and at the forefront of the AIDS discussion.

As a matter of fact, I was approached by a German Microbiology Professor, who has developed an immune barrier system for use during sexual intercourse. He asked me to help him with finding sponsors for his systems. Via personal contacts, I approached several companies, including Boehringer Ingelheim, Bristol Meyers-Squibb, Roche, MSD, SmithKline Beecham and others in South Africa, checking their interest in marketing such products. From all companies I received a negative response. There is no interest in the 'prevention' of AIDS. The companies are allocating research money only to their 'treatment' programs. After reading your book, I believe I understand their motives! With best regards." **Karl J. Stahl, PhD.Org.Chem.**

"I've been positive for sixteen years. In 1996, I came down with pneumonia, one of the hallmark AIDS diseases, and I began taking the cocktails. I felt my body was falling apart, not from the HIV, but from the drugs. I was always very aware of my body, and I could feel I was putting poison into it. I finally went to my doctors and told them I didn't want to take the drugs anymore. They called me a fool. They were very dramatic and told me it was suicide to stop. So instead of stopping I went onto a new combination of drugs. My speech was slurred and I kept losing my equilibrium. When I fell down a flight of stairs, that was the last straw. I stopped taking them. Two years after quitting the treatment, I feel better than ever." **Steven G.**

The Real 'Third World' War. I would like to thank Steven Ransom and Phillip Day for their book *The Truth About HIV*, in which they expose probably the greatest deception of our lifetime - the myth of HIV=AIDS. Initially, the book challenged my belief-system in the human condition, but in coming to terms with the substantiative evidence presented by highly qualified dissidents in this specialised field, I was left appalled. AIDS is where greed, opportunity and racism collide in a cynical, global, political network. It is genocide. WE have to be a voice of reason and TRUTH. I speak firstly as a human being, and then as a South African, where we as a people are being auctioned off to the pharmaceutical giants, and at the same time, gagged by poverty and debt. Stop and expose them. **Emily, London**

"Reading your book, *The Truth About HIV* was like a breath of fresh, mountain air. I have been an AIDS dissenter since 1991 and have experienced the complete denial by elected officials, other bureaucrats, and my friends and family, who can't seem to break their romance with the medical/pharmaceutical establishment. Your thorough work puts into easy-to-understand language a subject matter that others have so far made quite complicated, which has resulted in lay people not having much understanding or interest in the AIDS debate.

People who read this book should be prepared to be shunned by the denizens of ignorance, greed, and nobility who will chastise and condemn you for your 'foolishness' and 'audacity'. But truth sets you free - and you get an extra helping in this book! Thank you, Steven and Phillip, for an outstanding effort and let the AIDS bastions of lies, deceit, and murders begin their much-welcomed demise." **Bill Bissell, 'AIDS truth' campaigner and former substance abuse centre manager**

"I was diagnosed HIV+ more than 3 years ago and since then, I have felt that I have been on a journey towards hell. Tests, clinic appointments, doctors, more tests, depression, fear of getting ill, fear of death, are only some of the factors that almost drove me to insanity. It is very difficult for me to translate into words what I have felt for the past 3 years. Nobody told me that the hepatitis vaccination could cause an HIV-positive response.

In truth I was just waiting for AIDS to come and get me. Every simple illness (flu, fever, etc.) made me believe that this was the beginning of the onset of AIDS. I spend several months crying like a child. I lost my sense of humour, my spontaneity towards other people, and I built a wall around me to protect myself from the external world to cover the shame.

Eventually, a good friend of mine told me about a book called *The Truth About HIV*. It took 4 months to find the courage to buy it. Indeed, since my diagnosis I never found the courage to read anything related to HIV-AIDS, because I knew it could have discouraged and depressed me.

Thank God *The Truth About HIV* was a completely different book. For the first time, clear and honest information about HIV and AIDS was available for the public to access. I read the book in one sitting. By the time I had finished, I felt confused, and angry and disappointed in the media, the government and the scientists. How could they allow such a lie to exist? How can money ever be more important than human life?

Just reading the book made me feel completely different. I felt I had a new life; I felt I had been born again. I immediately became conscious of my eating habits and introduced minerals, vitamins, antioxidants into my diet. I chose not to waste any more time going to the clinic and getting my blood checked out. I chose to live!! Some of my friends did not agree with my choice (although they offered support), but they were relieved to see me happy and energetic. One of them told me: "I have never seen you so... well!!" And indeed I am. I am well and healthy and I have every intention of being so for many years to come. Thank you for giving my life back." **Vincenzo M, London**

"I have taken responsibility for my own life and have not allowed someone in a white coat to do it for me. Had I chosen the path they offered me, I know I would be dead. I'm a survivor because someone had the guts to tell me the truth about the HIV=AIDS=Death lie. It's bad science in the hands of bad government." **Scott Z.**

"Recently, we alerted you to the case of Baby Garfield, an 18-month-old boy from New York caught up in the system of mandatory, newborn HIV screening recently initiated in that state. After allegedly testing positive at birth (the actual test was missing from his medical

233

records) and following a series of inconsistent lab work and other questionable tests and recommendations, his mother sought a second opinion about the AIDS drug treatments prescribed for her healthy son.

A few days later, under orders from the department of social services, Baby Garfield was taken from his home by seven police officers. He was placed in foster care and put on an aggressive regimen of mandatory medication. His parents were allowed to see their child only one hour a week while awaiting a hearing to establish long-term arrangements for his custody.

When the parents found our organization Alive & Well, Garfield had been in a foster home for more than a month and the custody hearing was just a few weeks away. In record time, helped by your donations and good wishes, we pulled together a legal defense team led by Alive & Well's pro bono attorney Denis Sheils of Philadelphia. Although Denis is one of the best and busiest attorneys in the country, he gave his time, including weekends, to the effort to return Baby Garfield to his parents.

A coincidental interview with a national news program brought myself and my family to New York for the custody hearing. I am happy to report that the day after the hearing, Garfield was back in his mother's arms. The victory was resounding as the state has decided not to appeal the judge's decision. Outside the courtroom, after a round of hugs and tears of relief, I shared your e-mail messages with the family. It was a great honor to present them with all the good wishes and promises of donations from across the country and around the world. Help and concern came from as far away as Australia, Canada, England, and Iceland. Thank you!" **Christine Maggiore**

"Thank you for your information. Many people in South Africa and around the world have become aware of the conflicting debates around the issue of HIV/AIDS. What many people do not realise is that the contention that HIV may not cause AIDS is a lifeline for many people who have been given the death sentence (HIV-positive status).

From being depressed and sitting and waiting for death, they get hope that maybe *"I am not going to die from AIDS. Maybe I could go back to school, then maybe I could have children, and maybe I could live my life as though I am going to live to see my retirement."* This in itself brings life and productivity back to the sick person and we all benefit; the patient himself, the children who now have a healthy

234

parent, and the economy which now has a productive person.

I do not know what the answer is for those people who have been diagnosed as HIV-positive or who have AIDS. But from what I have read of AZT and other associated drugs, this is clearly not the answer. I hope in time the suspense will be lifted and the real truth about AIDS will be known and accepted for the benefit of all mankind. May God save us all from the world of capitalism; where dog eats dog and human beings eat each other alive just for the sake of worldly profits. Please keep me on your mailing list and keep the information coming. Thank you." **N.B., South Africa**

"Boy, am I glad this is coming out in the open. The press has to bear much responsibility in the dissemination of the AIDS panic. Please continue to report on new interpretations of the situation." **M.Schulgasser, USA**

"Dear Phillip, having just read your publications regarding Cancer and AIDS sufferers, I felt compelled to write to you in order to corroborate the authenticity and accuracy of your writings. I read through the articles with the greatest of sadness, as my own family has been touched with the tragedy of losing a loved one, perhaps unnecessarily, to a disease that has become a fashion statement for the various governments to be associated with. In my opinion, AIDS is a disease that brings millions of pounds of profit to the drug companies, all the while contributing to the suffering and ultimate death of its victims. Let me tell you why I believe this.

I had a young brother who was gay. He was a trained district nurse, fully conversant with the dangers associated with his lifestyle. He lived quietly with his long term partner for many years, but became diagnosed as 'HIV positive' after being accidentally jabbed with a needle whilst treating a patient.

Like most medically trained people, he trusted his peers when they advised him to take AZT in order to preserve his immune system. My brother was demonstrating no symptoms of AIDS when he commenced AZT. Little did he realise that AZT would ultimately cause the onset of the very diseases he was trying to avoid; opportunistic diseases that would kill him at just 44.

These AZT tablets were inordinately difficult for my brother to swallow and, in the first instance, produced ulcers all down his oesophagus, making it impossible for him to eat. An ordinary mouth ulcer is painful enough, but when you consider an open wound over two inches across in your throat, the pain must have been unbearable. Eventually, after several bouts of increasingly severe pneumonia, during which he was continuously hooked up to an antibiotic machine, he began to waste away, his weight falling from seventeen stone (238lbs) to five stone (70lbs).

His muscle tissue ceased working and became flabby, until he couldn't walk at all, eventually succumbing to terrible pains that racked his body. He was then prescribed amitriptyline as an antidepressant, which did no good whatsoever, all the time taking these awful AZT tablets. Merciful release only came with the morphine, addling his once-alert brain, until he could fight no more. Finally his heart just stopped and my brother died.

Other patients in St. Mary's Hospital, where my brother was admitted, refused to take AZT AND LIVED ON INDEFINITELY, in spite of the HIV diagnosis they were given. It is my opinion that AZT killed my brother, not 'AIDS'. Please accept my best wishes for your excellent book, which I feel sure will save many lives that would otherwise be lost." **Frank R.**

"I feel I perpetuated AIDS. I stood in front of Harvard Medical Center and demanded the release of ddI and ddC. I wonder how many people I harmed with my AIDS activism. And I'm really trying to figure out what my life has been devoted to. I feel we need to get to the bottom of this and put an end to the madness." - **Michael B.**

William's Senseless Act: "In 1990, I was diagnosed HIV positive after a short bout of pneumonia. I come from a wealthy Los Angeles family and the news devastated my parents. We all decided to keep quiet about what was the matter with me because my father was a successful and high-profile professional who strongly disapproved of my gay lifestyle. He was expecting a directorship of the entertainment company for which he worked and I don't think he needed the hassle.

I was advised by the clinic's doctors immediately to start anti-viral treatment with AZT in order to halt the spread of the HIV. My pneumonia had cleared up prior to taking the meds but I began to get a constant buzzing and ringing in my head, night sweats, assorted fungal infections and appalling body odor.

Right around Christmas of 1990, I was getting extremely sick. A friend gave me a private paper written by British researcher Phillip Day on the fraudulence of the HIV=AIDS connection and the dangers associated with AZT. At first I dismissed it. There was a lot of hype going around in those days about AIDS being a government germ warfare project, etc. etc. But I was curious. I did some more hunting and talked with other gays in the West Hollywood community. Two of them were quite up-front. They told me those who were taking the drugs (either clinical or recreational) were dying, while those who cleaned up their lifestyles, ate nutritiously and slept well were remaining symptomless.

I managed to track down Phillip, who was living in Los Angeles at that time. We met and talked. He took me through the information and answered all my questions, but told me the ultimate decision to quit my medication was down to me, not my doctors. I think mentally that had to be one of the most difficult decisions I had to make in my life. It was harder because I was considering going against the advice of some of the most brilliant minds in medicine on the West Coast.

Long story short, I decided to stop the meds and I actually flushed them down the toilet. When I later told my doctor what I had done with the drugs I'd bought, he got angry and said it was a 'senseless act'. Anyway, senseless or not, I can trace my recovery from that special day, and that was ten years ago, nine years more than that doctor gave me. I gained my weight back, my various problems checked themselves out and today I am older and wiser - angry and still confused about why this happened to me and why this insanity is allowed to continue. But the upside to this whole story? I am now in the very best condition of my life." – **William S.**

There are many more such testimonies and the number will only increase as the truth about AIDS and HIV spreads exponentially into the populations. If you have a story to tell, please write in confidence to us at Credence Publications, or email us at testimonies@credence.org and, if it is your wish, your testimony may well find its way onto our pages of conquerors.

FREQUENTLY ASKED QUESTIONS

Q: What exactly is AIDS?

A: AIDS is an acronym for Acquired Immune Deficiency Syndrome and is an umbrella term to describe a range of existing diseases, known to mankind, that afflict the patient as a result of immune suppression or immune system damage. That this immune damage is caused as a result of infection by a virus known as the Human Immunodeficiency Virus (HIV) has not only never been proven, the alleged virus has never even been isolated, its genetic material mapped and its proteins identified – the usual protocol for establishing the existence of a new viral micro-organism. Interestingly, Stefan Lanka states that the term AIDS is actually misleading. *"AIDS is an energy deficiency problem. The term 'AIDS' is absolutely misleading because it has nothing to do with immune defect or immune deficiency. 'AEDS' or Acquired Energy Deficiency Syndrome has a rational basis and can be treated."*434 This would seem to make sense, the deficiencies arising as a result of outside destructive toxins and/or lack of input of the necessary energy resources, and not as a result of initial immune system defects or a virus known as HIV.

Q: Why exactly can HIV NOT be the cause of AIDS?

A: Firstly, as mentioned, *HIV has never been isolated by any scientifically recognised procedure, its supposed presence has only been inferred.* Elements of blood detritus are sometimes called 'HIV'. Cells commonly occurring in placentas are called HIV. Secondly, for HIV to be the sole cause of AIDS (a hypothesis taught and accepted as fact by the medical establishment and thus by most of the public), HIV would have to occur in every case of AIDS. It doesn't. Thirdly, if HIV is the infective agent, it should proliferate and be easily detectable in patients suffering from AIDS in the final stages of their life (ie, when the opportunistic diseases are at their most rampant). But HIV cannot be traced in these patients, only inferred by a bewildering series of dubious markers. Fourthly, AIDS does not satisfy Koch's Postulates as an infectious syndrome, it does not satisfy Farr's Law as an infectious syndrome – these are two of medicine's most basic benchmarks for

---

434 *Zenger*, December 1998

identifying viral pathogens and infectious disease. Fifthly, AIDS does not behave like an infectious disease AT ALL. It hasn't spread equally into both sexes, it is still almost exclusively restricted to its original risk groups.[435] Viral epidemics are said to spread exponentially into the population, producing indiscriminate infection in men, women and children. AIDS hasn't done this, and the expected AIDS holocaust has of course failed to materialise.

Q: So is there actually such a thing as AIDS?

A: Yes, albeit an incorrect definition. In the early 1980s, certain victims began being identified with immune system damage. They went on to die from opportunistic infections that took advantage of their damaged immune system. The problems began when this 'new' syndrome was declared viral in nature, when there was no evidence to support this theory.

Q: So what causes AIDS?

A: All the evidence points to AIDS in the West being a syndrome of immune deficiency brought on by long-term exposure to recreational and pharmaceutical toxins and other immuno-suppressive behaviour. This being the case, It is no coincidence that AIDS appeared when it did. The late 1960s saw the start of the new global drug culture and the gay liberation movement. Part of this new, hedonistic lifestyle necessitated a chronic consumption of hard and soft recreational drugs, antibiotics, nitrite inhalants, promiscuous sex (risking STD infections and parasites), very little sleep, poor diet and constant alcohol abuse. This is the first time in history that this type of lifestyle has become prevalent and given the tacit endorsement of governments anxious to attract the powerful gay vote.[436]

---

[435] Cases where AIDS apparently affects heterosexuals can almost always be attributed to an HIV-positive diagnosis, after which the patient is prescribed AIDS drugs prior to exhibiting any symptoms at all. In many cases, these drugs themselves bring on the very symptoms of 'AIDS'. In the US, AIDS tests can be mandatory for couples getting married. An inadvertent positive test can result in a perfectly healthy individual being prescribed AZT or similar.

[436] During the 1993 Gay March on Washington, attended by 300,000 homosexuals, lesbians, transvestites and transsexuals, participants lobbied for a change in the 1964 Civil Rights Act, championed by Martin Luther King Jr three decades before, for the protection of black people. For the first time in American history, a gay and lesbian inaugural ball was held to celebrate a president's entry into the White House. During the ball, President Clinton, via video, thanked the gay and lesbian community for their support, and financial contributions to his successful campaign, declaring to them, *"I have a vision and you're part of it."* (*Gay Rights, Special Rights*, a video documentary, Jeremiah Films, PO Box 1710, Hemet, CA 92546 USA)

239

Sexual revellers and intravenous drug users over a period of time appear to have damaged their immune systems either reversibly or irreversibly with these lifestyles. It is interesting to note that deaths were occurring in the 1960s that looked remarkably like AIDS – wasting brought on by malnutrition, malabsorption of food, chronic diarrhoea, pneumonias, etc. These deaths were always as a result of chronic, long-term drug abuse or other immuno-suppressant behaviour and were understood clearly by the medical establishment at the time to be so caused. It is worth remembering that prior to Robert Gallo's 'AIDS as virus' announcement, the immune deficiency cases cropping up in San Francisco, Los Angeles and other gay metropolitan areas in the early 1980s were widely accepted to be caused by an excessive and drug-fuelled lifestyle – not a virus, sexually transmitted or otherwise.

Today the leading cause of AIDS in the Western world is believed by many to be the AIDS drugs themselves. Shocking though this might be to contemplate, AIDS is by no means the first syndrome where this has happened (see section entitled *Entrenched Scientific Error*). Recreational drugs and excessive lifestyles though still play a large part as, like pharmaceutical drugs, they are toxic by nature (foreign to the biological experience of the human organism) and so, by default, increase the toxic load on the subject. And then, of course, you can 'have AIDS' just by being presumptively diagnosed, being identified by medical science as belonging to a 'high risk group' or by having a low T-cell count. In this way, patients are often diagnosed as 'having AIDS' long before they have exhibited any immune deficiency diseases and are then prescribed the drugs which later fulfil the AIDS death prophecy.

The plain fact is, you do not need HIV to explain the phenomenon of Western AIDS. Erroneously administered AIDS-causing pharmaceutical treatments, as a result of submitting to an imprecise antibody test, poor diet and an excessive lifestyle all fit the criteria of Western AIDS to the letter. As we have already examined, it is malnutrition, poverty, polluted water supplies, and a whole host of pre-existing illnesses that equally account for AIDS in Africa and in any other nations deprived of the bare necessities for healthy living.

Q: Isn't putting out the message that AIDS is NOT spread sexually sending a dangerous message to those who have previously been practising 'safe sex'?

A: A good question, and one that is often used to counter any dissident views on HIV. We come back however to the central point: No evidence has ever been produced to demonstrate that AIDS is spread sexually, either through an HIV or any other medium. This has nothing to do with the issue of an individual routinely practising safe sex to protect themselves from other sexually transmitted infections. If HIV were transmitted sexually, we would definitely see a proliferation of infection spreading equally into both sexes and the rate of transmission increasing exponentially. As already reviewed, the predicted AIDS holocaust never materialised. Not only that, AIDS has remained almost exclusively within its declared risk groups for almost twenty-five years. This is absolutely not typical of an infectious, viral syndrome. Also, if you are going to declare AS FACT that HIV is being spread sexually, and that one virus is causing 29 disparate AIDS-defining diseases (no small undertaking), then you actually have to come up with this virus. Also, you have to demonstrate that this causal micro-organism can be identified in all cases of AIDS. A dedicated and unique viral agent has never been proven to exist that can directly or otherwise account for over two dozen of these supposed HIV=AIDS indicator diseases.

So, are we advocating a dangerous message here? Are we implicitly condoning liberal sexual practices as a result of the information we describe in this book? Absolutely not. We are recommending an end to toxic and extreme lifestyles that, over the long term, are creating cumulative toxicity within the body that is causing immune damage. The social issues of homosexuality, as society sees them, are not under discussion here and are not the focus of this book.

Q: You mentioned that over 100,000 papers have been written on HIV. How can so many people all be wrong about AIDS?

A: The first reaction of many members of the public when they hear a challenge to the HIV=AIDS hypothesis is usually one of disbelief. *"Everyone believes that HIV causes AIDS!"* First of all, not everyone believes it. Many well-qualified doctors and biochemists hold dissident positions on the HIV=AIDS issue. Secondly, even if everyone did believe HIV=AIDS, would that still make it FACT? Majority opinion is meaningless in an argument. All too frequently the majority can be wrong.

Public misconceptions arise when the medical opposition to a disease becomes centrally managed and a central hypothesis is accepted, for a wide variety of reasons, to guide the subsequent research. This state of affairs, although appearing at first to be a streamlined and efficient way forward, has one disastrous side-effect. It shuts out dissident views challenging the central hypothesis - a challenge which in the past has often performed the role of a check and balance system, exposing fraud, mismanagement and entrenched error.

Most people involved with AIDS have no access firsthand to the research, and so they go along with whatever scientific papers have already been published on the subject. They assume the experts know what they are talking about. It is also worth noting that peer pressure and fear of losing their grants or jobs has compelled many a professional to ignore science's fundamental laws to accommodate the establishment's view of AIDS.

This is by no means the only time this has happened in history! Consider that scurvy, beri-beri, and other metabolic diseases for a long time were viewed as infectious. Neurosyphilis, SMON and others were later found out to be conditions caused by the very medications prescribed to 'cure' them. With AIDS then, we are certainly not in virgin territory ground when it comes to widespread, catastrophic medical error.

Q: If AIDS is still inside its risk groups, what about those babies who are born with AIDS?
A: Firstly, you must ask yourself, "How are these babies being diagnosed with AIDS?" The answer is, if their mothers have been diagnosed with 'AIDS', the babies are given an HIV test which may turn up positive. Medical science interprets this positive result to mean that the baby is carrying HIV given to it by its mother. In reality, a positive ELISA is doing nothing more than highlighting the presence of antibodies in the baby's blood and therefore demonstrating that its immune system is functioning normally. HIV has never been isolated

and no antibody is specific to any one disease, so the test is not recognising HIV either directly or through antibody identification.

Now, the baby may be carrying a high toxic load if mum has been, for example, taking heroin and fast-tracking in the lead-up to birth. The baby may also inherit its mother's yeast or fungal overgrowths in the birth canal that can stir up immune system problems, especially if the infant is given a hepatitis B shot at birth (many are). So if we are right and the baby is suffering toxicity problems inherited from its toxic mother, then we should see these babies getting better once they are physically free from the mother after birth. And this is indeed what is happening. Babies diagnosed as HIV positive have been found to give an HIV-negative result within eighteen months in 87% of cases without therapeutic intervention.[437] The tragedy is, these little ones are often still treated with drugs and subsequently killed. [438]

The phenomenon of positive babies testing negative later is not supposed to happen in the AIDS world because HIV is portrayed as a relentless killer from which there is no escape. The facts state otherwise and, in the case of AIDS pediatrics, most definitely there are charges of negligent homicide to answer, perhaps even murder.

Q: Why has the medical establishment fixated so strongly on HIV to the exclusion of other potential causes for AIDS?
A: Because HIV is a huge money-earner and exposing toxic syndromes isn't. That's a harsh statement but a simple one. This question bears closer examination. Drug companies formulate drug 'solutions' to diseases. These drugs are patented by the drug companies and sold for huge profit. Pharmaceutical drugs are huge business. And when their drugs run out of appeal in the West, either because they are out of fashion or have been shown over time to be ineffective or dangerous, manufacturers often palm these leftovers off to Third

---

[437] **Peckham et al**. *Infant Seroconversion Profile*, London 1990. Also New York University Medical Center Pediatric Department, 1990

[438] *Los Angeles Times*, 30th March 1995, reports the child sero-conversion phenomenon. Then adds: *"In the past year, physicians have begun routinely prescribing the anti-HIV drug AZT to HIV-positive women who are pregnant. Studies show that the drug reduces transmission of the virus to the infants by two-thirds."* (p.A22) This, and other studies to do with AZT are funded by the manufacturers of the drug itself, Glaxo-Wellcome. When Credence researchers pressed to be given a copy of this research to investigate, no reply was forthcoming. The attitude was, *"It's just recognised..."*

World governments desperate for supposedly respectable Western medication. (These 'palmed off' medications are often interpreted by onlookers in the West as 'benevolent Third World aid'.)

So, when you have a disease as widely promoted by the media as AIDS, which has been officially classified as viral in cause, the demand created for drug treatments becomes very pronounced. With AIDS, you take a fearsome sounding disease, link it to two of mankind's most potent taboos – sex and death – then put out stories that this is the new bubonic plague which will devastate humanity. Then finish off by telling the public that you own the patent to the only drug treatments available to combat the coming plague and see what happens. Firstly, the share price of your drug company is going to sky-rocket. Secondly, you will be perceived as an authority on the disease because you have a potential answer for it. Thirdly, your company is going to have large sums of grant and research money thrown at it by government to encourage you to develop your drugs faster (for the benefit of humanity).

Alongside these endeavours, the media also plays its part, shaping public opinion to raise even more money and 'awareness' to give further credibility and speed to your work. At all costs, HIV must be seen to exist because HIV is the *vicious*, viral enemy your expensive drugs are being designed to combat. Without HIV, there are no profitable drugs and all funding will cease.

This more than adequately explains the highly charged rhetoric and unreasonable defence of HIV in the face of all the evidence to the contrary. Telling people the simple truth, such as "Don't do drugs!" does not make Mercedes payments. Telling people to clean up their toxic lifestyles and adopt proper nutrition will not please your shareholders. They will not earn out of this advice.

The handling of AIDS from the very beginning was steered in the direction of vested interests and the medical establishment, which originally misdiagnosed AIDS as viral in nature, and has now painted itself into a corner with all the publicity it has propagated. No doubt there are individuals within the AIDS establishment who are now desperately seeking some kind of exit from AIDS dogma before the truth emerges, as truth invariably does. What is holding back a public pronouncement that the medical establishment was so wrong about AIDS and HIV is the realisation that this admission would have catastrophic consequences for certain sections of the medical industry. Who would ever trust medicine again?

Q: Can all AIDS patients be saved by proper nutritional and detoxification procedures?

A. No. In certain cases, excessive drug-taking and immuno-suppressant behaviour have damaged the immune system beyond repair and the patient will eventually die of AIDS-related diseases. However, if drug abuse is viewed like alcohol and tobacco abuse, the model becomes clear. You are not likely to get irreversible lung cancer smoking a couple of cigarettes behind the bicycle sheds. Smoke enough of them over years, though, and you will. With drug abuse, there is no hard and fast point beyond which immune system damage becomes irreversible, only that eventually it will if the abuse continues. Ceasing highly toxic lifestyles and highly toxic 'medicines' can often bring immediate benefit, Professor Peter Duesberg reporting that *"one doctor took eleven of his worsening AIDS patients off AZT. The immune systems of ten immediately rebounded, and several continued improving."* [439]

Immediate cessation of toxic lifestyle and drug abuse (be it recreational or pharmaceutical) is essential. There are no guarantees that a patient will respond to nutritional therapies, but the place to start is by ending the abuse and lifestyle, and then setting forth a responsible program for proper rehabilitation.

Q: What other treatments are beneficial for those who have AIDS?

A: There are things to do, and then there are things NOT to do. Treatment for those manifesting AIDS-related diseases largely depends on the nature of the opportunistic infections afflicting them. Patients should closely examine the treatments offered to them in the light of increasing an already toxic situation. For instance, those manifesting any of the major epithelial cancers would do well to understand that toxic chemotherapy and harmful radiation treatments have no proven track record of extending life and can actually kill the patient before

---

439 Duesberg, Peter H, *Inventing...* op. cit.

the cancer does. Vitamin B17 Metabolic Therapy, on the other hand, is a simple nutritional protocol, outlawed by the medical establishment in many countries, that has been used to great effect in treating all forms of cancer.[440] Immune-deficiency diseases are, of course, a serious matter and qualified health advice should always be sought. But the patient should exercise strict discernment in accepting or rejecting the types of treatments offered to them by traditional medicine in the light of a diagnosis of 'AIDS'.

Symptomless individuals living with an HIV-positive diagnosis should get educated on the issues raised in this book. They might wish to consider moving into a detoxification and full nutrition regimen along the lines detailed in the next section of this book. The important point to remember is to stop the toxic build-up by ending the toxic lifestyle. This is the point where recovery begins.

Q: What do you say to rumours that AIDS was a covert US government project designed to wage war on the undesirable elements of society?
A: Most who have kept an ear open to the conspiracy theories surrounding AIDS will have heard them all: that AIDS came from the green monkey in Africa, that it was a biological warfare agent developed at Fort Detrick, Maryland, that it originated out of the Porton Down research facility in the UK.

The facts surrounding AIDS and HIV necessarily impose a number of restrictions that help us to determine what AIDS is and what it is not. Firstly, AIDS is clearly not viral, so any theories expounding some doomsday virus incubated in the beakers of mad scientists working in secret underground New World Order institutions hold little credibility. Even conspiring globalists are unlikely to unleash an unstoppable virus into a world where they themselves would be placed at risk. And then there is the matter of the accuracy and veracity of virus theory in general. The whole construct of virus theory needs a complete overhaul, as does the current understanding of germ theory. For an enlightening book on this fascinating subject, please read the Credence title, *Wake up to Health in The 21st Century* by Steven Ransom.

---

[440] Day, Phillip, *Cancer: Why We're Still Dying to Know the Truth*, op. cit.

246

In his book, *Emerging Viruses, AIDS and Ebola*,[441] Leonard Horowitz includes references to HIV as perhaps accidentally making its way into the populace as a result of biowarfare tinkering at various labs across the world. At no time does Horowitz spend time researching whether HIV actually exists. His work to uncover governmental corruption notwithstanding, his theories on 'HIV as germ warfare' are yet another example of an incorrect course followed with the maximum of precision.

Did HIV originate in Africa? The question is meaningless. First *find* HIV. Did AIDS originate in Africa? No. AIDS, or immune deficiency, manifests itself wherever there is chronic, long-term self-abuse and/or malnutrition that has been chronicled in world medical literature for centuries. Is there evidence that the authorities know about AIDS as a collection of illnesses brought on by fast-track, toxic lifestyle and/or malnutrition and are deliberately not considering it? Yes. Is there evidence that the authorities know how to save AIDS patients through removing toxicity and/or adding the necessary nutrition and basic medicines, but are not promoting this agenda? Yes. Do the authorities know that AIDS drugs kill adults and babies? Yes. Are there population control programs currently underway which are benefiting from a continued misunderstanding of the true facts about AIDS? To the very great shame of humankind - yes.

Q: A large number of influential Christians in America have been responsible for hyping AIDS as the wrath of God on wicked homosexuals and drug users. Where do you stand on this issue?

A: There is no question that certain powerful Christian platforms leapt on the AIDS bandwagon to promote their own agendas with regard to opposing gay rights and highlighting 'God's judgment on homosexuals'. One example is a famous annual Christian conference held in the Mid-West, organised by several large Christian groups, in which the 'AIDS on a doorknob' idea was given some airing and dark sentiments preached that God was exacting punishment on evildoers through the agency of AIDS.

---

[441] **Horowitz, Leonard** *Emerging Viruses, AIDS and Ebola*, Tetrahedron Publishing, 1998

247

There are also organisations who have used AIDS as a springboard for their own bigotries. It should be clear God is not wreaking havoc on homosexuals with AIDS. If AIDS were divine and exclusive judgment on homosexuals and drug-abusers, then why are only a small proportion of these demographic groups actually affected by the syndrome? Bigotry and AIDS have always gone hand-in-hand. Jesus Christ always taught people righteousness by His loving, non-judgmental actions as well as His words. Yes, the Bible does indeed promote morality and condemns certain behaviour. But just as clearly, the Bible speaks about there being only one Judge...and it isn't us. Our stance at Credence is that all people are equally loved by Jesus, and equally in need of our loving Father's forgiveness and personal mercy.

Q: Where does this information on AIDS leave the AIDS charities (both Christian and secular), as well as those celebrity charity concerts?
A: It was Vance Packard, the author of numerous works on subliminal advertising, who, in his book *Hidden Persuaders*, made the observation that in order to gain that moral/political/philosophical high ground in a given debate, your chances of gaining that ground are improved considerably by pre-empting the opening vocabulary. The work of 'God Bless the Child'[442] is a classic example. Funded by Abbott Laboratories, Bristol-Myers Squibb, Pharmacia & Upjohn and other financially interested parties, 'God Bless the Child' is currently distributing conventional AIDS medications to children in Romania, South Africa and Cambodia. To argue against this 'compassionate' and 'Godly' form of doctoring is seen as divisive and going against the flow of human kindness. In reality those children are being given known toxic medications. The emotive photography means nothing. In cynically using the word 'God' in their campaign, the think-tanks behind organisations such as these adequately fulfil the description of those who 'masquerade as angels of light'.

The Book from which church organisations draw their wisdom in dealing with social and political situations, warns quite clearly about being on guard against deception. The panoramic view of the 'plague of AIDS' looks real. But they have not heeded the warning to be on their guard. As a result, they have fallen for the lie, following the temptress

---

[442] www.iapac.org. The International Association of Physicians in AIDS Care.

248

unquestioningly (Prov 7:17). Genuine belief that AIDS is caused by a terrible virus, combated only by powerful pharmaceuticals, is leading these organisations to promote information that deceives their hearers, leading them *"like a bird, darting into a snare, little knowing it will cost him his life."* (Proverbs 7: 21-23)

METABOLIC PROCEDURES
FOR REVERSING IMMUNE DEFICIENCY

Please note: The following is provided for information purposes only and should not be construed as medical advice. No claims are made or implied in providing the following information. The reader must use his discretion and a qualified medical practitioner always consulted in the matter of serious illness.

A person exhibiting immune suppression will always become the target of opportunistic infections and illnesses. TB, pneumonia, fungal and yeast overgrowths, cancer, lupus, psoriasis, arthritis, sinusitis, Graves, Cushings, Hashimoto's, etc., are some examples. In rectifying extraordinary immune system function, it is first necessary to cease the antagonistic activity (drugs, bad diet, lifestyle, etc.)

Take action♥

If you have been diagnosed with 'HIV infection' or 'AIDS', the following protocol may be beneficial and is used by many nutritional doctors the world over. Please note that conditions diagnosed as AIDS are dangerous and life-threatening. The following regimen should always be followed under advice and supervision of a doctor acquainted with nutritional and detoxification protocols:

- **SUPERVISION:** Hire the services of a medical doctor (MD) or naturopathic physician (ND), trained in nutrition and aware of the AIDS/HIV deception
- **TIP:** Take no further 'AIDS tests'
- **PREVENTION:** Take advice on ceasing the use of AIDS medications, especially so-called 'nucleoside analogues', 'protease inhibitors' and 'DNA chain-terminators'. These are heavily immuno-suppressive and carcinogenic, bringing on the very symptoms of the problem the patient is trying to conquer
- **PREVENTION:** Cease taking ALL recreational drugs, including the sex-stimulant amyl nitrite ('poppers' - known to cause Kaposi's sarcoma). If you have a drug addiction, a

suitable clean-up program should be sought out and rigorously adhered to

- **PREVENTION:** If you are a homosexual, avoid sex and the lifestyle of the 'fast-track' homosexual community. Unprotected sex with multiple partners heightens the chances of contracting genuine, sexually transmitted diseases, such as herpes, gonorrhoea, syphilis, etc., along with the incessant drinking, taking of drugs, the ongoing regimens of antibiotics, not eating properly, etc., problems which themselves will generate antibodies that can be interpreted as AIDS-specific (they are not). Once you have triggered a positive AIDS test, physicians will usually prescribe dangerous cell toxins (AZT or other)

- **DIET: COMMENCE THE ANTI-*CANDIDA* DIETARY REGIMEN** (*see next section*) and alkalise your body's internal environment. Immune suppression thrives on an anaerobic environment which lacks oxygen and becomes a haven for fermentation and the proliferation of bacterial, fungal and yeast overgrowths. Alkali solutions prevent these problems because they attract large amounts of oxygen

- **DIET:** The main part of your diet will be fresh, <u>organic</u> vegetables, pulses, legumes, nuts and seeds <u>eaten raw</u>. A little broiled fish is OK. Juice green vegetables such as kale, cabbage, lettuce, spinach, beans, broccoli for their alkalising, antioxidant properties

- **DIET:** Small meals, consumed five to six times a day to even out blood sugar

- **DIET:** Drink at least four pints (2-3 litres) of clean, still water each day (not out of plastic bottles and avoid distilled water. Reverse osmosis-filtered water is best). Avoid all alcoholic drinks, including beer (which contains sugar, yeast, grains and alcohol)

- **DETOXIFICATION:** Eliminate ALL processed foods, meats, dairy products, sugar, grains, etc. These are often contaminated with chemicals and fungi

- **DETOXIFICATION:** Absolutely cut out sucrose, aspartame, saccharin and high-glycaemic carbohydrate foods (foods that break down rapidly into glucose, such as bread, pastas, potatoes, rice, bakery products). These feed

251

cancers as well as yeast and fungal growths. Also cut out high-glycaemic fruits such as grapes, raspberries, strawberries, mangoes, etc. Apples and pears in moderation (including their seeds) are OK

- **DETOXIFICATION:** Remove all toxic personal care and household products and damage triggers from your environment and lifestyle and replace with safe alternatives (see *The ABC's of Disease* by Phillip Day). Don't smoke and avoid second-hand smoke
- **DETOXIFICATION:** Conduct a two-week bowel cleanse with magnesium oxide (see *Colonics* by Phillip Day). Those with cancer or extraordinary bowel damage should also take advice on colon hydrotherapy for extra internal cleanliness
- **ANTI-PARASITE:** Follow the Anti-*Candida*/Anti-Fungal Supplementation (*see next sections*)
- **ANTI-CANCER:** Take an enzyme supplement away from food. This should contain, but not be limited to, bromelain (from pineapples), papain (papayas), thymus, trypsin, chymotrypsin, lipase, amylase, etc.
- **ANTI-CANCER:** Apricot kernels, 3 g per day, spread throughout the day, for the first few days, increasing as directed to a maximum of 28 g per day (ideal for a 200 lb male, or 140 lb female). Those with low bodyweight, (including children and pets), should reduce intakes according to body-weight
- **ANTI-CANCER:** 5-10 g vitamin C complex (ascorbates plus bioflavonoids) per day. 5 grams amounts to approximately one heaped teaspoon of C complex powder. Take one teaspoon in water every morning and another at night
- **COMMENCE A BASIC SUPPLEMENT PROGRAM,** ensuring liquid, colloidal minerals, antioxidants essential fatty acids. Also,
- Selenium, 200 mcg per day
- A priobiotic supplement to install beneficial flora
- **BOOSTING IMMUNITY:** Astragalus and echinacea for the immune system, as directed

- **PREVENTION:** Balance any hormonal irregularities with natural progesterone cream – cut out unfermented soy products (soy 'milk', soy 'meat', etc.)
- **PREVENTION:** Indulge in regular and vigorous exercise (unless health problems prevent this) to exercise and pump the lymphatic system, rid the body of waste products and draw oxygen into the body
- **PREVENTION:** Avoid behavioural and lifestyle problems that promote stress
- **PREVENTION:** Get plenty of regular rest
- **PREVENTION:** Avoid radiation scans and intrusive 'diagnostic' testing
- **PREVENTION:** The patient may consider absolutely avoiding conventional radiation, chemotherapy and other toxic treatments for any cancer unless life-threatening tumours require shrinkage in a hurry
- **TIP:** Consider surgery only if tumours are life-threatening
- **TIP:** Find out as much as you can about AIDS, as you have done by reading this book. Confront it, don't hide from it
- **TIP:** Use spiritual contemplation and prayer to focus your mind into taking action consistently
- **TIP:** Never give up, no matter how badly off you think you are. Go for it, one day at a time. Remember George Burns! *"The secret of a long life is to keep breathing."*

Herxheimer's reaction

During the detoxification and fungal-killing process, the body may become clogged with catabolic debris, swords, shields, ammunition, dead beasties and their resultant mycotoxins, including ammonia. You may feel ill as your symptoms apparently worsen. This is known as Herxheimer's reaction, after the venerable German dermatologist of the same name. It is temporary and will be experienced in proportion to the vehemence with which you apply your attack strategies. Symptoms may be alleviated by commencing the anti-*Candida* diet a full two weeks prior to starting on the anti-fungal/yeast supplements.

WHAT SHALL I EAT?

Changes in diet are essential for great health, either if you are sick, or if you don't want to suffer. Do not think you are going to have success unless you respect your body's requirements for proper nutrition.

The main culprit preventing a return to healthy immunity is the good old western diet, heavy in meats, sugars, milks, grains, saturated fats and chemicals, which boost levels of damaging fungi and yeasts, especially *Candida*, in the body. If you have 'AIDS', removal of all processed meats, as well as toxic foodstuffs such as additives, caffeine, refined sugars and chocolate, represents a vital start. Beneficial weight loss and a return of energy are almost immediate, and with these benefits comes a regular method of detoxifying the body as part of your future lifestyle.

A properly combined diet, rich in alkali-ash foods (unrefined and uncooked plant dietary) and low in animal proteins (20-40 g a day) is the way to go. The body takes in amino acids to build human proteins ideally from high quality vegetation, fruits and nuts, so you are not going to run short of protein any time soon. The watchwords are *balance* and *grazing*.

Two diet strategies now follow. The first is ideal for AIDS patients and is the **ANTI-*CANDIDA* DIETARY REGIMEN**, formulated by Nikki Zalewksi. The second is **THE *FOOD FOR THOUGHT* LIFESTYLE REGIMEN**, a more liberal diet, ideal for use by recovered patients and the public at large.

THE ANTI-CANDIDA DIETARY REGIMEN
Prepared by Nikki Zalewski

Although appearing to be extremely strict, after following this diet for a few days, you should notice increased energy, easier movement, better sleep, and less digestive problems

Foods to avoid:

All cow's milk products: cheese, yoghurt, whey – all cow's milk derivatives

All yeast products: alcohol, bread, (soda bread is allowed), Marmite, Oxo, Bovril, vinegars, mushrooms, processed and smoked fish and meats

All sugar products: honey, fructose, lactose, glucose, dextrose, Nutrasweet, Canderel, Equal and all aspartame and saccharin products

Nearly all fruit: over-ripe fruits are full of sugar and yeast (hence they go mouldy when over-ripe)

High-sugar root vegetables such as carrots, parsnips, sweet potatoes, beetroots. *NB: If you really can't live without potatoes, wean yourself off them slowly and try to end up with one a day.*

The list below shows you the foods *Candida* loves and thrives on. These need to be eliminated from your diet for between three to six months to start with.

Too much carbohydrate turns to glucose *rapidly*

Avoid:

- Sugar, and sugary foods
- Bread of all kinds and all of its pastry relatives: crackers, pastries, doughnuts, pies, muffins, cookies, etc.
- Cereals, hot or cold, sweetened or unsweetened
- Fast-food snacks, including crisps and pretzels
- White rice, potatoes and corn
- Products made with white flour such as pasta

- Most fruit
- Root vegetables such as carrots, turnips, parsnips and beetroot
- Chick peas, dried beans, lentils and pinto beans
- Coffee and other caffeine containing beverages
- Fizzy, canned drinks
- Alcohol in all forms
- Fruit juices and squash
- All convenience/junk foods, as they contain hidden sugars and other undesirable ingredients
- Cheeses (except non-cow's milk cheeses), milk and yoghurt
- All soy products
- Processed meats such as bacon, sausage, ham, salami, bologna, pastrami and hot dogs
- High salt foods such as processed meats and fish. Smoked fish contains unnecessary levels of sodium that can contribute to water retention
- Mushrooms and fungi, including quorn
- Condiments, such as pickles, toppings and all shop-bought sauces
- Hydrogenated fatty acids and partially hydrogenated fatty acids as contained in stick margarines and man-processed foods
- Saturated fats from tropical oil such as coconut oil
- Saturated fats, primarily from meat, dairy and eggs
- Health supplements containing lactose, gluten, citric acid

The following fruit and vegetables are best avoided until yeast and fungal complaints are under control:

Apricots, artichokes, asparagus, aubergine, avocado, blackberries, courgettes (zucchini), grapefruit, kumquats, okra, passion fruit, peaches, peas, plums, pumpkin, raspberries, sauerkraut, sugarsnap peas, squash, strawberries, tomato, watermelon.

SO what do I eat?!
Good food choices

The foods below have the lowest possible sugar/yeast content and are your best choices. You will notice there are several oils included as certain 'good fats' are vital for health (omegas 3, 6 and 9 essential fatty acids)

Eat plenty of the following foods:

- Alfalfa sprouts, bean sprouts, bell peppers, (sweet peppers), Bok choy, broccoli, Brussels sprouts, cabbage, cauliflower, celery, cucumber, endive, fennel, garlic, green beans, greens, hot chili peppers, kale, lettuce, onions, parsley, radishes, spring onions, spinach, swiss chard, turnips, yellow beans
- Free range eggs, fresh fish (deep and cold caught) and sea food (**not shellfish**), lamb and veal, poultry, chicken, turkey, (particularly skinless white meat), in **small** amounts.
- Use a juicer to produce two tall glasses of 'green' shakes, (one in the morning, one in the late afternoon), juicing cabbage, kale, broccoli, spinach, Brussels sprouts, beans, lettuce, etc. and using wheatgrass or other green mixes to fortify. Add the juice of one lemon to taste.

Fats (in moderation)

Avocado oil, cod liver oil, fish oil, flaxseed oil, grape seed oil, hemp oil, monounsaturated fats, olive oil, primrose oil.

Fluids

Try to drink 8 glasses of water each day: the body is 70% water, so needs fresh supplies daily for optimal hydration and to help flush out toxins. If you can get into the habit of drinking more water, the benefits are many – you'll notice increased energy, better concentration and clearer skin, to name but a few.

Herbal teas, especially Essiac and peppermint, are ideal

Although most fruits are taboo on the anti-*Candida* program, you may have one piece of *firm* fruit a day: apple, pear or kiwi. However, don't take fruit juice.

ANTI-*CANDIDA*/FUNGAL SUPPLEMENTATION

The following regimen will be of benefit to those suffering from yeast and fungal infestations. This is a long-term program, and must be adhered to for as long as the condition is in evidence. Many of these supplements need to be taken at least three times per day to ensure the body is washed with their ingredients:

- **COMMENCE A BASIC SUPPLEMENT PROGRAM**
- **DETOXIFICATION:** Commence a two-week magnesium oxide bowel cleanse (see *Colonics* by Phillip Day)
- **ANTI-PARASITE:** Allicin capsules may be taken, and Allicin cream and spray used for topical areas. Stabilised Allicin is 'the heart of garlic', and has been found to be dynamic in the treatment of AIDS-related conditions
- **ANTI-PARASITE:** Take fresh sticks of cinnamon (not the processed supermarket dust), and grind them down in a coffee grinder. Take a teaspoon of this ground cinnamon powder, mixed in a glass of warm water and drink two/three times a day
- **ANTI-PARASITE:** Take wormwood (*artemesia*) capsules, one four times a day, along with six to ten Allicin capsules per day (stabilised garlic element). A good wormwood and black walnut tincture is also beneficial
- **ANTI-PARASITE:** Enteric-coated capsules of the following oils are all effective antifungals: oregano, thyme, peppermint, rosemary, garlic. These should be taken at least three times a day, spread throughout the day
- **ANTI-PARASITE:** Colloidal silver, as directed
- **ANTI-PARASITE:** Brew Essiac tea properly and drink at least 2 oz, 4 times per day
- **ANTI-PARASITE:** Take a parasite purge formula (this should contain items such as black walnut, clove, ginger root, anise seed, pau d'arco, peppermint and fennel)
- **ANTI-PARASITE:** Take 3-5 grams of water soluble fibre such as psyllium husks or guar gum to help flush out the bowel as the killing proceeds apace. **THE ANTI-*CANDIDA* DIETARY REGIMEN** will also provide you with haystacks full of bowel-scraping fibre to help broom your innards clean

THE *FOOD FOR THOUGHT* LIFESTYLE REGIMEN
Ideal for long-term maintenance

➤ Little or no meat in the diet. Any meat consumed should be hormone and pesticide-free. White meat is better than red. Avoid pork
➤ Avoid sugar, dairy, coffee and alcohol
➤ Eat properly constituted, organic, whole, living foods, a high percentage raw. If you want 'hot', briefly steam your veggies, do not murder them. Remember that heat kills enzymes over 45°C. Excellent recipes are provided in our companion guide, *Food For Thought*.
➤ The ideal balance is: 80% alkali/20% acidic ash foods. Most diets today comprise 90% acid/10% alkali!
➤ Some broiled fish, deep and cold caught, eaten sparingly is OK
➤ Avoid the foods below
➤ Hydrate the body (2 litres (4 pints) of clean, fresh water a day minimum). Reverse-osmosis-filtered water is best
➤ Keep high-glycaemic fruit intake down. Eat more fruits that have low sugar-conversion, such as pears and apples
➤ Eat six *small* meals a day, ensuring a) that you don't go hungry, and b) that the body has a constant supply of nutrients
➤ **A basic supplement program** will consist of ionised colloidal trace minerals, antioxidant tablets, Vit C and B complexes and essential fats
➤ Exercise (to get everything moving and assist in detoxing the body in an oxygen-rich environment). A regular walk in the early morning air is also healthy and very invigorating
➤ Rest. Rest. Rest. Rest. Rest
➤ Reduce environmental toxicity (avoid jobs using dangerous chemicals, radiation, etc.)
➤ Use safe personal care products
➤ Use safe household products

Foods to avoid

> Pork products (bacon, sausage, hot-dogs, luncheon meat, ham, etc.) These are high in nitrites and are known homotoxins which can cause high blood urea and dikitopiprazines, which cause brain tumours and leukaemia.[443]

> Scavenger meats (inc. ALL shellfish and other carrion-eaters – see Leviticus 11 in the Bible). Carrion-eaters, pork and shellfish in particular, concentrate toxins of other animals in their tissues, which we then consume to our detriment. The same goes for the elimination organs of commercially raised animals, such as liver and kidney, which can be high in drug and pesticide residues

> Aspartame/saccharin, artificial sweeteners. These are known mental impairment problems and cancer risks

> Refined sugar/flour/rice. SUCROSE FEEDS CANCER AND YEAST COMPLICATIONS!!! Restricted amounts of wholegrain bread are OK. Use only wholegrain rice. No sugars should be consumed other than those contained naturally in whole foods

> Hydrogenated & partially hydrogenated fats (margarine)

> Junk (processed) food, including fizzy sodas and other soft drinks containing sugar, artificial sweeteners or phosphoric acid, which are drunk out of aluminium cans

> Fat-free foods. Essential fats are *essential!*

> Olestra, canola, soy, etc. Avoid fake or synthetic fats. Soy, in its unfermented state (meat and milk substitute products), disrupts the hormone (endocrine) system, blocks the absorption of calcium and magnesium, and acts like estrogen in the body. Small usage of unfermented soy and fermented soy products (soy sauce and miso) is OK

> Polluted water (chlorinated or fluoridated – see *Health Wars*, 'Water Under the Bridge')

> Caffeine products

> Alcohol products

> Excess refined salt. It's better to spice food with ground kelp or natural sea-salt to maintain a healthy iodine intake

---

443 Day, Phillip, *Food for Thought*, op. cit; *Biologic Therapy*, "Adverse influence of pork consumption on human health", Vol. 1, No. 2, 1983

ACRONYMS

AIDS	Acquired Immune Deficiency Syndrome
APHIS	Animal, Plant Health Inspection Services
CAFMR	Campaign Against Fraudulent Medical Research
CDC	Centers for Disease Control (US)
CIA	Central Intelligence Agency (US)
DFID	Department For International Development (UK)
DOD	Department of Defense (US)
EIS	Epidemic Intelligence Service (US)
FBI	Federal Bureau of Investigation (US)
HIPCs	Heavily Indebted Poor Countries
HIV	Human Immunodeficiency Virus
HL23V	Human Leukaemia 23 Virus
HTLV1	Human T-cell Leukemia Virus
ICPD	International Conference on Population and Development (Cairo, 1994)
ICPD+5	Five years on from the International Conference on Population and Development
IL2	Interleukin 2
IMF	International Monetary Fund (UN)
JAMA	Journal of the American Medical Association
KS	Kaposi's Sarcoma
LAV	Lymphadenopathy-associated Virus
NCI	National Cancer Institute (US)
NIH	National Institutes of Health (US)
OPA	Office of Population Affairs (US)
PCP	Pneumocystis Carinii Pneumonia
PCR	Polymerase Chain Reaction
SMON	Subacute Myelo-Optico-Neuropathy
T-Cell	Immune system lymphocyte cells
UCLA	University of California Los Angeles
UN	United Nations (global)
WHE	Whole Human Embryo
WHO	World Health Organization (UN)

TESTING, TESTING 1-2-3

Aside from the HIV test, other medical tests can often be worthlessly inaccurate or downright fraudulent. Medical writer Oliver Clerc:

> *"People are still being manipulated by their fears and childish hopes. They are still told that the source of their problems is outside them, and that the solution can only come from the outside. They are not allowed to do anything by themselves and they must have the mediation of priest-physicians, the administration of drug-hosts, and the protection of vaccine-absolutions."*[444]

Gene Franks:

> *"However irrational it may seem, we seek reassurance from the Doctor/Priest: 'Doctor, I have sinned. Consult the Oracle and tell me what I must do to be saved.' The Doctor then performs the high-tech hocus-pocus we have been taught to believe in and solemnly gives us the Oracle's decision. If our sins have been grave, a heavy penance is exacted. What we long to hear is: 'What you feared was cancer is only gastro-esophageal reflux. Take these magic pills. Go and sin no more.'"*[445]

A frank and damning admission from the UK Royal College of General Practitioners should have made the front page of every newspaper. The College accused drug companies of inventing fictitious diseases and exaggerating the severity of symptoms to boost drug sales. Labelled 'disease-mongering', the College explained that pharmaceutical companies were taking the UK's National Health Service to the brink of collapse by hyping both these diseases and the assortment of prescription drugs used to treat their symptoms. Dr Maureen Baker, RCGP's Honorary Secretary, declared:

> *"It is always difficult to draw a simple line between what is normal and what is an illness, but it is very much in the*

---

[444] **Clerc, Olivier** *Médecine, Religion et Peur; l'influence cachée des croyances* (The hidden influence of beliefs and fears), Editions Jouvence, France, 1999
[445] Ibid.

interest of the pharmaceutical industry to draw a line which includes as large a population as possible within the 'ill' category. After all, the bigger this group is, the more drugs they can sell." [446]

The power of the establishment has never been greater as government grants itself wider Orwellian powers. A patient diagnosed 'clinical depressed' can, in certain countries, be placed on antidepressant drugs by law. Parents disdaining drugs for natural therapies and nutrition can see their door broken down and their child removed, now they are 'recklessly endangering the life of their child' and thus 'too mentally incompetent' to care for their offspring. Prominent AIDS critic Michael Ellner:

> *"It's pretty clear that the pharmaceutical industry wants to define everybody in the population as being sick, even if you think you are healthy and deny the fact that you have any diseases whatsoever. They could diagnose you with 'Denial Disorder' (DD) by sending you to the right psychiatrist. There are lots of drugs readily available for DD, just as there are for other fictitious diseases like social anxiety disorder or fear of public speaking. Is there really a person alive who isn't afraid of public speaking in the first place? This isn't a brain chemistry disorder. This is a Big Pharma con-game of redefining natural emotions as 'brain chemistry imbalances'.... They redefine normalcy as illness, and once they give it a disease name, suddenly everybody's taking prescription drugs for it."* [447]

The public is, of course, the unwitting protagonist. Buying into 'If you think you are healthy, you simply have not had enough tests yet', we submit to an ever-widening battery of diagnostics. Blindly we trust that the experts know what they're talking about. Consider this from a discussion on drug testing in the criminal justice system:

> *"While the reliability of the standard urine drug test is aggressively asserted by the companies that make money off the testing, the tests, as administered, are not scientifically*

[446] "RCGP warns against unhealthy pharmaceutical industry", 17th August 2004 at www.medicalnewstoday.com/ medicalnews.php?newsid=12177

[447] Michael Ellner eNewsletter, 21st December 2004, commenting on the story at www.newstarget.com/002581.html

assessed for reliability. In Dr. Kent Holtorf's book 'Ur-ine Trouble', published by Vandalay Press, Holtorf begins by pointing out the myriad ways in which drug testing laboratories can and do make mistakes. For instance, a test can come out positive for marijuana as the result of ingesting Ibuprofen, found in Advil and Motrin.

A number of over-the-counter medications may produce a positive test result for amphetamines. Holtorf claims more false positives than accurate tests are reported by drug testing laboratories. Holtorf also points out that second-hand smoke from marijuana and crack cocaine is taken up in a person's hair, which produces a positive test result when hair is sampled for drugs. The more melanin in a person's hair, claims Holtorf, the greater the concentration of the illegal substance. And since African-Americans tend to have higher concentrations of melanin in their hair, the chances are also great that they are at much greater risk than whites of testing positive when their hair is tested - even if the substance got there through second-hand smoke." [448]

Dr Ronald Siegel, a psycho-pharmacologist at University of California, states:

"The widespread testing and reliance on tell-tale traces of drugs in the urine is simply a panic reaction invoked because the normal techniques for controlling drug use haven't worked very well. The next epidemic will be testing abuse." [449]

The same web page is in possession of a quite damning document from Syva Company, makers of the widely used, work-place drug testing kit, 'EMIT'. The document, leaked by a disillusioned Syva employee, lists more than 250 over-the-counter medications and prescription drugs that can cause a false-positive drug test, despite the Syva web-page boasting, "a comprehensive portfolio of products that have been used for more than 32 years, and its reputation as the 'Gold Standard' stands strong." [450]

---

[448] Drug Tests: Junk Science? A discussion of drug tests as a part of the criminal justice system at http://www.nolo.com/lawcenter/ency/article.cfm/objectID/D00957F8-B3EE-48F0-8C57D9F29BD18CC8

[449] www.alwaystestclean.com/false_positive_causes.htm

[450] Village Health Page at www.dadebehring.com/edbna2/ebusiness/products

Consider this letter sent in to an infectious disease Q & A column, hosted by virus expert Dr Harold Oster.

Q: *"All my life I have had false-positive tests for TB and syphilis. Further testing always showed I was free of disease. I am now eight weeks pregnant. Not only was my syphilis test positive, but so was the follow-up test. My husband and I live on a dairy farm and have a lifestyle as distant as possible from any of the ways of transmitting syphilis that I know of. However, the lab tech says the test is 100 percent accurate. Is this true? Is there some way to get syphilis other than extramarital relations, drug use or blood transfusions?*

A: *"Given what you have told me, it is likely that your results are false positive. It is true that the test is highly accurate in showing that a person was once infected with the syphilis organism, but it is not 100 percent accurate. However, this does not mean that I would not consider treating you for syphilis. If there is a chance that you have the infection, it may be wise to treat you in order to prevent the very small risk of your baby becoming infected. It is not common for a foetus to be infected before the fourth month, so even if you do have syphilis, the baby is probably still okay. Syphilis is treated with penicillin, which is considered safe in pregnancy."*[451]

Great! An unreliable test, but we'd like to treat you anyway. And you *were* infected with syphilis at one time, Madam, just trust me on that. It is just not true that these treatments are safe in pregnancy. Syphilis penicillin can cause premature labour and foetal distress.[452] On the eMedicine syphilis page, a Dr Liu admits: *"These tests have high false-positive rates. Other factors (eg, lupus, concomitant viral or bacterial infection, recent immunization, pregnancy) may give false-positive readings."*[453] So, just as with the HIV test, pregnancy is a contributory factor to consider in any supposedly positive syphilis reading.

/discipline.jsp?sDiscipline=Drug+Monitoring
[451] iVillage medicine home page at www.ivillagehealth.com
[452] Antibiotics for syphilis [side-effects] at www.uhseast.com/118958.cfm
[453] www.emedicine.com/MED/topic2224.htm

Hearing those dreaded words, *"You have cancer"*, can be a devastating enough experience in itself. But what if you accepted your doctor's diagnosis and endured the subsequent treatment, only to discover it was all completely unnecessary? An Internet search on *'cancer misdiagnosis'* reveals a very high number of lawyers advertising their services. The level of lawyer interest in any given litigious angle is usually a good indicator of that angle's ability to pay off. In the case of cancer, lawyers have gathered thick and fast around what has been found to be a lucrative and stable source of income. The science of cancer diagnosis is by no means exact. Smartlight Mammographics is a major manufacturer of radiography and mammography equipment. The organisation admits that radiographic testing procedures are inaccurate. Amazingly, this organisation has posted links that proffer the following information: *"We expected error rates to be around 30%, but the wide range of results (10%-90%) was an eye-opener."* and: *"Radiologists can differ substantially in their mammographic recommendations."*[454]

And in the UK, a report was released concerning the case of an elderly pathologist who misdiagnosed more than 200 cancer patients. The report was ordered after it emerged that 79-year-old Dr James Elwood, a consultant pathologist, had wrongly diagnosed more than 200 cancer patients at the Princess Margaret Hospital in Swindon. Dr Elwood had worked as a locum pathologist in three other Trusts - the Royal United Hospital Bath Trust, the Mid-Sussex Trust and Frimley Park Hospitals Trust - between 1995 and 1999. In a statement to the press, the Swindon and Community Health Council said the report was *"a damning indictment of a system that has failed to protect patients from poorly performing locum consultants."* [455]

But still a system that allows the public to be aggressively assaulted by poorly performing tests and testing procedures and toxic drugs. And lastly, a very brief word on genetics testing procedure. The following two-line sentence from leading genetics testing facility, Lawrence Berkley Laboratory in the US, sums up the situation quite plainly:

454 Smartlight Mammographics: www.smartlight.com/dfvcenter/misdiagnosis.html
455 *'I'm sorry,' Says Bungling Doctor: Brighton Evening Argus,* 14th June 2000

"Since genetic tests are expensive and not 100% accurate, it is important to have a good reason for doing them."[456]

And what good reason is that? If it's not accurate, why submit to it at all? If you are being recommended a diagnostic test of any nature by your doctor, it is wise to test that test before getting tested! So far as the 'HIV test' is concerned, the next section includes the very latest information all pregnant mothers need to know.

---

[456] www.lbl.gov/Education/ELSI/Frames/genetic-testing-results-f.html

PREGNANCY AND THE HIV TEST

Information you need to know

In the UK, it is now standard National Health policy at midwifery level to recommend the HIV test to all expectant mothers. As such, you, your sister, wife, daughter, girlfriend, mother even, has every chance of being exposed to a test that falsely indicates the presence of a so-called killer disease where none is present. And there are moves afoot to increase the take-up in these tests. Here is an excerpt from the September 2004 *National Library of Medicine Journal*:

"The UK Department of Health recommends that all pregnant women are offered screening for infection with human immunodeficiency virus (HIV) and had encouraged maternity units to achieve uptake targets of 90 per cent by the end of 2002. Many maternity units fail to meet this target and there is concern that those women who are still refusing testing may include a higher proportion of women at high risk of infection.

There is good evidence that women refusing HIV antenatal screening have a higher prevalence of another blood-borne virus, indicating clearly that further effort must be made to increase the screening uptake and fully integrate HIV screening with other antenatal tests."[457]

If you are pregnant, then, as part of your standardised antenatal care service, you will be recommended to take the HIV test. The dangers concerning this test need to be made more accessible to the general public. To facilitate this process, the information on the following two pages has been designed specifically for easy photocopying. Please distribute this information as widely as possible.

---

[457] *Antenatal screening for HIV; are those who refuse testing at higher risk than those who accept testing?* at
http://www.ncbi.nlm.nih.gov/entrez/query.fcgi?cmd=Retrieve&db=pubmed&dopt=Abstract&list
_uids=15454598

The following facts about the HIV test and certain AIDS drugs are listed here for your suggested reading.

The HIV test can give a false positive reading. Leading manufacturers are all too aware of the imprecise nature of their tests, and include the following or similar disclaimer in with their HIV blood test products: "At present, there is no recognised standard for establishing the presence or absence of antibodies to HIV-1 and HIV- 2 in human blood."(1)

The reason for this disclaimer is because the test does not indicate the presence of a virus in the blood sample. The test has been designed to measure raised levels of antibody activity in the sample supplied. Raised levels of antibody activity are a normal occurrence in the bloodstream and primarily indicate a well-functioning immune system. Unfortunately, this antibody activity in the blood can be misinterpreted by the test as indicating the presence of HIV.

As a result of this misinterpretation, men, women and children are being wrongly diagnosed as HIV positive. Conventional scientific literature has so far recorded in excess of 60 different medical conditions which can cause sufficient levels of antibody activity in the blood to trigger a false HIV positive reading. These separate conditions include flu, the flu jab, malaria, tetanus jab, Hepatitis B, Hepatitis jab, renal failure, haemophilia, organ transplant, alcohol and drug use and even pregnancy.(2) The secondary tests that are then employed by the laboratories to confirm the initial positive reading all carry similar disclaimers.

Receiving an HIV positive diagnosis may well lead your doctor to recommend a course of anti-HIV drugs for you and your baby. The current drug licensed for use in the UK is Azydothimidine, also known as AZT, ZDV, zidovudine or Retrovir. This drug is highly toxic. It has the well-documented capacity to harm the mother, and also to severely deform and even kill the unborn child.(3)

The current level of spending on AIDS and HIV drugs in the Western World is very high. So too are the profits enjoyed by the drug manufacturers. As a result, the information contained in this leaflet is largely being ignored by the orthodox medical establishment. This is not an unexpected reaction. The pursuit of corporate profit at the expense of human health is an everyday reality in western healthcare today.

Please consider this information carefully as you decide on whether to be tested for HIV. Show this leaflet to your doctor. Ask questions. You are quite within your rights to decline the test.

References

1. Extract from a disclaimer included in all Abbott AXSYM HIV tests, the world's leading supplier of HIV test kits.

2. **Johnson, Christine** *Continuum* magazine, September 1996; **Maggiore, Christine** *What if Everything You Knew about AIDS was Wrong?* An Alive and Well Publication, April 2000; **Ransom & Day** *The Truth About HIV*, Credence Publications, January 2005 at www.credence.org. Refer to www.virusmyth.net for a comprehensive list of known false positive indicators.

3. **Kumar et al** *Journal of Acquired Immune Deficiency Syndromes*, 7; 1034-9, 1994, records spontaneous abortions, birth defects, heart defects, mis-shapen faces and other abnormalities; *The Lancet*, Vol 354, 25th September 1999, **Blanche et al.**, discusses deaths of children who received AZT *in utero* and after birth; *Journal of American Medical Association*, 5th January 2000, describes incidence of liver damage; *The Truth About HIV*, Credence Publications, AZT and its links to enlarged crania in infants.

For more information:
Credence UK – Tel: (01622) 832386

* * * * *

OK. SO WHAT CAN YOU DO?

King Cnut was told by a fawning courtier that even the waves of the sea would obey him. Upon arriving at the water's edge however, Cnut's famous demonstration was actually carried out to show England even the mighty are subject to the laws of nature (history does not record what happened to the courtier). The tide of AIDS, however, is not of nature, but of man. And with the concerted effort of man, this tide can be turned back. So what can each of us do?

Listed on the following pages are a wide variety of useful names, addresses and telephone numbers of organisations who, in one way or another, are worthy of inclusion. They are divided into self-explanatory sections.

ADDING YOUR VOICE TO THE DEBATE

The Truth About HIV is ideal for giving people the facts they need on this subject. Why not do further research with some of the sources contained in this book? Let everybody know about this book and have a chance to end their fear of AIDS. We believe also that every time you tune in to a public service provider such as CNN or the BBC reporting on HIV and you hear those expressions "HIV, the virus that causes AIDS" or "Africa devastated by AIDS", that station should receive your emails, faxes and telephone calls by the thousand. As enlightened viewers and listeners, you can make a difference. Tell them *"This debate is fundamentally dishonest. We're not taking it any more!"* Nothing is more powerful. People take notice of strident voices – especially yours!

Write to your local politician, your local doctor, to the health authorities, to national government bodies, to local and national newspapers. In so doing, you run the risk of becoming... a dissident! The Collins dictionary defines a dissident as *'a person who disagrees with a government or powerful organisation.'* This current section will give you all the names, addresses and phone numbers to lodge your legitimate, dissident view.

If you have seen or read something on AIDS that you would like to raise with the appropriate bodies, here are a few simple guidelines.

271

Strike while the iron is hot. If writing, be polite and concise. Always be prepared to give your name and address, the date, time and title of the program concerned, and state precisely what you liked or what caused you offence. If phoning, consider first what you want to say and stay calm. If you are not satisfied with the answer you are given, write to the program producer. Part of the inscription above the door at BBC Broadcasting House, Portland Place in London reads as follows, "...that *everything offensive to decency and hostile to peace will be expelled, and that the nation will incline its ear to those things which are lovely, pure and of good report and thus pursue the path of wisdom and virtue.*" Let's hold them to it.

Listed below are the major UK and US media consortia and regulatory bodies. Go for it!

Independent Television Commission
(regulates all commercially funded television)
33 Foley St
London
W1P 7LB
Tel: 020 7255 3000
Fax: 020 7306 7800
e-mail:
publicaffairs@itc.org.uk

The Broadcasting Standards Commission
(considers complaints about standards and fairness)
7 The Sanctuary
London
SW1P 3JS
Tel: 020 7233 0544
Fax: 020 7233 0397
e-mail: bsc@bsc.org.uk

Radio Authority
regulates radio programming
Holbrook House
14 Great Queen St
Holborn
London
WC2B 5DG
Tel: 020 7430 2724
Fax: 020 7405 7062
e-mail:
info@radioauthority.org.uk

UK TV and RADIO STATIONS

BBC Television Centre
Tel: 0208743 8000
Fax: 0208576 7450
e-mail: Vlc@bbc.co.uk

BBC Radio 1-5
Tel: 020 7580 4468
Fax: 020 7705 3030
e-mail: Vlc@bbc.co.uk

Carlton Television
Tel: 020 7240 4000
Fax: 020 7240 4171
e-mail:
dutyoffice@carltontv.co.uk

GMTV Ltd
Tel: 020 7827 7000
Fax: 020 7827 7001
e-mail: talk2us@gmtv.co.uk

Independent Television News Ltd (ITN)
Tel: 020 7833 3000
Fax: 020 7430 4228
e-mail:
viewer.liaison@itn.co.uk

Channel 4
Tel: 020 7396 4444
Fax: 020 7306 8347
e-mail: viewer-enqs@channel4.co.uk

British Sky Broadcasting Ltd
Tel: 020 7705 3000
Fax: 020 7705 3030
e-mail: feedback@sky.co.uk

US TV NEWS STATIONS

NBC
Dateline NBC -
dateline@nbc.com
Meet the Press - mtp@nbc.com
NBC Nightly News -
nightly@nbc.com

Today Show - today@nbc.com
(718) 656 1350

CBS
www.cbsnews.cbs.com,
Feedback section
(212) 975 4321

ABC
www.abcnews.go.com
(212) 456 7777

CNN
www.cnn.com - Feedback
section
(212) 714 7800

OTHER GROUPS

UK All-Party Parliamentary Group on AIDS
Houses of Parliament
Westminster
London SW1
Tel: 020 7219 6916

World Health Organisation
Avenue Appia 20
1211 Geneva 27
Switzerland
Tel: +41 22 791 2111
Fax: +41 22 791 3111
e-mail: Dr Gro Harlem Brundtland
Director General
info@who.ch

UNAIDS
As above (WHO)

UNFPA
220 East 42nd Street
New York
NY 10017
USA
Tel: (212) 297 5279
e-mail: Dr Nafis Sadik
ryanw@unfpa.org

World Bank
1818 H Street, NW,
Washington DC, 20435
USA
Tel: (202) 477 1234
How to report fraud
www.worldbank.org
e-mail re African campaign
rtoye@worldbank.org
e-mail Dr Peter Piot
unaids@unaids.org

PEOPLE
HELPING
PEOPLE
TO RETURN
TO HEALTH

HEAL is a non-profit, community based education network with independent chapters throughout the United States and around the world. Originally founded in 1982 as an AIDS support group under the direction of president Michael Ellner and science advisor Dr Frank Buianoukas, HEAL New York became the inspiration for an international movement challenging the validity of the HIV=AIDS hypothesis and the efficacy of HIV-based treatment protocols.

For more than a decade, HEAL has been the leading source for comprehensive information on effective, non-toxic approaches to recovery from AIDS defining illnesses and has served as a consistent voice calling for honesty in AIDS issues.

HEAL
Tel: +1 (1) 212 873 0780
Fax: +1 (1) 212 873 0891
E-mail: healintl@aol.com

ALIVE & WELL AIDS ALTERNATIVES
ALIVE & WELL questions the HIV=AIDS=Death paradigm based on a growing body of scientific, medical, and epidemiological data. This organisation also promotes awareness of life-affirming facts to HIV positive diagnosed persons and concerned citizens worldwide. In addition to sponsoring scientific and medical studies, ALIVE & WELL offers a yearly calendar of free community events,

produces books, videos, and other materials that present alternative views of AIDS, and shares resources with ALIVE & WELL affiliates and other organisations around the world that support informed choices for people affected by HIV and AIDS.

ALIVE & WELL

Christine Maggiore, Director
11684 Ventura Boulevard
Studio City
CA 91604 USA
Toll-Free: +1(1) 877 92-ALIVE
Fax: +1(1) 818 780-7093
Email:
christine@aliveandwell.org

THE NATIONAL VACCINE INFORMATION CENTER (NVIC)

Founded in 1982 by parents of vaccine-injured children, the **NVIC** is a non-profit, educational organisation dedicated to preventing vaccine injuries and deaths through public education and defending the right of all citizens to informed consent to vaccination. NVIC takes the position that scientific evidence to date is not sufficient to prove HIV causes AIDS and that if any HIV vaccine is made available to the public in the future, no citizen should be required to use it without their voluntary, informed consent. NVIC maintains that the ethical principle of informed consent, which is applied to all other medical procedures carrying a risk of injury or death, must be applied to all vaccinations, including any future AIDS vaccine.

THE NATIONAL VACCINE INFORMATION CENTER

512 West Maple Avenue, Suite 206, Vienna, VA 22180 USA
Tel: +1 (1) 703 938-0342
Fax: +1 (1) 703 938-5768

REAPPRAISING AIDS

This is the monthly publication of the Group for the Scientific Reappraisal of the HIV/AIDS Hypothesis. Every issue offers very readable and highly informative insights into the facts behind the current AIDS news. An excellent guide to understanding the realities of the latest claims, number games and hype from the AIDS establishment:

THE GROUP

7514 Girard Avenue #1-331
La Jolla
CA 92037
USA
Tel: +1 (1)810 772 9926
Fax: +1 (1) 619 272-1621

ORGANISATIONS WORTHY OF SUPPORT

PARTAGE TANZANIE
Box 1404
Bukoba
Kagera
Tanzania
Africa

PARTAGE (French for 'share') supports some four thousand people in and around the Kagera area. The Krynen's outreach program brings them into direct contact with families, widows, orphans and destitute children. Donations to this valuable work can be made direct to the organisation's above address.

WATERAID
FREEPOST (SW1644)
Prince Consort House
27-29 Albert Embankment
LONDON SE1 7YY
Tel: +44(0)20 7793 4526

2 billion people around the world (a third of the world's population) do not have access to basic sanitation. Over 1 billion do not have a safe supply of water close to their homes. Every six seconds, one person dies from a water-contamination illness.

The **WATERAID** vision is of a world where everyone has access to safe water and effective sanitation. To date, WATERAID-funded projects have enabled over 5 million people to gain access to safe water. Tax-deductible donations are gratefully accepted at the above address or credit card line.

CONTACTS! CONTACTS! CONTACTS!

If you wish to purchase more copies of this book or find out where you may obtain any of Credence's other book and tape products, please use the contact details below. Credence has local sales offices in a number of countries. Please see our website at **www.credence.org** for further details on how to contact them:

> **UK Orders:** (01622) 832386
> **UK Fax:** (01622) 833314
> **www.credence.org**
> **e-mail:** sales@credence.org

Obtaining health products

If you need more information or help on any of the materials discussed in this book, such as where to find them, please use the above contact details. Alternatively, why not visit our comprehensive web-site at www.credence.org, which contains secure on-line global stores, our famous testimonies section, and many other great features (Please note: Items not available in your regional shop may be obtained through the Rest of World store). Alternatively, you may contact us at:

Credence Publications
PO Box 3
TONBRIDGE
Kent TN12 9ZY
England
(01622) 832386
info@credence.org

THE CAMPAIGN FOR TRUTH IN MEDICINE

WHAT IS CTM?

The Campaign for Truth in Medicine is a worldwide organisation dedicated to educating the public on health issues and pressing for change in areas of science and medicine where entrenched scientific error, ignorance or vested interests are costing lives. Our ranks comprise doctors, scientists, researchers, biochemists, politicians, industry executives and countless members of the world public, all of whom have made at least one observation in common. They have recognised that, in certain key areas of global disease, drug treatments and overall healthcare philosophy, the medical, chemical and political establishments are pursuing the wrong course with the maximum of precision, even when their own legitimate, scientific research has illustrated the dangers of pursuing these courses.

CTM STANDS FOR CHOICE IN HEALTHCARE

CTM founder, Phillip Day: *"Millions of people today use nutritional supplements and alternative health strategies for themselves and their families, and yet, increasingly, the public's freedom to choose is being eroded by government legislation and attempts by the pharmaceutical conglomerates to 'buy out' the massive alternative health market. CTM stands for the people's right to choose the healthcare system they feel is right for them, free of big business interference, pointless government regulation, and coercion by the medical establishment which often attempts to compel its own dubious remedies upon an unwilling public."*

CTM - SPREADING THE GOOD NEWS

Every month, CTM sends out EClub, its global online bulletin, which is forwarded free to CTM subscribers around the world to keep them informed of the latest news, developments, scandals and great news in healthcare and other relevant issues. Within EClub, doctors, researchers, journalists, scientists, leading healthcare advocates, researchers and members of the public share their tips, views and strategies with hundreds of thousands around the world. EClub represents the news you are not being told; information that can literally change and even save your life. Don't miss out on this vital resource.

WHAT YOU CAN DO NOW

Why not add your voice immediately to the hundreds of thousands around the world who are uniting, mobilising and making a difference through CTM in so many lives. Join for FREE today by completing the form in this brochure and sending it in. Alternatively, you may wish to join via our web-site at www.campaignfortruth.com.

Let's be part of a different future.
One that celebrates life!

INDEX

C

Cable News Network (CNN), 191, 192, 200, 201, 202, 208, 212, 271, 273
Calcium, 260
Callen, Michael, 117, 119, 121
Camden, 98, 99
Cancer, 13, 15, 26, 27, 29, 34, 35, 37, 38, 55, 77, 83, 85, 106, 112, 114, 191, 195, 197, 245, 260
Candida albicans, 251, 253, 254, 255, 257
Candidiasis, 13
Canola oil, 260
Carnegie, Andrew, 195
Carty, Todd, 23
CBS, 190, 273
CDC, 14, 15, 16, 17, 18, 19, 20, 23, 28, 39, 45, 47, 48, 49, 66, 70, 80, 134, 186, 221
Center for Strategic and International Studies, 196
Chemotherapy, 13, 77, 79, 245
Child Protection Services (US), 99
China, 164, 192, 196
Chirac, Jacques, 41, 170
Chirimuuta, Richard, 130, 137
Chocolate, 254
Cholera, 169
CIA (Central Intelligence Agency), 168, 170
Clumeck, Nathan, 134
CNN, 172
Cocaine, 109, 111, 113, 120
Cohen, Richard, 77, 113, 190
Columbia, 168
Compound S, 81
Concorde study, 83, 84
Condoms, 171, 172
Conference on Retroviruses and Opportunistic Infections (1996), 86
Connor, Steve, 55, 56
Conrad, Joseph, 133, 134, 154, 209, 213
Continuum (UK), 29, 46, 53, 55, 56, 58, 62, 66, 88, 91, 95, 108, 141, 142, 152, 159, 182, 190
Council on Foreign Relations (CFR), 190, 191, 208

Credence Publications, 27, 35, 55, 66, 67, 76, 88, 101, 122, 160, 208, 209, 217, 237, 243, 248
Crixivan, 86, 87
Curran, James, 14, 39

D

d4T, 76, 97
Daily Telegraph (UK), 23, 63, 84, 209, 210
ddC, 76, 86, 236
ddI, 76, 86
Department for International Development (DFID), 178, 179, 180, 181
Department of Defense (DOD) (US), 185, 197
Depression, 78, 111, 230
Dewar, Michael, 174, 175, 200, 202
Diarrhoea, 19, 35, 76, 78, 79, 91, 95, 140, 158, 161, 178, 219, 240
Dikitopiprazines, 260
Dogs, 260
Drug Enforcement Agency (DEA), 109
Duesberg, Peter, 13, 15, 16, 19, 20, 46, 48, 49, 50, 51, 53, 62, 81, 82, 109, 111, 112, 113, 114, 197, 245
Duke University, 81
Durban 2000, 185, 186, 212
Durex, 137
Dysentery, 169

E

East Enders, 23
Egypt, 168
EIS, 16, 17, 18, 19, 23, 28
El Salvador, 177, 192
ELISA, 60, 61, 65, 66, 67, 95, 98, 135, 155, 228, 242
Ellison, Bryan, 17, 19, 28, 29
Emerson, Valerie, 96
Emery, Frank, 132, 133
Emphysema, 112
Enfield, 95
England, 277
Enzymes, 259

282

Human Immunodeficiency Virus (HIV), 5, 6, 7, 12, 21, 22, 23, 25, 36, 37, 38, 39, 40, 43, 44, 45, 46, 47, 48, 49, 50, 51, 52, 53, 54, 55, 56, 57, 58, 59, 60, 61, 62, 63, 64, 65, 66, 67, 69, 70, 71, 75, 76, 78, 79, 80, 84, 85, 88, 89, 91, 93, 94, 95, 96, 97, 98, 99, 103, 104, 108, 111, 112, 113, 114, 116, 117, 123, 124, 134, 135, 138, 141, 142, 143, 145, 155, 159, 160, 181, 182, 184, 185, 202, 203, 213, 217, 218, 219, 220, 221, 225, 228, 229, 230, 231, 233, 236, 237, 238, 239, 240, 241, 242, 243, 244, 245, 246, 247, 271, 274, 275

Human Life International, 176

Hume, David, 132

Hurricane Mitch, 179

Huxley, Julian, 167

Hydrogenated fats, 260

I

I G Farbenindustrie (IG Farben), 196

Independent, The, 56

India, 12, 97, 168, 192

Indonesia, 168

International Monetary Fund (IMF), 138, 146

International Planned Parenthood Federation, 196

Internet, 266

Isaacson, Walter, 190

J

Jackson Memorial Hospital, 19

Jaffe, Harold, 47, 111, 113

Jesus Christ, 248

Johns Hopkins University (JHU), 16

Johnson, Christine, 61, 62

Jubilee Campaign, 178

Justice Department (US), 109

K

Kagera, Tanzania, 144, 276

Kaletsky, Anatole, 209, 210

Kaposi's Sarcoma, 14, 15, 250

Kasun, Jacqueline, 162, 163, 172, 177, 178, 179, 186

Kay, Cathy, 107

Kissinger, Henry, 167, 168, 178, 190, 197, 208

Koch, Robert, 47, 48, 238

Koch's Postulates, 47, 48, 238

Krafeld, Karl, 52, 53

Krynen, Philippe, 141, 142, 143, 146, 158, 161, 181, 186

Kumah, Opiah Mensah, 174

L

Lamb, David, 157, 158

Lancet, 39, 62, 83, 87, 111, 135, 228

Langmuir, Alexander, 16

Lanka, Stefan, 46, 51, 52, 53, 57, 78, 79, 123, 238

Lauritsen, John, 48, 49, 79, 85, 86

Lellouche, Pierre, 170, 171

Leo Africanus, 131

Leonard, Mark, 165

Lesser Developed COuntries (LDCs), 167

Leukaemia, 260

Liberace, 23

Like cures like, 88

Litton Bionetics, 29, 33, 34, 197

Liver, 260

London, 243

Los Angeles, 11, 13, 14, 20, 22, 29, 49, 61, 70, 108, 236, 237, 240, 243

Lymphocytes, 114

Lymphoma, 85

M

Macnamara, Robert, 162

Maggiore, Christine, 27, 49, 55, 61, 66, 69, 70, 71, 77, 83, 84, 86, 87, 89, 95, 100, 156, 218, 231, 274

Magnesium, 260

Malaria, 61, 99, 155, 156, 158

Malnutrition, 19, 20, 27, 79, 139, 141, 147, 149, 158, 169, 182, 240, 247

Mammography, 266

Marijuana, 141
Marlow, Charles, 133
Maxensia, Namuburu, 157
Mbeki, Thabo, 148, 203, 204, 205
Media, 20, 21, 22, 47, 54, 69, 75, 76, 83, 121, 123, 138, 141, 189, 190, 191, 192, 198, 200, 207, 209, 220, 221, 244, 272
Medicines Control Council, 184
Mengele, Josef, 167, 208
Merck, 86, 87, 88, 191
Mercury, Freddie, 23
Mexico, 168
Miami, 19
Milk, 253, 255, 256, 260
Millennium Design Council, 91
Millennium Dome (Greenwich, UK), 91
Miller, James, 176
Montagnier, Luc, 38, 39, 40, 41, 45, 53, 66
Morgan-Witts, Max, 17
Mullis, Kary, 45, 46, 67
Mulondo, Sam, 158
Mwebe, Winifred, 158, 159
Mycotoxins, 253

N

National Academy of Sciences, 24, 25, 42
National Cancer Institute, 26, 29, 48, 81
National Healthcare Advocates, 107
National Institute of Child Health and Human Development (US), 177
National Institutes of Health (NIH), 26, 29, 36, 40, 48, 221
National Security Council, 167
Nausea, 35, 82, 84, 87, 219
NBC, 53, 273
New World Order, 246
New York, 14, 15, 18, 35, 36, 47, 48, 65, 70, 79, 88, 89, 90, 95, 106, 108, 114, 116, 120, 159, 188, 196, 208, 243, 274
New York Press Club, 188
New York Times, 15, 188
Nicaragua, 176, 177
Nigeria, 138, 168, 176, 177, 198
Nilsson, Lennart, 115
Nitrites. *See* Poppers

Non-Governmental Organizations (NGO), 155, 212
NSSM 200, 167, 168, 172, 178, 191, 197, 202, 208
Nujol, 195
Null, Gary, 47, 69, 76, 77, 109, 110, 112, 119, 120
Nussbaum, Bruce, 81, 82

O

Observer Online, 100
Office of Research Integrity, 40, 50, 118
Oriel College, Oxford, 118
Orphan, 142, 143, 160
Overseas Development Council, 196

P

Packard, Vance, 248
Pakistan, 168
Pancreas, 86
Papadopulos-Eleopulos, Eleni, 58, 59, 198
Paralysis, 17, 18
Parasites, 19, 61, 63, 140, 239
Parsons, Richard, 190
Partage, 141, 161, 276
Paxman, Jeremy, 207, 208, 209
Pearlstine, Norman, 190, 191
People Magazine, 96
Pharmacia & Upjohn, 88, 248
Philadelphia, 17, 23, 87
Philippines, 168, 176, 177
Phosphoric acid, 260
Pinching, Tony, 84
Piot, Peter, 228, 229, 274
Placebo, 82, 83
Pliny the Elder, 131
Pneumocystis carinii, 13, 29
Pneumonia, 13, 17, 18, 29, 62, 231, 236
Poppers, 14, 109, 250
Population control, 161, 163, 164, 165, 168, 174, 175, 176, 177, 178, 180, 181, 185, 186, 194, 198, 199, 247
Population Council, 177, 196, 198
Pork, 260
Porter Adventist Hospital (Denver), 90

284

Tocino, Pedro, 53
Toxic load, 113, 240, 243
Toxins, 70, 239
Tuberculosis (TB), 19, 61, 62, 70, 74, 140, 141, 155, 156, 158, 159
Turkey, 168
Turner, Ted, 192, 193, 200, 202, 208, 212

U

UCLA, 13
Uganda, 135, 143, 144, 155, 158, 159, 183
UN Development Program, 144, 177
UNAIDS, 146, 155, 159, 160, 180, 273
UNFPA, 145, 155, 161, 164, 165, 172, 176, 177, 179, 180, 181, 192, 212, 274
United Nations, 49, 146, 161, 167, 185, 192, 198
Universite Libre, Brussels, 134
US Congress, 16, 17, 18, 19, 20, 26, 27, 50, 64, 197, 198
US military, 201, 202
USAID, 145, 146, 155, 164, 165, 174, 175, 176, 177, 181, 186, 212

V

Vaccine, 17, 18, 27, 35, 61, 62, 176, 177, 181, 182, 183, 185, 191, 202
Verney-Elliott, Michael, 55
Vietnam War, 112, 239
Virodene, 184
Virology, 55, 57
Virus hunters, 21, 23, 26, 29
Vitamin B17, 246
Vitamin B17 Metabolic Therapy, 246
Voronoff, Serge, 135

W

Walker, Martin, 57, 58, 189, 190
Wall Street Journal, 63, 118
Washington, George, 13, 24, 40, 41, 57, 145, 159, 164, 185, 197, 274
Water, 19, 100, 139, 141, 142, 155, 157, 158, 161, 182, 186, 271, 276
Wattenberg, Ben, 171
Watts, Geoff, 117
Waxman, Henry, 20
Weiss, Robin, 47, 111, 113
Wellcome, 80, 81, 83, 86, 88, 89, 207, 243
West Hollywood, 22, 237
White House, 17
Willner, Robert, 53, 54
Windscale, 86, 180
World Bank, 144, 145, 146, 147, 149, 150, 159, 160, 162, 163, 165, 172, 174, 175, 177, 178, 179, 180, 186, 206, 208, 212, 274
World Health Organization (WHO), 12, 144, 156, 159, 176, 185, 227, 228, 273
World Medical Assembly (Helsinki), 104

Y

Yeast infection, 13, 62
Yeast infections, 251, 253, 255, 257, 258
Yokohama, Japan, 134

Z

Zambia, 139, 145
Zimbabwe, 145, 147, 180

SPECIAL THANKS

Photographs

A very special thank-you to photographer Loel Poor and colleague Jack Forest of the Forest Foundation for the photographs of Eddie and Arnie, and those featured in 'Loving Ministrations'. To Melissa Springer for 'Death of a Twelve Year Old'. To *Continuum* Magazine for 'Huw Christie, Joan Shenton, Stefan Lanka, Eleni Eleopulos, Paul B, Robert Gallo, Peter Duesberg, Luc Montagnier, Robert Giraldo, AIDSvax, Global Murder, Missing Virus'. To Christine Maggiore for 'Chris and Charlie'. To Philippe Krynen for 'Philippe, Lucy and Joseph, Deus and Jovina, Partage group, AIDS orphans'. To *Renewal* Magazine for 'Hungry'.

Inspiration

A big thank-you to all who have encouraged us throughout the writing of this book. To our loved ones, who have borne with us as we burned the midnight oil. And finally, a special 'thank-you' to our loving God, whose inspiration it was in the first place to believe in the possibility of this book.